Preface

Normal, healthy skin is no longer regarded merely as a physical, protective barrier to the environment, but as a complex immunological organ. This book reviews the immune mechanisms used by healthy skin to protect the body from environmental insults, including those revealed by the recent progress made in the field of innate immunity, and uses this information as a basis for understanding the immunopathogenesis of various inflammatory skin diseases such as SLE, atopic dermatitis and psoriasis.

The findings presented here show the considerable progress that has been made in skin disease research over the past decade, particularly in the search for disease susceptibility genes. Furthermore, increased understanding of the mechanisms involved in inflammatory skin diseases has led to the development of new biological therapies, particularly for psoriasis, which selectively target mediators of the disease process.

With thanks to Professor Lionel Fry and Dr Nick Francis for generously providing clinical and histological slides, respectively.

Barbara S. Baker

Formerly a lecturer in Immunodermatology at Imperial College, London, Dr Barbara Baker has been involved in skin disease research for 25 years. Her main research interest has been the immunopathogenesis of psoriasis, but her work has also included other inflammatory skin diseases such as acne, eczema and dermatitis herpetiformis.

List of Colour Plates

Contents

2. Skin Immune System: Humoral

PART II: Immune Responses in Skin
3. Skin Immune System: Innate Immunity

4. Acquired immune Responses: Immunological Hypersensitivity Reactions

PART III: Immunological Mechanisms of Skin Disease
5. Antibody-Mediated Skin Diseases

6. Systemic Lupus Erythematosus

7. Allergic Contact Dermatitis

8. Atopic dermatitis

9. Psoriasis

PART I: Immune Components of Skin

$$\boxed{1}$$

Skin Immune System: Cellular

Normal human skin is no longer regarded merely as a physical, protective barrier to the environment, but as a complex immunological organ. The term "Skin Immune System" (SIS) was first coined by Bos and Kapsenberg in 1986 and encompasses the epidermal cell types originally included in the term "skin-associated lymphoid tissues": recirculating T lymphocyte subpopulations, Langerhans cells and keratinocytes, and a variety of immunologically active cells present in both epidermal and dermal layers (Table 1.1). The latter include mast cells, tissue macrophages, polymorphonuclear neutrophils, dermal dendritic cells, Langerhans cell precursors, vascular endothelial cells, and afferent lymphatic endothelium beginning in the dermis. Fibroblasts, which were omitted in the original classification, have also been included here. Immunocompetent cells in the skin can be resident, recruited and/or recirculating. For example, eosinophils are recruited to the skin only in certain pathological states, unlike T lymphocytes, which are resident in small numbers and recirculate between the skin and the skin-draining lymph nodes.

In addition to the cellular constituents of the SIS, a variety of inflammatory and immune mediators are also present in normal skin. These will be discussed in Chapter 2.

1.1 T lymphocytes

The characteristics of T lymphocytes in normal skin are described below; a summary is given in Table 1.2.

1.1.1 T cell subpopulations

With the development of monoclonal antibody hybridoma technology by Kohler and Milstein in 1975, it became possible to identify subpopulations of immune cells using highly specific probes for surface markers. T lymphocytes, which have matured in the thymus from bone-marrow-derived precursors, can be subdivided into two functionally distinct subpopulations based upon the expression of CD4 or CD8 molecules expressed on the cell surface.

CD4$^+$ T cells interact with Major Histocompatibility Complex (MHC) class II molecules on the surface of antigen-presenting cells (APCs), such as dendritic cells, B cells and macrophages. These cells functions as "helper" T cells assisting B cells to produce immunoglobulins, and inducing the maturation of cytotoxic T cells via the production of cytokines. CD4$^+$ T helper (Th) cells can be further subdivided according to their cytokine profile into Th-0, Th-1 and Th-2 cells, which was first described for murine clones. Th-1 cells produce interferon (IFN)-γ, interleukin (IL)-2 and tumour necrosis factor (TNF)-β, and promote the production of opsonising and complement-

Table 1.1 Cellular constituents of the SIS

Cell type	Epidermis	Dermis
Recirculating T lymphocytes	✓	✓
Langerhans cells	✓	
Keratinocytes	✓	
Langerhans cell precursors		✓
Dermal dendritic cells		✓
Macrophages		✓
Polymorphonuclear neutrophils		✓
Mast cells		✓
Vascular endothelial cells		✓
Afferent lymphatic endothelium		✓
Fibroblasts		✓

fixing antibodies, macrophage activation, antibody-dependent cell cytotoxicity and delayed-type hypersensitivity. Th-2 cells, on the other hand, produce IL-4, IL-5, IL-6, IL-9, IL-10 and IL-13, and provide help for humoral immune responses, including IgE and IgG_1 isotype switching, as well as mucosal immunity through induction of mast cell and eosinophil growth and differentiation, and IgA synthesis. Th-0 cells produce both Th-1 and Th-2 cytokines. There is strong evidence for the existence of similar subsets of human $CD4^+$ T helper cells, although the expression of some cytokines such as IL-2, IL-6, IL-10 and IL-13 may be less restricted.

$CD8^+$ T cells interact with MHC Class I molecules present on the surface of all nucleated cells and function as cytotoxic cells or as suppressors of antigen-specific B and T cell responses. $CD8^+$ cytotoxic (Tc) cells can also be subdivided into two subtypes, Tc-1 and Tc-2, with similar cytokine profiles to their respective Th counterparts.

Antigenic peptides bound in the groove of Class I or Class II molecules bind to the antigen-specific T cell receptor (TCR) on $CD8^+$ and $CD4^+$ T cells, respectively, and induce activation. As a result molecules such as the IL-2 receptor and human leukocyte antigen (HLA)-DR (one of the MHC Class II antigens), which are absent from resting T cells, are up-regulated on the surface of both $CD4^+$ and $CD8^+$ T cells.

1.1.2 Intraepidermal and dermal T cells

A small number of T cells are present in the epidermis of normal skin. Intraepidermal T cells account for less than 2% of the total number of skin T lymphocytes, are predominately $CD8^+$, and about 70- 80% express the more common TCR consisting of a heterodimer of α and β chains (TCRαβ). The remaining 20-30% express the TCRγδ heterodimer (see section 1.1.3).

Table 1.2 Characteristics of T lymphocytes in skin

Intraepidermal T cells
- < 2% of skin T cells
- CD45RO$^+$ CD8$^+$
- 70-80% TCRαβ$^+$, 20-30% TCR γδ$^+$

Dermal T cells
- <98% of skin T cells
- CD45RO$^+$ CD4$^+$= CD45RO$^+$ CD8$^+$
- 80-90% TCRαβ$^+$, 2-9% TCRγδ$^+$
- Activated: HLA-DR$^+$, IL-2R$^+$
- Expanded TCR Vβ2 and Vβ6 families
  - High junctional diversity
  - Superantigen-driven e.g. SPE-A, SPE-C, SEB
- Expanded TCR Vβ3, Vβ12 and Vβ17 families
  - Identical junctional sequences
  - Specific antigen clonal expansion; antigens unknown
- Oligoclonal TCR γδ$^+$ T cells

The majority of T cells in normal skin are clustered in 1-3 rows around post-capillary venules of the papillary vascular plexus or adjacent to cutaneous appendages. Dermal T cells are predominately TCRαβ$^+$, 2-9% being TCRγδ$^+$, and consist of approximately equal numbers of CD8$^+$ and memory CD4$^+$ T cells which mostly express HLA-DR and IL-2R molecules. Memory T cells have been previously activated by antigen in the context of MHC Class II molecules and can be identified by the expression of a particular isoform of the leukocyte CD45 molecule, CD45RO. Naïve CD4$^+$ T cells that express the CD45RA isoform are relatively rare in normal skin. This contrasts with peripheral blood in which approximately 50% of circulating CD4$^+$ T cells are CD45RA$^+$ and only small numbers of T cells express activation markers. It is not known whether these T cells enter the skin in an activated state or are activated in situ, but the latter is more likely because of the spatial relationship to APCs such as dermal dendritic cells, and the chronic exposure of the skin to exogenous stimuli.

B lymphocytes whose main function is to produce antibodies are very rarely seen in normal (or diseased) skin.

1.1.3 TCR and Antigens/Superantigens

The T cell receptor (TCR) is composed of one of two types of heterodimers, α,β-dimers or γδ-dimers. Both α and β chains consist of V (variable), J (joining) and C (constant) regions, with an additional region D (diversity) in the β chain [1](Fig. 1.1). These regions are encoded in gene segments that rearrange to form the final product. During rearrangement, a variable number of non germ line-encoded bases can be added to or deleted from the junctions between Vα and Jα, Vβ and Dβ or Dβ and Jβ segments. These additions or deletions are responsible for the diversity of the complementarity determining region 3 (CDR3) encompassing the hypervariable VDJ segments. CDR3 interacts with more than half of the surface of the peptide in the MHC peptide-binding groove and in this way contributes substantially to antigen specificity. Thus T cells with identical antigen specificity share conserved CDR3 amino acid sequence motifs. Another hypervariable region, the complementarity determining region 2 (CDR2) of both α and β chains, interacts with the MHC molecule.

In contrast to recognition of antigenic peptides bound to MHC proteins which involves contributions from all the variable components of the TCR, bacterial toxins stimulate T cells almost exclusively via the Vβ region of the TCR expressed by T cells (Fig. 1.1). Streptococcal pyrogenic exotoxins (SPE) and staphylococcal enterotoxins (SE) are potent T cell mitogens which can activate 5-30% of peripheral blood T cells, compared to only $1:10^5$ antigen-specific T cells which respond to an antigenic peptide. They are therefore commonly termed superantigens. Each toxin stimulates T cells bearing particular Vβ families, which vary for each toxin. Stimulation of T cells by toxins is dependent upon the presence of MHC Class II-positive cells in the cultures; however, unlike antigenic peptides, the toxins bind outside of the antigen-binding groove of the MHC molecules

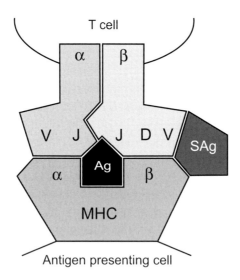

Figure 1.1   Schematic representation of binding of superantigen (SAg) and antigen (Ag) to MHC Class II and TCR on antigen-presenting cells and T cells, respectively. (Source: Baker B.S. *In* Recent Advances in Psoriasis: The Role of the Immune System, 2000, with permission from Imperial College Press, London, UK.)

1.1.4 Restricted TCR Vβ families in skin

The TCR repertoires in normal human skin are characterised by restricted TCRBV gene usage. Preferential usage of BV2 (representing on average approximately one third of the total TCR expressed) and, to a lesser extent, BV6 was detected by reverse-transcriptase PCR assay in adult skin compared to peripheral blood [2]. The majority of the TCRBV2 and BV6 transcripts were heterogenous with high junctional diversity, suggestive of polyclonal activation by superantigens. Several of the bacterial superantigens, such as SPE-C, SEA and toxic shock syndrome toxin-1 (TSST-1) are known to be stimulatory for Vβ2+ and/or Vβ6+ T cells [3].

In addition, certain other TCRBV genes (TCRBV3, BV12 or BV17) were more highly expressed in skin than blood in individual samples [2]. In contrast to TCRBV2 and BV6, analysis of these TCRBV genes revealed numerous identical transcript sequences that were not detected in blood. These dominant TCR rearrangements implicate clonal expansion of T cells by antigenic peptides in skin.

Thus both superantigens and antigens appear to affect TCRBV gene usage, not only in diseases such as psoriasis, but also in normal skin.

1.1.5 Restricted TCR δ families in skin

In normal, human skin only a small number of CD3+ T cells express the TCRγδ heterodimer and these are located mainly in the dermis. These cells, which are also found in the lung and epithelium of the gut and genitourinary tract, probably contribute to the initial defence against infection. They recognise non-peptide, unprocessed antigen and have been suggested to form a bridge between innate and acquired immune responses. CDR3 spectratyping of the TCR DV1 and DV2 genes, and subsequent nucleotide sequencing revealed that normal skin is composed of clonally expanded γδ+ T cells which are widely distributed [4]. Furthermore skin DV TCR sequences were not found in peripheral blood. The function of oligoclonal skin γδ+ T cells may be to recognise antigens such as stress-induced self-antigens or conserved foreign antigens as part of the skin's innate immune defence system.

1.1.6 T lymphocyte homing to skin

Recruitment of T lymphocytes to skin involves three stages; tethering and rolling on the vessel wall, adhesion and transmigration/extravasation [reviewed in ref 5] (Fig. 1.2).

1.1.6.1 Tethering and rolling

The initial transient attachment of T lymphocytes to the vessel wall involves the selectins, P-selectin (CD62P) and E-selectin (CD62E) expressed on endothelial cells. Selectins are single-chain transmembrane adhesion molecules with a lectin-like domain that binds to ligands displayed on glycoproteins. P-selectin is rapidly mobilized to the surface on activation of endothelial cells, whilst E-selectin expression is induced by inflammation. E-selectin is also expressed in non-inflamed skin, but is restricted to a subset of vessels in the mid to upper dermis and shows focal variation of expression within individual vessels.

Figure 1.2   Recruitment of T lymphocytes to skin showing the involvement of selectins, integrins and chemokines: a) tethering and rolling on the vessel wall, b) adhesion, and c) transmigration/extravasation.

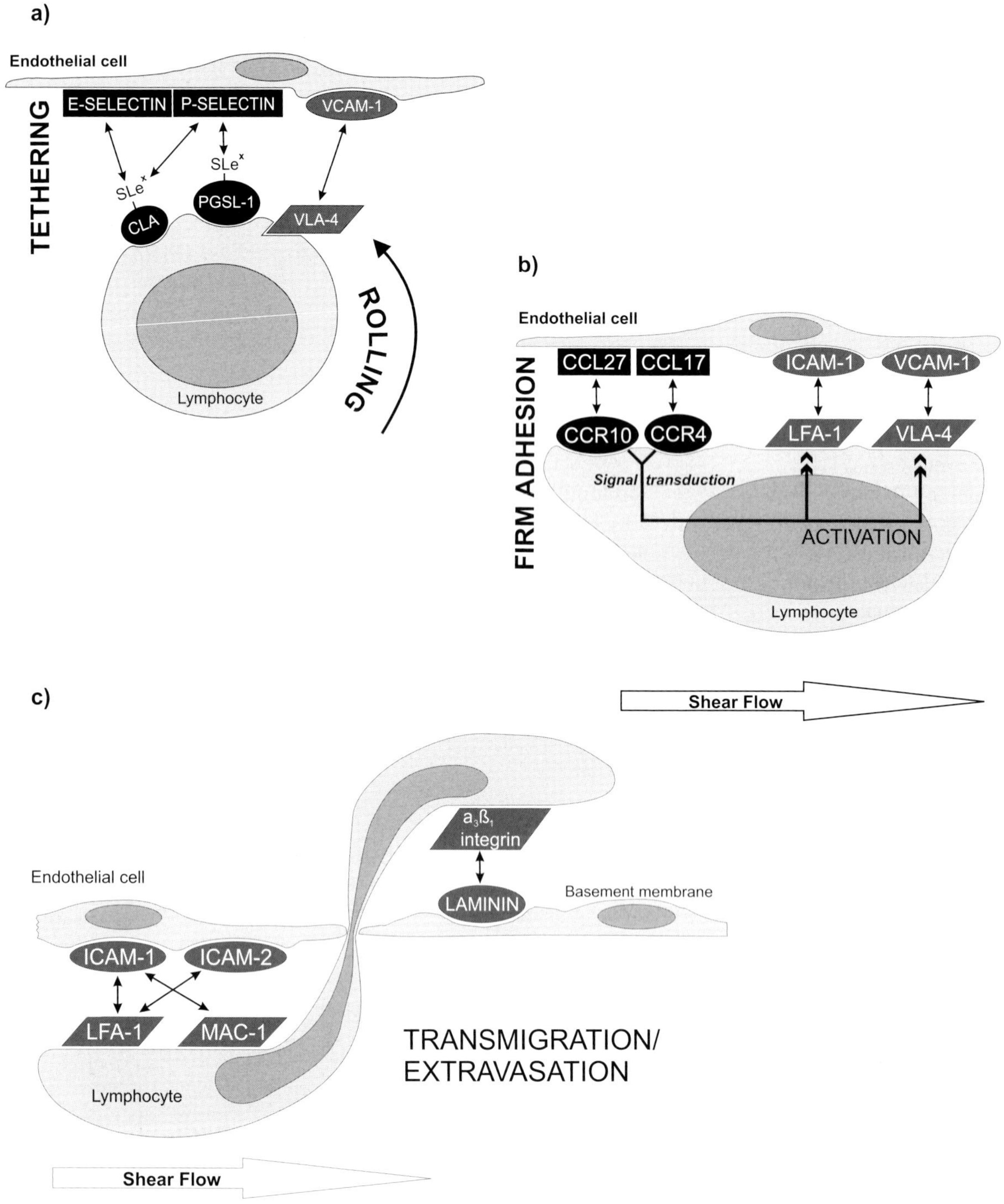

T cells express transmembrane glycoproteins with sialyl-Lewis^x groups which act as ligands for E- and P- selectins. T cells specifically homing to the skin express cutaneous lymphocyte-associated antigen (CLA) which is an inducible carbohydrate modification of P-selectin glycoprotein ligand-1, a surface glycoprotein constitutively present on all peripheral blood T cells. CLA is expressed on a minor subset of CD45RO$^+$ memory T cells in peripheral blood, but by the majority of such cells in cutaneous sites of chronic inflammation such as psoriasis in which E-selectin expression by endothelial cells is unregulated. CLA expression is selectively induced on T cells during virgin to memory transition in skin-draining peripheral lymph nodes and is regulated by microenvironmental factors such as the cytokine transforming growth factor (TGF)-β_1.

In addition to selectins, a heterodimeric adhesion receptor of the integrin family called very late antigen-4 (VLA-4, $\alpha_4\beta_1$-integrin, CD49d/CD29) also mediates rolling of certain leukocyte subsets. VLA-4 binds to vascular cell adhesion molecule-1 (VCAM-1), a member of the immunoglobulin superfamily expressed on the endothelial cell surface.

1.1.6.2 Firm adhesion

After transient rolling, leukocytes attach firmly to the endothelium via β_2-integrins such as lymphocyte function-associated antigen-1, LFA-1 (also called CD11a/CD18, $\alpha_L\beta_2$) on lymphocytes or Mac-1 (CD11b/CD18, $\alpha_M\beta_2$) on macrophages and natural killer (NK) cells which bind to intercellular adhesion molecule-1 (ICAM-1) constitutively expressed on endothelial cells. The VLA-4/VCAM-1 pair of molecules is also involved in leukocyte-endothelial cell adhesion, in addition to rolling of leukocytes as described above. In inflammatory skin diseases, cytokines such as IFN-γ, TNF-α and IL-1 induce ICAM- and VCAM-1 expression by endothelial cells and facilitate further T cell localization.

Circulating leukocytes express integrins (see Section 1.3.3) which are in a non-adhesive state to avoid non-specific binding to blood vessels. To enable leukocytes to bind firmly to the endothelium, the integrins must be activated in order to increase avidity and resist detachment by disruptive shear flow. This activation is achieved by chemokines, small polypeptides that comprise a large family of 50 ligands and 20 G-protein-coupled receptors with overlapping function. The chemokines are retained on the surface of the endothelium, via their binding sites for heparins and related glycosaminoglycans, having being transported by a process of transcytosis from the cytoplasm. Chemokines can be subdivided into two main subclasses depending on whether the two N-terminal cysteine residues are separated by an amino acid (CXC) or are adjacent (CC). They are constitutively produced for basal leukocyte trafficking, and/or are inducible and up-regulated in response to stress and tissue injury. Two chemokines and their receptors appear to be particularly relevant for T cell homing to inflamed skin; chemokines CCL27 (also called cutaneous T cell-attracting chemokine, CTACK) and CCL17 (also known as thymus- and activation-regulated chemokine, TARC) and their receptors CCR10 and CCR4, respectively.

CCL27 is a skin-associated CC chemokine expressed preferentially by basal keratinocytes (KCs) in normal epidermis, but present throughout the epidermis in skin lesions of psoriasis and atopic dermatitis. Basal KCs release large amounts of CCL27 into the dermis where the protein is found on extracellular matrix, fibroblasts and endothelial cells of the superficial plexus (Fig. 1.3). Scattered expression of CCR10 is observed on T cells in the superficial dermal plexus of normal skin, but not by T cells within the epidermis. These observations suggest that endothelial-bound CCL27

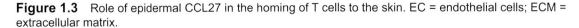

Figure 1.3   Role of epidermal CCL27 in the homing of T cells to the skin. EC = endothelial cells; ECM = extracellular matrix.

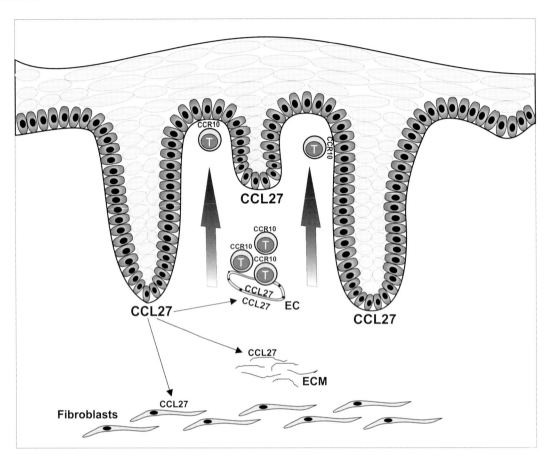

plays a role in lymphocyte homing to normal and inflamed skin by mediating firm adhesion and initiating transendothelial migration. In addition, CCL27 attached to dermal extracellular matrix and fibroblasts may contribute to a chemokine gradient directing T cells towards the epidermis.

Constitutive and inducible expression of CCL17 has also been demonstrated on post-capillary venules in the dermis, and CLA$^+$ T cells commonly co-express CCR4. The receptor/chemokine pair CCR4/CCL17 have been shown to play a role in homing of CLA$^+$ T helper-2 (Th-2) cells in a number of allergic diseases, especially atopic dermatitis, and in some types of cutaneous T cell lymphoma.

Another chemokine CCL20 (macrophage inflammatory protein (MIP)-3α, and its receptor CCR6 have also been implicated in the arrest of a subset of memory T cells by dermal endothelial cells, a process which is relevant to psoriasis. CCL20 is constitutively present in dermal vessels, whilst CCR6 is highly expressed on skin-homing CLA$^+$ memory T cells.

The particular chemokines and their receptors that are expressed will determine the type of cell that is attracted. (Usually only activated effector T cells will respond to chemokines as naïve T cells lack the appropriate receptors). This pattern is regulated by cytokines; IFN-γ induces chemokines that attract monocytes, polymorphonuclear neutrophils (PMNs) and T helper-1 (Th-1) cells whilst IL-4 and IL-13 induces chemokines that attract eosinophils, mast cells and Th-2 cells.

1.1.6.3 Transmigration/Extravasation

The process of transmigration across endothelial cells has not been fully elucidated. Transmigration involves the movement of adherent cells in between endothelial cells at the contact site and requires that the lymphocytes be continuously exposed to fluid shear. The process is promoted by chemokines bound to the endothelial cell surface. Once extravasated, the lymphocytes move through the dermal extracellular matrix by binding via $\alpha_1\beta_1$-, $\alpha_2\beta_1$- and $\alpha_5\beta_1$- integrins to various extracellular matrix components such as collagen type I, fibronectin, chondroitin sulphate, laminin, or hyaluronans. Lymphocytes also use the CD44 and LFA-1 receptors to bind to dermal hyaluronate and interstitial ICAM-1, respectively, and various β_1-integrins to bind to components of the epidermal basement membrane such as collagen type IV, epiligrin and laminin. The latter interactions may be enhanced by cytokines such as IL-7 produced by keratinocytes (KCs).

It is not clear what the mechanisms are for localization of T cells within the epidermis. Although intraepidermal T cells express β_1-integrins, which are therefore implicated in epidermotropism, extracellular ligands for these integrins are not expressed in the epidermal layers. The $\alpha_E\beta_7$-integrin, which is expressed by the majority of intraepithelial T cells in the intestine, is also present on epidermal T cells in some inflammatory skin diseases and in cutaneous T cell lymphomas. Furthermore, the ligand for the $\alpha_E\beta_7$-integrin, E-cadherin is also expressed on epithelial cells in these diseases, supporting a functional role for this integrin in the skin.

In inflammatory skin diseases, the initial entry of T cells into the epidermis is probably facilitated, at least in part, by ICAM-1 induced on basal KCs by cytokines. Another adhesion molecule, LEEP-CAM (glycoprotein lymphocyte endothelial-epithelial cell adhesion molecule) which is constitutively expressed on suprabasal epidermal layers in normal and inflamed skin, may also be involved in the localization of T cells in the epidermis. However, the ligand for LEEP-CAM on T cells has not yet been identified.

1.2 Antigen-presenting cells

APCs in normal skin include epidermal Langerhans cells, and Langerhans cell precursors, dermal dendritic cells and macrophages present in the dermis.

1.2.1 Langerhans cells

Dendritic cells are potent APCs that migrate as progenitors from the bone-marrow via the blood to non-lymphoid tissues where they may become resident immature cells. Langerhans cells (LCs), which are used as a prototype for studies of dendritic cells, reside in the suprabasal layer of the epidermis forming a regular network with their dendrites (Fig. 1.4, colour plate). Immature dendritic cells such as LCs are capable of antigen uptake and processing, MHC production and the formation of antigenic peptide-MHC complexes. Under the influence of inflammatory stimuli, they mature and migrate out of non-lymphoid tissues into the blood and/or afferent lymph as veiled cells. Mature

Table 1.3 Surface markers on skin dendritic cells

Surface marker	LC	LC Precursors	DDC
MHC Class II	✓	✓	✓
MHC-Class I-like CD1			
CD1a	✓	✗	(✓)
CD1b	✗	NT	(✓)
CD1c	✓	NT	✓
CD1d	✗	NT	✓
Adhesion molecules			
ICAM-1	✓	✓	✓
ICAM-3	✓	NT	NT
LFA-1 (CD11a)	✗	NT	✓
Mac-1 (CD11b)	✗	✓	✓
LFA-3	✓	NT	✓
E-cadherin	✓	NT	NT
Co-stimulators			
CD80	✗	✓	✗
CD86	✓	✓	(✓)
CD40	✓	✓	✓
Activation/maturation			
CMRF-44	✗	NT	(✓)*
CD83	✗	✗	(✓)
Chemokine receptors			
CCR3	✓**	NT	✓
CCR6	✓	✓	✗
CCR7	✗	NT	✓
CXCR4	✓	NT	NT

Surface marker	LC	LC Precursors	DDC
Other molecules			
Langerin	✓	✓	✗
CLA	✓	NT	✓
CD14	✗	✓	(✓)
Factor XIIIa	✗	✗	✓
FcγRII (CD32)	(✓)	NT	✓

* Present on a subset of cells; ** Present on mature Langerhans cells.
Brackets denote weak expression; NT, not tested.

dendritic cells pass into secondary lymphoid organs and home to the T cell-rich areas where they initiate antigen-specific primary T cell responses (see Chapter 4).

LCs express an array of surface markers including MHC antigens, MHC Class I-like CD1 molecules, adhesion and costimulatory molecules, chemokine receptors and a cell-specific protein called langerin (Table 1.3).

1.2.1.1 Surface markers associated with antigen presentation

MHC Class II subtype HLA-DR is highly expressed on the LC surface with concomitant constitutive expression of HLA-DQ and HLA–DP. In addition LCs express CD1, a non-polymorphic MHC Class I-like molecule encoded for by genes that map to chromosome 1q22, in contrast to MHC molecules which map to chromosome 6p21. The human CD1 locus contains 5 genes; the protein products of three of these genes CD1a, CD1b and CD1c have been identified as β_2-microglobulin-associated cell surface glycoproteins on immature thymocytes. CD1a is highly expressed on LCs and is specific for this cell type in epidermis. CD1c is also present on the LC surface but CD1b and CD1d are absent. In contrast to MHC Class I and II molecules, CD1 proteins present lipids and glycolipids, rather than proteins, to T cells. In addition, adhesion molecules ICAM-1 and ICAM-3, LFA-3 and E-cadherin, and costimulator molecules CD86 and CD40 present on the surface of LCs facilitate interaction and antigen presentation to T cells.

1.2.1.2 Immune receptors

Unlike other dendritic cell populations, LCs express the chemokine receptor CCR6, which is the sole receptor for macrophage inflammatory protein (MIP)-3α/CCL20. This chemokine is produced mainly by epithelial cells and is up-regulated under inflammatory conditions such as those found in lesional psoriatic skin and in tonsils. Thus CCL20 appears to play a central role in the recruitment of LCs into the epidermis during inflammation. A lesser role is played by constitutively expressed CXCR4 on LCs and its ligand, stromal cell-derived factor-1a (SDF-1α, CXCL12), a weak chemoattractant produced by basal KCs. In addition, CLA expressed on the LC surface contributes to the specific homing of this dendritic cell subtype to the skin. LCs also express the low affinity Fc receptor for IgG (FcγRII, CD32) which, together with complement receptors, is involved in phagocytosis.

1.2.1.3 Birbeck granules/Langerin

LCs are characterised by the presence in the cytoplasm of Birbeck granules, unique rod-like organelles (named after the person who first described them), which are found in association with small vesicles forming racket-like structures. The precise functions of these organelles are unknown but are probably involved in the uptake and trafficking of molecules internalised through the C-type lectin langerin (CD207). Langerin, a type II transmembrane protein specific to LCs, may act as a pattern recognition receptor with specificity for mannosides.

1.2.1.4 Proinflammatory cytokines

In common with KCs (see below), LCs are a source of the proinflammatory cytokines, IL-1 and TNF-α in the epidermis. IL-1 occurs in two forms, IL-1α and IL-1β, which are the products of separate genes but which have almost identical biological activities. They are produced as precursors, but while pro-IL-1α is biologically active, the IL-1β precursor becomes active only after proteolytic cleavage by IL-1β-converting enzyme. Unlike KCs, LCs are able to synthesize this enzyme and consequently the active IL-1 they produce is predominately of the β form.

Thus LCs have a characteristic profile of surface markers that differs from that of other dendritic cell subpopulations. This profile is probably determined by their unique epithelial microenvironment, which includes the cytokine TGF-β_1 that appears to be essential for the development of LC characteristics. LCs are capable of pinocytosis (clathrin- or caveolin-mediated uptake of small particles) and processing of soluble antigens targeted by the cells' membrane molecules, which are subsequently expressed as peptide-MHC complexes at the cell surface. However they are immature and unable to initiate primary immune responses.

1.2.2 Langerhans cell precursors

LC precursors are resident in the dermis of normal skin [6]. They differ from LCs in their expression of CD14 and Mac-1, molecules usually present on monocytes and/or macrophages, but lack CD1a, which is characteristically expressed by Langerhans cells (Table 1.3). However, these precursor cells display langerin and CCR6 chemokine receptors on their surface, which are characteristic for the LC population. When cultured with TGF-β alone, the LC precursors have the potential to differentiate into epidermal LCs, whilst culture with granulocyte macrophage-colony-stimulating factor (GM-CSF) and IL-4 induces differentiation into mature dendritic cells. It has therefore been hypothesised that these dermal CD14$^+$ cells migrate to the epidermis in response to CCL20 produced by KCs where they differentiate into immature resident LCs. Under inflammatory conditions, further differentiation may take place to produce more mature LCs with enhanced T cell stimulatory function.

1.2.3 Dermal dendritic cells

Dermal dendritic cells (DDC) are present around the vessels of the papillary dermis of normal skin and express MHC Class II, various adhesion and costimulatory molecules and, in some cases, the myeloid CD14 marker (Table 1.3). In contrast to the homogenous population of LCs in the epidermis, there are several different subsets of dendritic cells in the dermis. One subpopulation of DDC can be characterised by the expression of Factor XIIIa, an intracellular form of fibrin stabilizing factor [7]. Unlike LCs which constitutively express CD1a but not CD1d, only a subset of DDC express CD1a at low levels, whilst CD1d is constitutively expressed. In addition, DDC lack LC-specific langerin. A subpopulation of CD1a$^+$ DDC has recently been shown to express the maturation and activation markers CMFR-44 and CD83, respectively [8]. Most of these activated cells were in close contact with T lymphocytes, which also displayed an activated phenotype, and were observed mainly in the adnexal regions. The costimulator molecule CD86 was expressed by the T cell-associated DDC, implicating an on-going antigen-specific immune response.

1.2.4 Macrophages

In normal skin, abundant macrophages with a spindle-shaped or dendritic morphology are found in the superficial dermis around small blood vessels and adnexal structures, and scattered in the reticular dermis. Macrophages are bone-marrow-derived cells, which were regarded as distinct from dendritic cells but are now considered to be derived from a common precursor whose differentiation is influenced by its environment. In contrast to dendritic cells, macrophages are highly phagocytic and act as scavengers of microorganisms, apoptotic (dying) cells, immune complexes and cellular debris. In addition, they have various anti-microbial mechanisms for elimination of bacteria. Although macrophages can present antigen to T cells they are less efficient than dendritic cells.

1.3 Keratinocytes

It is now widely accepted that KCs function as immunocompetent cells and, as such, play a vital role in the skin immune system. Thus KCs are the major source of proinflammatory and immunomodulatory cytokines and chemokines in the epidermis, produced in response to a variety of non-specific stimuli. They can also respond, in an autocrine or paracrine manner, to many of these cytokines via specific receptors on their surface resulting in effects on proliferation, differentiation and cytokine production. In addition, upon activation KCs up-regulate expression of cell surface molecules involved in antigen presentation and interaction with other cell types, especially LCs and T cells.

1.3.1 Cytokines and Cytokine receptors

KCs constitutively produce low levels of a vast array of different cytokines [9]. These levels can be substantially increased by various stimuli such as physical trauma, ultraviolet (UV) light, bacteria and chemicals, together with *de novo* synthesis of further cytokines. In addition, they express receptors for the cytokines they produce, and for some that they do not, enabling them to respond functionally in both an autocrine and paracrine manner.

1.3.1.1 Proinflammatory cytokines

Proinflammatory cytokines, as their name suggest, induce inflammation via pleiotropic effects such as the up-regulation of adhesion molecule expression on endothelium and the induction of various cytokines which act on inflammatory leukocytes. They include IL-1α, IL-1β, IL-6 and TNF-α (Table 1.4).

IL-1α and IL-1β are constitutively synthesized and stored by KCs in normal epidermis, ready to be released following injury to the epidermis. Although the IL-1α produced is biologically active, KCs (unlike monocytes and LCs) do not synthesize IL-1β-converting enzyme necessary for activation of the IL-1β precursor. However, bioactive IL-1β has been detected in lesional epidermis from patients with psoriasis suggesting that biologically active IL-1β may be generated via a different mechanism.

Two types of IL-1 receptor (IL-1R) have been characterised; IL-1RI, which transduces IL-1-mediated signals, and IL-1RII, which does not due to its short cytoplasmic tail. The latter appears to act as a decoy target for the cytokine. The extracellular domains of both receptors can be shed and act as IL-1 inhibitors. Another inhibitor is the IL-1 receptor antagonist (IL-1ra), which can bind to IL-1R without inducing signal transduction thus blocking the IL-1 response. IL-1ra exists in one secreted and two intracellular isoforms; the intracellular forms in the cytosol of KCs may bind to IL-1R present on the nuclear membrane.

IL-6 (formerly known as B cell stimulatory factor-2) is produced in low amounts by normal KCs, but is markedly up-regulated in skin lesions of psoriasis (see Chapter 9). It plays a central role in the host response to injury and infection via its multiple effects on many cell types. These include stimulation of acute-phase protein synthesis by the liver, enhancement of the proliferation of T and B cell lines, induction of B cell differentiation and immunoglobulin production, and stimulation of cytotoxic T cells and NK cells via the induction of IL-2. IL-6-specific receptors are expressed by KCs, in common with various other cell types, enabling them to respond in an autocrine manner to the cytokine.

TNF-α is a multifunctional cytokine produced mainly by activated macrophages, T cells and mast cells. However KCs also produce very low amounts of the cytokine, which are markedly up-regulated by stimulation with endotoxin (lipopolysaccharide) or UV light. The wide range of effects exerted by TNF-α include necrosis of transplanted tumours (hence its' name), endotoxic shock mediation, growth modulation of normal cells and inflammatory, immunoregulatory and anti-viral responses. These effects are mediated via two immunologically distinct TNF-α receptors, TNF-R1 (55 kDa) and TNF-R2 (75 kDa), which have different cytoplasmic domains and are independently regulated. Furthermore, these receptors are differentially expressed on different cell types. KCs preferentially express TNF-R1, which are distributed throughout the epidermal layers in a predominately intracellular perinuclear location [10].

1.3.1.2 Immunomodulatory cytokines

KCs constitutively produce the immunomodulatory cytokines IL-7, IL-12, IL-15 and IL-18 which can be substantially up-regulated by various stimulatory factors such as other cytokines, allergens and UV light (Table 1.4).

IL-7 exerts a variety of effects in addition to its original description as a growth factor for B cell progenitors, including the activation of monocytes, and stimulation of the growth, cytokine production and expression of IL-2 α-chain (CD25) receptor by T lymphocytes.

IL-12 is a heterodimeric molecule composed of two covalently linked chains, p40 and p35, both of which are required for biological activity. The p35 chain of IL-12 is widely expressed by various cell types whilst the p40 chain is more restricted in its distribution. IL-12 is a potent inducer of IFN-γ in T and NK cells, a growth factor for pre-activated T and NK cells, and an enhancer of cytotoxic activity in CD8$^+$ T and NK cells. IL-12 is synthesized by macrophages, B cells and dendritic cells and plays a vital role in the generation of Th-1 cells, and in the optimal differentiation of cytotoxic cells. KCs also produce a small amount of IL-12 which may be biologically active as mRNA specific for both p35 and p40 chains has been detected by reverse-transcriptase (RT)-PCR in the epidermis of normal skin.

IL-15 is a cytokine that, in common with IL-2, stimulates T cell proliferation and activates NK cells. It also inhibits Fas-induced apoptosis (programmed cell death) of T cells (see Section 1.3.6). However, unlike IL-2, IL-15 is not synthesized by T cells but by monocytes/macrophages, dermal fibroblasts and KCs. Expression of IL-15 can be induced by UVB irradiation, and high levels are observed in skin lesions of psoriasis.

IL-18 or IFN-γ-inducing factor is another growth and differentiation factor for Th-1 cells with similar functions to that of IL-12. In common with IL-1β, the inactive IL-18 precursor is cleaved by IL-1β-converting enzyme to produce the mature, active form of the cytokine. IL-18 is produced by macrophages and dendritic cells, and also in small amounts by KCs, the levels of which can be increased by stimulation with contact allergens or double-stranded RNA (dsRNA).

Another cytokine, the cytokine synthesis inhibitor IL-10, whose other effects include the inhibition of macrophage-dependent proliferation of T cells, the stimulation of B cells, and the ability to act as a chemoattractant for CD8$^+$ T cells and an inhibitor of IL-8-induced CD4$^+$ T cell migration, is not produced constitutively by KCs. However, IL-10 synthesis by KCs can be induced by UVA irradiation, tape stripping or by application of a recall antigen such as poison ivy antigen. KCs express the receptor for IL-10; the effects of IL-10 on KCs may involve inhibition of IFN-γ-induced HLA-DR expression.

Receptors for the T cell-derived cytokines IL-4, IL-13 and IL-17, are also expressed by KCs. Cytokine-specific stimulation of KCs via these receptors results in modulation of functions such as cytokine production and expression of ICAM-1 induced by IFN-γ, TNF-α and/or IL-4.

1.3.1.3 Suppressors of cytokine signalling

Cytokine-stimulated KCs are able to regulate cytokine signalling via the production of at least two members of the suppressors of cytokine signalling (SOCS)/cytokine-inducible SH2 containing protein (CIS) family, SOCS-1 and SOCS-3 [11]. SOCS-1 and SOCS-3 are absent from normal epidermis, but are up-regulated in skin lesions of psoriasis and allergic contact dermatitis, and after UVB irradiation.

The SOCS/CIS molecules are negative regulators of signal transducers and activators of transcription (STAT) molecules, which transmit cytokine-derived signals to the nucleus of the cell. Different isotypes of STAT molecules are associated with different cytokines; for example, STAT-1

Table 1.4 Keratinocyte-expressed cytokine/cytokine receptors

Cytokine	Constitutive	Inducers	Receptor
Proinflammatory			
IL-1-α/β	✓	UVB	IL-1 RI, RII
IL-6	✓	IL-1α, IFN-γ, IL-17, UVB	IL-6R
TNF-α	✓	Endotoxin, UV	TNF-RI
Immunomodulatory			
IL-4	✗	Not known	IL-4R
IL-7	✓	IFN-γ	Absent
IL-10	✗	Tape stripping, recall antigens e.g. poison ivy	IL-10R
IL-12	✓	Allergens	Absent
IL-13	✗	Vaccinia virus	IL-13Rα1
IL-15	✓	IFN-γ, UVB	IL-15R
IL-17	✗	Not known	IL-17R
IL-18	✓	Contact allergy, dsRNA	IL-18R
Growth Factors			
TGF-α	✓	TGF-α, EGF, AR, HB-EGF, Epiregulin	ErbB1 (ErbB2, ErbB3)
AR	✓	TGF-α, EGF, AR, HB-EGF, Epiregulin	ErbB1, (ErbB2, ErbB3)
HB-EGF	✓	TGF-α, EGF, AR, HB-EGF, Epiregulin	ErbB1 (ErbB2, ErbB3)
Epiregulin	✓	TGF-α, EGF, AR, HB-EGF, Epiregulin	ErbB1 (ErbB2, ErbB3)
TGF-$β_1$, TGF-$β_2$	✓	UVB	TGFβ-RI, RII (and RIII)
FGF-2 (Basic FGF)	✓	Wound healing	KGFR
FGF-10	✓	Not known	KGFR
IFG-II	✓	Not known	IGF-IR

Cytokine	Constitutive	Inducers	Receptor
PDGF-A, -B	✓	Wound healing	PDGFR-α, -β (follicular KC)
NGF	✓	Active Vitamin D$_3$	p75, TRK
VEGF	✓	HGF/SF	Absent
ET-1	✓	TGF-α, EGF, UVB, TNF-α, IL-1α	ETA, ETB
SCF	✓	Not known	Absent
Colony stimulating Factors			
GM-CSF	✓	Wound healing, tumours	GM-CSFR
G-CSF	✓	Wound healing, tumours	G-CSFR
M-CSF	✓	Wound healing, LPS	M-CSFR
Interferons			
IFN-α/β	✗	Viruses, UVB, dsRNA	IFN-α/βR
IFN-κ	✓	Viruses, dsRNA, IFN-α/β	IFN-α/βR
IFN-γ	✗	Not known	IFN-γ-R
Chemokines			
CXCL1 (GROα)	✓	TNF-α ± IFN-γ, UVB	CXCR2
CXCL8 (IL-8)	✓	TNF-α	CXCR2
CXCL9 (Mig)	✓	IFN-γ	Absent
CXCL10 (IP-10)	✓	IFN-γ, TNF-α	Absent
CXCL12 (SDF-1α)	✗	Not known	CXCR4
CCL11, 24, 26 (Eotaxin-1,2,3)	✗	IL-1α, TNF-α + IFN-γ, TNF-α + IL-4	CCR3
CCL20 (MIP-3α)	✓	IL1α, TNF-α	Absent
CCL27 (CTACK)	✓	Nickel exposure, TNF-α, IL-1β	Absent
CCL2 (MCP-1)	✗	TNF-α, IFN-γ	Absent
CCL5 (RANTES)	✗	TNF-α, IFN-γ	Absent

and STAT-2 with IFN-α, -β, and -γ, STAT-3 with IL-6 and IL-10, and STAT-6 with IL-4 and IL-13.

SOCS-1 is induced by IFN-γ or IL-4 and is a crucial regulator of IFN-γ/STAT-1 and IL-4/STAT-6 signalling in KCs. Thus SOCS-1 may contribute to homeostasis of the Th-1 and Th-2 signals in KCs.

SOCS-3 is induced by IFN-γ or IL-6, and regulates IFN-γ/STAT-1 and IL-6/STAT-3 signalling. Unlike monocytes, IL-6 does not enhance the expression of SOCS-1 in KCs, nor does the latter inhibit IL-6/STAT-3 signalling. Furthermore, epidermal growth factor (EGF), which phosphorylates STAT-3, has no effect on the levels of SOCS/CIS molecules.

1.3.1.4 Growth factors

KCs constitutively produce, at low levels, several different families of growth factors and their receptors (Table 1.4). Autocrine and paracrine effects of these growth factors serve to regulate KC proliferation and differentiation. Dysregulation of this process results in diseases of epidermal hyperproliferation such as psoriasis.

EGF-family growth factors

Members of the EGF family of growth factors have a structure consisting of one or more EGF domains, a transmembrane domain and six conserved cysteine residues. Their membrane-anchored precursors undergo enzymatic cleavage to release mature soluble forms, which act as autocrine growth factors. In addition some members of the EGF family can act as growth factors to adjacent cells whilst still attached to the membrane.

Transforming growth factor (**TGF**)-**α** is a polypeptide structurally related to EGF, which binds to EGF receptors inducing a variety of effects on target cells. These include induction of tumour cell growth and oncogene expression, promotion of angiogenesis (blood vessel formation) and induction of wound healing. TGF-α was initially assumed to be an embryonic growth factor that is inappropriately expressed during neoplasia, until it was discovered that it was synthesized by primary cultures of normal, human KCs. Furthermore the addition of exogenous TGF-α or EGF to the cultures increased the levels of TGF-α mRNA expression demonstrating an auto-induction effect via EGF receptors expressed on basal KCs. There are four tyrosine kinase EGF receptors, ErbB1 (also called EGFR), ErbB2, ErbB3 and ErbB4, the first three of which are present on KCs. ErbB1, the main receptor expressed in normal epidermis, is essential for KC function and binds the four EGF family members synthesized by KCs (see below).

Amphiregulin (**AR**), heparin-binding EGF-like growth factor (**HB-EGF**) and **epiregulin** are additional members of the EGF family also involved in the regulation of epidermal growth, but are present in lower amounts in the epidermis than TGF-α. All of the EGF family members are capable of inducing other EGF family growth factors in a process termed cross-induction.

TGF-β

TGF-β is a member of a complex family of structurally related growth and differentiation factors. In contrast to TGF-α, the homodimer TGF-β has a reversible inhibitory effect on KC growth, although it stimulates proliferation of some fibroblast cell types in culture. In addition, TGF-β stimulates secretion of KC-derived fibronectin and plasminogen activator activity, and modulates lymphocyte function by suppressing IL-2 activity and inhibiting lymphocyte proliferation. Three subtypes of TGF-β (TGF-$β_1$ -$β_2$ and -$β_3$) are present in humans in various combinations in most nucleated cell types; KCs constitutively produce TGF-$β_1$ and TGF-$β_2$. The proteins are synthesized as inactive precursors, which must be cleaved to form active dimers. The various forms of TGF-β bind to a set of three structurally and functionally distinct cell surface receptors present on most cell types including KCs; high affinity types I and II, and low affinity type III. Transduction events are triggered when type I and type II receptors associate during TGF-β binding.

Fibroblast growth factors

Keratinocyte growth factor (KGF) is a fibroblast-derived member of the fibroblast growth factor (FGF) family, designated FGF-7, which is a potent mitogen for KCs. The KGF receptor (KGFR) is a transmembrane tyrosine kinase that is a splice variant of the FGFR-2 gene and binds both KGF and acidic FGF (FGF-1) with high affinity, and basic FGF (FGF-2) at low affinity. Epithelial cells selectively express KGFR, whereas FGFR-2 is present on a variety of different cell types. Basic FGF, produced by KCs, accelerates skin repair during wound healing whilst KGF is involved in the growth of hair follicles. Another fibroblast growth factor, FGF-10, has been detected in dermal papilla cells, outer sheath cells and KCs and may act as a growth factor for hair.

Insulin-like growth factors

Insulin growth factor-I (IGF-I), previously called somatomedin C, is a 7.5 kDa polypeptide present in most tissues and in high concentrations in plasma, and produced by melanocytes and fibroblasts in the skin. KCs produce IGF-II, a member of the same family of structurally related hormones. Both factors regulate KC proliferation and differentiation via synergistic interactions with EGF or EGF-like factors. The receptor for both IGF-I and IGF-II (IGF-1R) is expressed by basal KCs in normal epidermis and is composed of a 125 kDa protein that is extracellular and binds ligand, and a 95 kDa transmembrane protein with extracellular and cytoplasmic domains. IGF-1R binds with high affinity to IGF-I and with low or intermediate affinity to insulin and IGF-II, respectively. KCs also produce IGF-binding proteins (IGFBPs) that modulate these interactions; IGFBP-3, which inhibits both IGF-I and IGF-II, and IGFBP-6, which is a relatively specific inhibitor for IGF-II.

Other growth factors

Other growth factors produced by KCs that have autocrine and/or paracrine effects include platelet-derived growth factor (PDGF), nerve growth factor (NGF), vascular endothelial growth factor (VEGF), endothelin-1 (ET-1) and stem cell factor (SCF).

PDGF consists of two related polypeptide chains A and B that form disulphide-linked homo- or hetero-dimers with overlapping biological activities, which are secreted to the outside of the plasma membrane. KCs synthesize all the isoforms of PDGF (AA, AB and BB), but only follicular KCs express PDGF-specific receptors (A and B receptors), consistent with the effects of the growth factor on hair follicle development. The main effects of PDGF are, however, on the proliferation of dermal cells such as fibroblasts, microvascular endothelial cells and smooth muscle cells, and as a chemoattractant for PMNs, monocytes, fibroblasts and smooth muscle cells during wound healing.

NGF is a peptide synthesized by KCs that has regulatory effects on the survival and differentiation of sensory and sympathetic neurons, and is implicated in skin re-innervation during wound healing. NGF has an autocrine effect on the proliferation of KCs, via low affinity (p75) and high affinity (TRK) NGF-specific receptors. Melanocytes also express NGF receptors and are prevented from undergoing UV-induced apoptosis by the effects of NGF.

VEGF stimulates angiogenesis and hyperpermeability of dermal blood vessels, as well as inducing the endothelial cell production of PDGF and HB-EGF via the VEGF receptors, kdr and flt-1. Levels of VEGF are induced by hepatocyte growth factor/scatter factor (HGF/SF) produced by fibroblasts and smooth muscle cells and by cytokines such as TGF-α and EGF.

ET-1 is a potent vasoconstrictive peptide produced by both endothelial cells and KCs. KCs express the ETA and ETB receptors and respond to ET-1 by proliferation through the ETA receptor, and by down-regulation of ET-1 via the ETB receptor. Melanocytes also respond to ET-1, which induces proliferation, melanogenesis and dendrite formation. Levels of KC-derived ET-1 are increased by UVB irradiation, TNF-α and IL-1α.

SCF is a growth factor for cells expressing the c-kit marker. In skin it is produced by KCs, and acts on mast cells and melanocytes.

1.3.1.5 Colony stimulating factors

GM-CSF, G-CSF (granulocyte colony stimulating factor) and M-CSF (monocyte colony stimulating factor) are constitutively produced by KCs and up-regulated during wound healing (Table 1.4). CSFs are pleiotropic cytokines that affect the differentiation and function of various leukocyte types, and of non-lymphoid cells such as fibroblasts and endothelial cells. KC-derived GM-CSF is of particular importance for LC viability and functional maturation. In addition, CSFs regulate KC proliferation via expression of CSF-specific receptors and induce the production of other cytokines such as TGF-β.

1.3.1.6 Interferons

Interferons (IFNs) comprise a family of cytokines that exert anti-viral, anti-proliferative, anti-tumour and immunomodulatory effects. They can be subdivided into members of type I, including 13 IFN-α and one IFN-β, and of type II which is represented by IFN-γ alone. KCs do not constitutively produce IFN-α, IFN-β or IFN-γ, but, in common with most cell types, can be induced to synthesize the type I IFNs by various factors such as viruses, double-stranded RNA and UVB. In contrast, a novel type I IFN called IFN-κ, which has 30% homology to the other type I IFNs, has recently been detected which is constitutively synthesized by KCs alone [12]. IFN-κ, which binds to the same receptor as IFN-α and IFN-β, can also be induced by viral infections and double-stranded RNA. The type I receptor is composed of two chains, IFNAR1 and IFNAR2c and differs from the receptor for IFN-γ; both are expressed by KCs.

1.3.1.7 Chemokines

Chemokines are polypeptides that play a vital role in the recruitment of leukocytes into inflammatory skin [9]. CXCL8 (IL-8) and GRO (or melanoma growth stimulatory activity) are heparin-binding 8 kDa polypeptides which are potent PMN and/or T lymphocyte chemoattractants. Three different GRO genes have been identified, α (CXCL1), β (CXCL2) and γ (CXCL3) which are 85-90% homologous at the protein level. CXCL8 and CXCL1 are constitutively produced by KC, as are CXCL9 (monokine induced by interferon-gamma, Mig) and CXCL10 (IFN-γ-inducible protein, IP-10) at low levels (Table 1.4). However KCs express the chemokine receptor CXCR2, but not CXCR3, enabling them to respond to CXCL8 and CXCL1, but not to CXCL10.

KCs also synthesize, but lack receptors for, the chemokines CCL20 (MIP-3α) and CCL27 (CTACK) (see Section 1.1.6.2). In addition, KCs are capable of producing two other CC chemokines, CCL5 (regulated on activation, normal T expressed and secreted, RANTES) and CCL2 (monocyte chemoattractant protein (MCP)-1) after IFN-γ or TNF-α stimulation. Conversely, KCs express the receptor CCR3 which is specific for eotaxins-1, 2, 3 (CCL11, CCL24, CCL26) produced by various cell types, but not constitutively by KCs. Eotaxins are important factors in asthma and allergy, and attract eosinophils and Th-2 cells into the lungs and skin. In addition, KCs express CXCR4, the receptor for CXCL12 (stromal cell-derived factor (SDF)-1α), which is produced by epithelial cells of sweat glands, but not by KCs.

1.3.2 Response to cytokines

KCs respond to cytokines by increased/decreased proliferation, differentiation, the upregulation of surface molecules and/or the production of cytokines and chemokines. The ability of KCs to respond to a cytokine is dependent upon both the expression of specific receptors at sufficient levels, and a functional signal transduction pathway.

1.3.2.1 Proliferation/Differentiation

Various cytokines can affect the proliferation of normal, human KCs *in vitro*. Some are stimulatory, such as IL-6, IL-8 (CXCR8), TGF-α /EGF and possibly IL-1 and GM-CSF, whereas others are inhibitory in a reversible manner such as TNF-α, TGF-β, IFN-γ and IL-10. TGF-β, and possibly IFN-γ also exert effects on the differentiation of KC in culture. In addition, the culture conditions in which the cells are grown appear to play an important part in the type and degree of response. For example, IL-6 is stimulatory for normal KC proliferation under serum-free conditions, but not in the presence of serum.

1.3.2.2 Up-regulation of surface molecules

KCs in normal skin express adhesion molecules at low levels, but these can be up-regulated by stimulation with cytokines (summarised in Table 1.5). After stimulation by non-specific stimuli, KCs release the proinflammatory cytokines IL-1 and TNF-α, and express ICAM-1. IL-1 and TNF-α activate dermal endothelium resulting in up-regulation of the expression of the addressins ICAM-1, E-selectin and VCAM-1. This enables adhesion of circulating leukocytes such as CLA+ memory T cells and PMNs to the dermal endothelium (see Section 1.1.6). Interaction between T cells and KCs involves LFA-1 and its ligand ICAM-1, respectively.

IFN-γ produced by activated T cells in the skin contributes to ICAM-1 up-regulation on KCs, but also induces MHC Class II (predominately HLA-DR and HLA-DQ), a Class II-like molecule

Table 1.5 Cytokine-induced surface molecules on keratinocytes

ICAM-1
- Adhesion molecule that interacts with LFA-1 on T cells

MHC Class II
- HLA-DR, -DQ, -DM, invariant chain
- Involved in antigen/superantigen presentation to T cells

BB-1 (B7-3)
- Binds to CD28 on T cells
- Non-functional costimulatory molecule?

CD40
- Binds to CD40L on T cells
- Activation induces KC cytokine production, upregulation of ICAM-1 and anti-apoptotic Bcl-x

CDw60
- Ganglioside in plasma membrane
- Involved in cell proliferation and differentiation

HLA-DM, and invariant chain expression by KCs which normally lack or express low levels of these molecules. All of these molecules are required for the generation of functional MHC Class II/peptide complexes for presentation to T cells (see Section 1.3.4). In addition, IL-8 can also induce HLA-DR expression by KCs, whilst IL-10 inhibits the induction of HLA-DR by IFN-γ.

Activated KCs also express BB-1, a ligand for CD28 expressed by T cells. BB-1 is one of a family of B7 molecules (B7-3) expressed by professional APCs which, on binding to CD28, delivers a costimulatory signal required for optimal activation of T cells via the TCR/CD3 complex. However, in contrast to the B7 molecules B7-1 (CD80) and B7-2 (CD86), BB-1 on the surface of KCs may not be stimulatory (see Section 1.3.4).

In addition to lymphoid cells, CD40, a member of the TNF-α superfamily, is functionally expressed by normal human KCs. The CD40/gp39 pathway is an important feature of B cell/T cell collaboration leading to activation, proliferation or differentiation of B cells. KC CD40 expression is markedly up-regulated by stimulation with IFN-γ, but not with TNF-α or IL-1β. Activation of KC by monoclonal CD40 antibody or ligation with soluble gp39 (the CD40 ligand, CD40L), results in an increase in secretion of IL-6, IL-8 and TNF-α by the activated KCs and up-regulation of ICAM-1 and Bcl-x, an inhibitor of apoptosis (see Section 1.3.5). Furthermore, ligation of CD40 on KC by CD40L-transfected L cells, or by soluble CD40L, leads to inhibition of proliferation, and differentiation of the cells.

Another molecule, CDw60, is restricted to melanocytes in normal skin, but is expressed by KCs in the lesional skin of psoriasis patients. CDw60, which is involved in T cell activation, is present on approximately 25% of peripheral blood T cells. The UM4D4 antibody that detects CDw60 has been shown to bind to the o-acetylated form of ganglioside GD3, Gangliosides, sialylated glycosphingolipids located in the plasma membrane, are thought to play a role in the control of cell proliferation and differentiation, as well as in cell surface recognition.

1.3.2.3 Cytokine/chemokine production

The interaction of a cytokine with its specific receptor on KCs may lead to induction of its own synthesis, (TGF-α) and/or to the production of other cytokines (the induction of IL-8 by TNF-α). Alternatively, stimulation by one cytokine may lead to the down-regulation of the receptors for a different cytokine such as IL-8 and IL-10R, respectively. Cytokines can also act in synergy, for example, IFN-γ and TNF-α, or can cross-induce other members of the same family, as in the case of the EGF family of growth factors. Cytokines may also stimulate KCs to produce chemokines, as in the case of CCL5 (RANTES) and CCL2 (MCP-1), which are produced after IFN-γ or TNF-α stimulation.

1.3.3 Integrins

The integrins are a family of heterodimeric membrane glycoproteins, expressed on the cell surface but linked to the cytoskeleton, which mediate cell-cell and cell-extracellular matrix adhesion, and transmit signals, both into and out from cells. Each integrin consists of two non-covalently associated subunits, α and β, of which at least 18 different α and 8 different β subunits have been identified. Several α chains can associate with a single β chain; the reverse is also true, although to a lesser extent. In human epidermis, integrin expression is largely confined to the basal layer where they mediate cell adhesion and migration, and regulate stratification and the initiation of terminal differentiation [13]. Furthermore, the integrin heterodimers, four of which contain the β_1 subunit, are located to discrete KC membrane domains (Table 1.6). Thus $\alpha_2\beta_1$ and $\alpha_3\beta_1$ integrins are arranged on the lateral surface of basal cells and on adjacent suprabasal cells implicating a role in cell-cell adhesion of epithelial cells. In contrast, $\alpha_6\beta_4$ is strictly restricted to the basal aspect of basal KCs, and hemidesmosomes, suggesting a role as a basal lamina receptor. This polarisation of expression is markedly altered in situations in which epidermal cells hyperproliferate, such as during wound healing, when integrins are expressed on suprabasal KCs.

1.3.4 Antigen/Superantigen Presentation

As described earlier, KCs can be induced to express MHC Class II antigens and accessory proteins in response to IFN-γ. This raises the possibility that these cells can present antigen to T cells. Recognition of antigenic peptides presented by professional APCs such as macrophages or dendritic cells leads to T cell activation. In contrast, antigen presentation by cells which lack accessory function can lead to a state of specific non-responsiveness (anergy), characterised by a failure of T cells to produce IL-2.

Early studies showed that presentation of antigen by KCs pre-treated with IFN-γ induced anergy in T cell clones, suggesting that KCs did not provide the accessory signals required for T cell activation. However, subsequent studies have shown that KCs can present *M.leprae* antigens or herpes simplex virus-related antigens to cytotoxic and/or proliferative T cells and induce a functional response [14,15]. Furthermore, IFN-γ-treated KCs have been shown to provide the necessary costimulatory

Table 1.6 Keratinocyte-expressed integrin heterodimers and their ligands

Integrin heterodimer	Constitutive/ Induced (C/I)	Ligand	Location
$\alpha_2\beta_1$	C	Collagen	Lateral surface of basal KCs Suprabasal KCs
$\alpha_3\beta_1$	C	Laminin 5	Lateral surface of basal KCs Suprabasal KCs
$\alpha_v\beta_5$ (weak)	C	Vitronectin	Basal KCs
$\alpha_6\beta_4$	C	Laminin	Basal aspect of basal KCs. In hemidesmosomes
$\alpha_v\beta_6$	I	Fibronectin, Tenascin	Basal KCs
$\alpha_5\beta_1$	I	Fibronectin	Basal KC plasma membrane
$\alpha_9\beta_1$	C/I	Tenascin	Basal KCs
$\alpha_v\beta_8$	C	Vitronectin	Suprabasal

signals required to support a T cell-mediated response to two bacterial-derived superantigens, staphylococcal enterotoxins A and B [16]. These signals were induced by interaction between LFA-1 and ICAM-1, an adhesion molecule ligand pair involved in T cell/KC adhesion. However, KCs failed to stimulate the proliferation of T cells from a genetically non-identical (allogeneic) individual.

These conflicting findings probably arose from differences in culture conditions including the use of adherent versus suspensions of KCs, different numbers and ratios of T cells to KCs, nature of the antigen etc. Thus overall it seems that, if the culture conditions are optimal, HLA-DR$^+$ KCs are capable of functioning as professional APCs, albeit with a different mechanism of costimulation.

1.3.5 Apoptosis

Apoptosis or programmed cell death is an active process of cell deletion that can be differentiated from necrosis by characteristic features such as chromatin condensation, DNA fragmentation and blebbing of the plasma membrane. In addition to embryogenesis, tissue atrophy and tumour regression, there is now convincing evidence that apoptosis occurs in normal skin, contributing to epidermal homeostasis by removing excess cells and maintaining normal cell numbers [17]. KC apoptosis has been postulated to be involved in hair bulb cycling, response to sunburn and prevention of neoplasia and can be triggered by various factors including growth factor deprivation, UVB irradiation, and by oligomerization of Fas (CD95) by the Fas ligand (FasL, CD95L) or anti-Fas antibody. Fas antigen is a transmembrane molecule that belongs to the nerve growth factor/TNFR superfamily. Its corresponding ligand is a type II transmembrane protein belonging to the TNF-α family, which includes other cell surface molecules that promote (p55 TNF-αR) or prevent (CD40) apoptosis. Both Fas and FasL are minimally expressed, if at all, in normal epidermis. However, Fas is markedly up-regulated on KCs in a number of inflammatory and infectious skin diseases, and after culture with IFN-γ or a tumour promoter (12-O-tetradecanoylphorbol-13-acetate, TPA) [17]. FasL, which is present on activated T cells, can also be induced on KC by UVB irradiation. Normal KCs also express at very low levels the anti-apoptotic molecules Bcl-2 and the long form of Bcl-x (Bcl-x$_L$). Another anti-apoptotic molecule, CD40, present on basal KCs in normal epidermis, was described earlier in Section 1.3.2.2.

1.4 Mast cells

Mast cells are bone-marrow-derived cells that are released as committed precursors into the blood, from which they migrate into tissues and develop into mature mast cells under the influence of cytokines.

Mast cells in the skin are located in the dermis, and not at the interface with the external environment as are mast cells of the bronchial or nasal mucosa. Mast cells at mucosal and connective tissue sites can be differentiated by their neutral protease content. In intestinal mucosa, most mast cells contain tryptase alone and are therefore termed MCT. In the skin, most mast cells contain chymase and carboxypeptidase, as well as tryptase and are termed MCTC.

1.4.1 Mast cell activation

Mast cells are characterised by the cell surface expression of high affinity receptors for IgE, termed FcεR1, the α subunits of which bind to the Fcε chain of IgE. Cross-linking of IgE by the interaction of allergen with specific determinants on the Fab part of the immunoglobulin brings the receptors into juxtaposition and initiates mast cell activation. In addition, skin mast cells, unlike those of the lung, tonsil or large intestine, may also be activated by non-immunological stimuli, for example, substance P present in nearby sensory nerves in the dermis. Other non-immunological stimuli include vasoactive intestinal peptide (VIP), somatostatin and the complement anaphylatoxins C5a and C3a. Once activated, mast cells produce a variety of factors, including enzymes, mediators and cytokines (Table 1.7).

1.4.2 Mediators and cytokines

Mast cells produce three main types of mediators involved in the production of the symptoms of immediate hypersensitivity or allergic reactions; histamine, prostaglandins and leukotrienes. Histamine is a primary amine synthesized from histidine in the Golgi apparatus and then transported to the granules where it is stored bound to the glycosaminoglycan side chains of heparin. After mast cell activation, histamine is disassociated from the granules and, upon rupture of the cytoplasmic membranes, is released from the cell. Extracellular histamine has a wide variety of biological effects mediated via specific H1, H2 and H3 receptors. For example, in the skin, factor XIIIa expression is induced on DDC (which express H1 and H2 receptors) after mast cell degranulation. Furthermore, after allergen injection, local vasodilation and oedema leads to the formation of a weal, whilst flare

Table 1.7 Mast cell-derived molecules

Enzymes
- Tryptase
- Chymase
- Carboxypeptidase

Mediators
- Histamine
- Prostaglandin PGD_2
- Leukotriene LTC_4

Cytokines
- Proinflammatory: IL-1β, TNF-α, IL-6
- Th-2: IL-4, IL-13, IL-5

Chemokines
- CXCL8 (IL-8)

is associated with vasodilation mediated by histamine-induced axon reflexes (see Chapter 5).

Activation of mast cells also results in the release of the fatty acid, arachidonic acid, from phospholipids in the cell membrane. Arachidonic acid can be metabolised to form either prostaglandins via the cyclo-oxygenase pathway, or leukotrienes via the lipoxygenase pathway (see Chapter 2). The major prostanoid in mast cells is prostaglandin D_2 (PGD_2), which has vasodilator properties in skin, whilst the only lipoxygenase identified is leukotriene C_4 (LTC_4). Leukotrienes promote increased permeability of post-capillary venules, manifested as a prolonged weal response to intradermal injection of allergen.

Interestingly, the characteristics of IgE-dependent and neuropeptide-induced mediator release from skin mast cells differ markedly [19] (Fig. 1.5). Thus IgE-dependent activation leads to a relatively slow, 5 minute degranulation and production of PGD_2 and LTC_4, whilst, in contrast, neuropeptide activation results in a rapid release of preformed mediators, without production of PGD_2 and LTC_4, after 15 seconds. The latter enables skin mast cells to extend their potential effects to control of local inflammation, blood flow regulation and angiogenesis.

Mast cells synthesize a variety of cytokines including proinflammatory IL-1β, TNF-α and IL-6, the Th-2 cytokines IL-4, IL-13 and IL-5, and the chemokine CXCL8. These cytokines are released, preformed or newly generated, upon mast cell activation and contribute to up-regulation of allergic inflammation via their effects on T cells and eosinophils.

1.5 Dermal endothelial cells

The endothelial cell lining of dermal blood vessels are characterised by flat squame-like cells which contrast with the tall columnar or cuboidal endothelial cells of the high endothelial venules (HEV) found in lymphoid organs. HEV can also be found at sites of chronic inflammation or persistent antigenic inflammation such as the dermis in psoriasis and the synovium in rheumatoid arthritis. Inside endothelial cells, Wiebel-Palade bodies store P-selectin and chemokines such as IL-8 whose production is induced by proinflammatory cytokines.

1.5.1. Leukocyte recruitment

The recruitment of leukocytes into tissues involves interaction between an array of adhesion molecules expressed by both leukocytes and endothelium cells (described in Section 1.1.6.).

Figure 1.5 Different characteristics of IgE-dependent and neuropeptide-induced degranulation of mast cells. PLC/PLD = phospholipase C/D; PKC = protein kinase C; COX = cyclooxygenase; 5-LP = 5-lipoxygenase; PSG = pertussis-sensitive G protein.

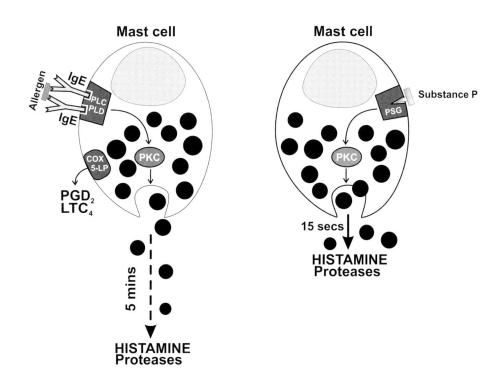

Circulating cells enter the tissues via intercellular junctions, which consist of a complex network of transmembrane molecules linked to cytoskeletal proteins inside the endothelial cell. The structure of these junctions can be rapidly altered in a reversible manner to accommodate the passage of cells from the blood. However, the mechanisms responsible for the opening of intercellular junctions remain unknown. PECAM-1 (platelet endothelial cell adhesion molecule, CD31), which is constitutively expressed by endothelial cells, is localised at intercellular junctions where it plays an important role in adhesion of endothelial cells and diapedesis of leukocytes.

1.5.2 Cytokines and cytokine receptors

Endothelial cells both synthesize cytokines and chemokines (mostly after activation), and respond to a range of cytokines via specific receptors (Table 1.8) resulting in the activation of distinct functional activities, including those of immunity, inflammation and angiogenesis.

Table 1.8 Cytokines, chemokines and receptors produced by dermal endothelial cells

Mediator	C	Inducers	Receptor	Comments
Proinflammatory				
IL-1	✓	IL-1, TNF-α	IL-1 RI	No IL-1ra or IL-1RII
IL-6	✗	IL-1, TNF-α (IL-4, IL-13)	Soluble IL-6R	IL-6/IL-6R induces chemokines
TNF-α	✗	IL-1β, LPS	TNF-RI TNF-RII	RI in Golgi and cytoplasmic vacuoles RII in membrane
Other cytokines				
IL-3	✗	✗	IL-3R	Weak agonist of migration/proliferation
IL-4	✗	✗	IL-4R	IL-4 induces VCAM-1 (and MCP-1)
IL-13	✗	✗	IL-13R	IL-13 induces VCAM-1 (and MCP-1)
IFN-γ	✗	✗	IFN-γR	IFN-γ + TNF-α induce MHC Class II and augment IL-3Rα
Colony Stimulating Factors				
SCF	✓	IL-1, TNF-α, LPS	c-kit	
G-CSF	✓	IL-1, TNF-α, LPS	G-CSFR	Weak agonist of migration/proliferation
M-CSF	✓	IL-1, TNF-α, LPS	✗	
GM-CSF	✓	IL-1, TNF-α, LPS	GM-CSFR	Weak agonist of migration/proliferation
EPO	✗	✗	EPO-R	Weak agonist of migration/proliferation
Chemokines				
CXCL1	✗	IL-1, TNF-α	✗	
CXCL5	✗	IL-1, TNF-α	✗	
CXCL8	✓	IL-1, TNF-α	CXCR1	
CXCL10	✗	IL-1, TNF-α, IFN-γ	CXCR3	
CCL2	✓	IFN-γ, IL-1, TNF-α	✗	
CCL5	✗	IL-1, TNF-α + IFN-γ	CCR3	
CCL7	✗	IL-1, TNF-α	CCR3	
CX3CL1	✗	IL-1, TNF-α	✗	
CCL17	✓	TNF-α, IFN-γ	CCR4	
CCL20	✓	IL-1,TNF-α	✗	

1.5.2.1 Proinflammatory cytokines

Endothelial cells release endogenous IL-1α and express the activating receptor IL-1RI, but do not produce the IL-1 antagonist IL-1ra or express the decoy IL-1 receptor IL-1RII suggesting a lack of regulation of IL-1 activity. Unlike KCs, endothelial cells preferentially express the TNF-R2 receptor for TNF-α on the endothelial cell membrane. However, although the TNF-R1 receptor is only expressed at low levels on the endothelial cell surface, it is abundantly present in the Golgi apparatus and in cytoplasmic vacuoles and is the main receptor used for activation of endothelial cells by TNF-α.

IL-1 and TNF-α induce the production of various cytokines by endothelial cells including IL-1 itself and IL-6. IL-6 together with soluble IL-6 receptor has an unexpected functional effect on endothelial cells; the induction of chemokine production, implying a role for the cytokine in leukocyte migration into tissues. In addition, IL-1 and TNF-α induce production of the prostaglandin PGI_2, nitric oxide (NO) and platelet-activating factor (PAF) by endothelial cells. PGI_2 and NO act as vasodilatory mediators facilitating the migration of leukocytes from blood into tissues. In contrast, NO also appears to inhibit cytokine-induced expression of adhesion molecules and cytokine production by endothelial cells. These effects are mediated by inhibition of the transcription factor, nuclear factor (NF)-κB, via induction and stabilization of NF-κB inhibitor.

TNF-α, in combination with IFN-γ, increases expression of the α chain of the IL-3 receptor (IL-3Rα) on endothelial cells, whilst IL-3 and TNF-α act together to increase IL-8 (CXCL8) and adhesion molecule levels.

1.5.2.2 Th-2 cytokines/growth factors

IL-4 selectively induces expression of VCAM-1 by endothelial cells, an adhesion molecule recognized by VLA-4 on the surface of eosinophils, whilst inhibiting ICAM-1 and E-selectin expression. In addition, IL-4, together with other mediators, induces endothelial cell production of IL-6 and MCP-1. IL-13 has similar effects on endothelial cells and probably acts through shared IL-4 and IL-13 receptor subunits. These effects may be involved in the local development of Th-2-type responses such as the recruitment of eosinophils and basophils.

VEGF produced by KCs induces synthesis of PDGF and HB-EGF by dermal endothelial cells via the VEGF receptors, kdr and flt-1. VEGF is probably responsible for induction of angiogenesis during wound healing and in psoriatic skin, which is characterised by dilated and tortuous capillaries in the papillary dermis.

1.5.2.3 Colony stimulating factors

Endothelial cells produce various haematopoietic growth factors, including stem cell factor (SCF), GM-CSF, G-CSF, and M-CSF whose levels can be induced or increased by stimulation with IL-1 and TNF-α, and other stimuli such as LPS. Endothelial cells also respond to G-CSF, GM-CSF, IL-3 and erythropoietin (EPO; a hormone produced by the liver or kidney), but not M-CSF, via specific receptors. These factors have relatively weak effects on migration and proliferation of endothelial cells, but increase their responsiveness to other signals.

1.5.2.4 Chemokines

Chemokines produced by dermal endothelial cells include IL-8, Mig, IP-10, epithelial-neutrophil activating peptide 78 (ENA78) and GRO-α (CXCL8, CXCL9, CXCL10, CXCL5, CXCL1), MCP-1, MCP-3 and RANTES (CCL2, CCL7, CCL5) and fractalkine (CX3CL1) (Table 1.8). Chemokine production may be induced by IL-1, TNF-α and adhesion molecules expressed by monocytes and platelets in close apposition to endothelial cells. In addition, IFN-γ induces CCL2 in microvascular endothelial cells in common with its effects on monocytes. Chemokines displayed on the surface of endothelial cells play a vital role in the multistep process of leukocyte recruitment; see Section 1.1.6. Dermal endothelial cells also express various receptors for chemokines (Table 1.8).

1.5.3 Antigen presentation

In common with KCs, endothelial cells may present antigen to T cells under certain circumstances [20]. This requires that they express sufficient levels of MHC Class II molecules, which are up-regulated by IFN-γ at sites of inflammation. The costimulatory molecule used by endothelial cells in antigen presentation is LFA-3, which binds to CD2 and ICAM-1 on T cells. Neither endothelial cells nor KCs express the B7 costimulatory molecules, CD80 and CD86. The interaction between endothelial cells and CD4$^+$ T cells may prime the latter for subsequent stimulation with antigen or cytokines present at inflammatory sites. Furthermore adhesion molecules may be induced on endothelial cells as a result of endothelial cell CD40/T cell CD40L interactions.

1.6 Fibroblasts

Fibroblasts are dermal cells of mesenchymal origin present in the connective tissue, which synthesize extracellular matrix proteins (ECM) such as collagen, fibronectin and tenascin. They play an important role in wound healing and in regulation of the proliferation and differentiation of KCs in the epidermal layer via the production of cytokines and growth factors.

1.6.1 Cytokines, growth factors and chemokines

Fibroblasts produce a variety of cytokines, growth factors and chemokines (Table 1.9). Proinflammatory cytokines produced include IL-6 and IL-1α, IL-1β and the IL-1 inhibitor IL-1ra, which are retained in the cytosol. However, TNF-α is not synthesized by fibroblasts. Production of these cytokines is up-regulated by stimulation of fibroblasts with 0.5M NaCl, H_2O_2, or the Gram-negative bacterial components, LPS and porins, which also induce ICAM-1 expression. Fibroblasts also produce TGF-β whose levels are increased by treatment with heparin, and express receptors for GM-CSF, but the latter has no effect on cell growth.

Fibroblasts produce KGF and IGF-I, which stimulate KC proliferation, and HG/SF that induces KC VEGF production. The two growth factors target KCs, but are not synthesized by KCs themselves. KGF production is up-regulated by IL-1, IL-6, TGF-α (produced by KC) and PDGF-BB (also a mitogen and chemoattractant for fibroblasts).

Fibroblasts express receptors for the Th-2 cytokines IL-4 and IL-13. These cytokines, or TGF-β,

Table 1.9 Production and response to cytokines by fibroblasts

Production of cytokines/growth factors
- IL-1α, IL-1β, IL-6, IL-1ra, TGF-β
- KGF and IGF-I stimulate KC proliferation
- HG/SF stimulates KC production of VEGF

Response to cytokines
- IL-4/IL-13 stimulate collagen and TIM-1
- IL-4/IL-13 inhibit IL-1β-induced MMP1 and MMP3 production
- TGF-β stimulates collagen, VEGF and CTGF production
- IL-17 stimulates release of various cytokines
- IL-4 induces TARC and eotaxin
- TNF-α induces TARC
- TNF-α and IFN-γ induce fractalkaline, IL-8, MCP-1 and RANTES

stimulate production of collagen, which is suppressed by interferons (α, β or γ). Furthermore, IL-4 or IL-13 inhibit IL-1β-induced increases in fibroblast-derived matrix metalloproteinases (MMP)-1 and MMP-3, enzymes that degrade ECM and, conversely, stimulate the production of tissue inhibitor of metalloproteinase (TIMP-1). In addition, fibroblasts respond to another CD4$^+$ T cell-derived cytokine, IL-17 by the release of cytokines.

TGF-β also induces fibroblast production of VEGF and connective tissue growth factor (CTGF), a mitogen and chemoattractant for fibroblasts, which is not constitutively produced by fibroblasts. The effects induced by TGF-β are inhibited by TNF-α, probably via its down-regulatory effects on the type II, TGF-β receptor (TbetaRII).

Two chemokines, CCL17 (TARC) and CCL11 (eotaxin) are produced by fibroblasts after stimulation with IL-4. TNF-α also induces CCL17, and, in combination with IL-1β or (more effectively) IFN-γ, induces delayed production of soluble CX3CL1 (fractalkine), and rapid production of CXCL8 (IL-8), CCL2 (MCP-1) and CCL5 (RANTES).

Summary

The cellular skin immune system consists of:

- Activated memory CD4$^+$ and CD8$^+$ T cell subsets expressing specific TCR Vβ families that are either oligoclonally (antigen) or polyclonally (superantigen) expanded, and a small subset of oligoclonally expanded TCR γδ+ T cells.
- LCs, immature dendritic cells with a characteristic profile of surface markers including receptors for antigen presentation, homing to skin and facilitating phagocytosis. LCs take up and process antigen in the epidermis and then, as mature cells, migrate to regional lymph nodes and initiate antigen-specific primary T cell responses.
- DDC comprising a heterogenous population of efficient APCs.
- Highly phagocytic macrophages whose main function is to scavenge microorganisms, apoptotic cells, immune complexes and cellular debris.
- KCs, the major source of proinflammatory and immunomodulatory cytokines and chemokines in the epidermis, whose function is modulated by various cytokines in an autocrine or paracrine manner.
- Mast cells, activated by binding of IgE or neuropeptides to specific receptors, that release a mixture of mediators involved in local inflammation, blood flow regulation and angiogenesis.
- Endothelial cells that mediate the recruitment of leukocytes, and produce cytokines and chemokines.
- Fibroblasts, which play an important role in wound healing and regulate KC proliferation and differentiation via the production of cytokines and growth factors.

References

1. Bentley G.A. & Mariuzza R.A. The structure of the T cell antigen receptor. Ann.Rev. Immunol. 1996; **14:** 563-90.

2. Menssen A., Vollmer S., Trommler P., Sander C., Prinz J.C. Analysis of the TCRBV repertoire of T cells in normal, human skin: Evidence for a restricted diversity. J.Invest.Dermatol. 2000; **115:** 66-73.

3. Alouf J.E. & Muller-Alouf H. Staphylococcal and streptococcal superantigens: molecular, biological and clinical aspects. Int.J.Med.Microbiol. 2003; **292:** 429-40.

4. Holtmeier W., Pfander M., Hennemann A., Zollner T.M., Kaufmann R., Caspary W.F. The TCR δ repertoire in normal human skin is restricted and distinct from the TCR δ repertoire in the peripheral blood. J.Invest.Dermatol. 2001; **116:** 275-80.

5. Schon M.P., Zollner T.M., Boehncke W.-H. The molecular basis of lymphocyte recruitment to the skin: clues for pathogenesis and selective therapies of inflammatory disorders. J.Invest.Dermatol. 2003; **121:** 951-62.

6. Larregina A.T., Morelli A.E., Spencer L.A. *et al.* Dermal-resident CD14+ cells differentiate into Langerhans cells. Nat. Immunol. 2001; **2:** 1151-8.

7. Nestle F.O., Zheng X.-G., Thompson C.B., Turka L.A., Nickoloff B.J. Characterisation of dermal dendritic cells obtained from normal human skin reveals phenotypic and functionally distinctive subsets. J.Immunol. 1993; **151:** 6535-45.

8. McLellan A.D., Heiser A., Sorg R.V., Fearnley D.B., Hart D.N.J. Dermal dendritic cells associated with T lymphocytes in normal human skin display an activated phenotype. J.Invest.Dermatol. 1998; **111:** 841-9.

9. Uchi H., Terao H., Koga T., Furue M. Cytokines and chemokines in the epidermis. J.Dermatol. Sci. 2000; **24 (Suppl 1):** S29-S38.

10. Kristensen M., Chu C.Q., Eedy D.J., Feldmann M., Brennan F.M., Breathnach S.M. Localization of tumour necrosis factor-alpha (TNF-alpha) and its receptors in normal and psoriatic skin: epidermal cells express the 55-kD but not the 75-kD TNF receptor. Clin.Exp. Immunol. 1993; **94:** 354-62.

11. Yamasaki K., Hanakawa Y., Tokumaru S. *et al.* Suppressor of cytokine signaling 1/JAB and suppressor of cytokine signaling 3/cytokine-inducible SH2 containing protein 3 negatively regulate the signal transducers and activators of transcription signalling pathway in normal human epidermal keratinocytes. J.Invest.Dermatol. 2003; **120(4):** 571-80.

12. LaFleur D.W., Nardelli B., Tsareva T. *et al.* Interferon-kappa, a novel type I interferon expressed in human keratinocytes. J.Biol.Chem. 2001; **276:** 39765-71.

13. Watt F.M. Role of integrins in regulating epidermal adhesion, growth and differentiation. EMBO J. 2002; **21:** 3919-26.

14. Mutis T., De Bueger M., Bakker A., Ottenholff T.H.M. HLA class II+ human keratinocytes present *Mycobacterium leprae* antigens to CD4+ Th1-like cells. Scand.J.Immunol. 1993; **37:** 43-51.

15. Cunningham A.L. & Noble J.R. Role of keratinocytes in human recurrent herpetic lesions. Ability to present herpes simplex virus antigen and act as targets for T lymphocyte cytotoxicity

in vitro. J.Clin.Invest. 1989; **83:** 490-6.

16. Nickoloff B.J., Mitra R.S., Green J. *et al.* Accessory cell function of keratinocytes for superantigens. Dependence on lymphocyte function-associated antigen-1/intercellular adhesion molecule-1 interaction. J.Immunol. 1993; **150:** 2148-59.

17. Weisfelner M.E. & Gottlieb A.B. The role of apoptosis in human epidermal keratinocytes. J.Drugs Dermatol. 2003; **2:** 385-91.

18. Wrone-Smith T. Discordant expression of Bcl-x and Bcl-2 by keratinocytes *in vitro* and psoriatic keratinocytes *in vivo*. Am.J.Pathol. 1995; **146:** 1079-88.

19. Church M.K., Lowman M.A., Robinson C., Holgate S.T., Benyon R.C. Interaction of neuropeptides with human mast cells. Int.Arch.Allergy Appl.Immunol. 1989; **88:** 70-8.

20. Pober J.S., Kluger M.S., Schechner J.S. Human endothelial cell presentation of antigen and the homing of memory/effector T cells to skin. Ann.N.Y.Acad.Sci. 2001; **941:** 12-25.

2

Skin Immune System: Humoral

The humoral component of the skin immune system consists of various factors including complement components, prostaglandins, leukotrienes, secretory immunoglobulins, cytokines, chemokines, neuropeptides, and anti-microbial peptides (Table 2.1). A detailed description of anti-microbial peptides will be given in Chapter 3.

2.1 Complement components

The complement system participates in both the innate (see Chapter 3) and acquired immune responses to pathogens and other foreign antigens. The epidermis contains the complement components necessary for generation of the initial C3 convertase of the alternative pathway. In addition KCs synthesize complement regulatory proteins, which allow them to modulate complement activation and protect the epidermis from damage.

2.1.1 C3 and B

KCs produce two components of the alternative complement pathway, C3 and B [1] (Fig. 2.1).

C3 is a central component of the alternative and classical complement pathways and is composed of two polypeptides linked by disulphide bonds. In the alternative complement pathway, a spontaneously formed C3 convertase cleaves C3 to give C3b and the anaphylactic C3a fragment. C3b has an intramolecular thioester bond, which allows it to bind to nearby cell surface molecules and immune complexes, and multiple binding sites for complement components. Binding of factor B, factor D and properdin (factor P) to cell-bound C3b results in the formation of stable C3 convertases (C3bBb), which can cleave C3 to generate more C3b.

Factor B is a single chain polypeptide that, on binding to C3b, is cleaved by factor D. The smaller Ba fragment is released, whilst the second fragment Bb, which contain domains with homology to the catalytic chains of other serine proteases, remains associated with C3b.

In this way, huge numbers of C3b molecules are generated which coat the surface of the bacterial cell and act as opsonins for uptake by phagocytes expressing complement receptors CR1, CR2, CR3 and CR4, or trigger activation of the terminal pathway of complement resulting in assembly of the membrane attack complex and eventual cell lysis.

Synthesis of C3 and B by cultured KCs is constitutive, and can be increased further by various proinflammatory cytokines, particularly TNF-α and IFN-γ, respectively [1]. Moreover, KC-derived C3 is regarded as a potential source of C3d,g, a constituent of the sublamina densa region of normal epidermal basement membrane. C3d,g is formed from C3b as a result of two cleavage steps by

Table 2.1 Humoral components of the SIS

Components	Epidermal producer cell types	Dermal producer cell types
Complement system		
C3	KCs	None
B	KCs	None
CR1	KCs	None
Membrane cofactor protein	Intercellular spaces, particularly of basal layers	Endothelial
Decay accelerating factor	Basement membrane	Elastic fibres
CD59	KCs	None
Polyunsaturated fatty acid metabolites		
13-HODE	Lamellae in stratum corneum	None
PGE_2, $PGF_{2\alpha}$, PGD_2	KCs	Fibroblast - PGE_2
15-HETE	KCs	None
LTB_4	KCs, converted from PMN-derived $LT-A_4$	None
Secretory Immunoglobulins		
Secretory component	Basement membrane, KC surface, sweat glands	None
IgA	None	Sebaceous and eccrine sweat glands
Cytokines and Chemokines		
Proinflammatory, immunomodulatory cytokines, growth factors, CSFs and/or interferons	KCs and LCs	Endothelial, T, mast, dendritic, macrophage, fibroblast, sebaceous gland
CXCL and CC chemokines	KCs and LCs	Endothelial, T, mast, dendritic, macrophage, fibroblast
Neuropeptides		
Substance P	Sensory neurons	Sympathetic nerves
CGRP	Sensory nerve endings close to LCs	Sensory nerves surrounding blood vessels, in sweat glands
Neuropeptide Y	Nerve fibres in basal layer, (LCs in atopic dermatitis)	Around blood vessels, sweat glands

Components	Epidermal producer cell types	Dermal producer cell types
Somatostatin	KCs, on LC membrane	Dendritic cell subset, Meissner corpuscles, mast cells
VIP	None	Sweat and apocrine glands, arterial blood vessels, hair follicles, mast cells
PACAP	None	Close to E/D junction, sweat glands, blood vessels, hair follicles
POMC-derived peptides	KCs, LCs and melanocytes	Endothelial, fibroblast
Protease-activated receptors		
PAR-1	KCs	Endothelial, fibroblast, vascular smooth muscle
PAR-2	KCs, highest in granular layer	Endothelial, hair follicles, sweat glands, dendritic
Vanilloid receptors		
Vanilloid receptor-1	KCs, sensory nerves	Sweat and sebaceous glands, blood vessels, hair follicles, mast cells

factor I in combination with various cofactors (see below), with the release of fragments C3f and C3c. In various inflammatory skin diseases a greater C3d,g reactivity is observed and is typically associated with C3c deposition.

2.1.2 Complement regulatory proteins

Four complement regulatory proteins, CR1, MCP, DAF and CD59, whose role is to protect KCs from damage induced by complement activation, are present in normal skin [2] (Fig 2.1).

CR1 (CD35) is a highly polymorphic, single-chain membrane protein that binds C3b via sites in its repeat domains, and has cofactor and delay accelerating activity. It is expressed by nearly all human peripheral blood cells and by KCs in the skin.

MCP (Membrane cofactor protein; CD46) is a membrane-bound complement regulatory protein that has cofactor activity for factor I, a serine protease which degrades C3b. It is composed of four short consensus repeats, a sequence of serine, threonine and proline residues, and a transmembrane region. MCP is located in the intercellular spaces of epidermis, being higher in the basal layers than in the granular layer, and on endothelial cells in the dermis.

DAF (Decay accelerating factor; CD55) is a membrane-bound complement regulatory protein whose function is to regulate the formation of C3 convertases and to decrease their stability.

Figure 2.1   The alternative complement pathway. CR1 = complement receptor 1; DAF = decay-accelerating factor; MCP = membrane cofactor of proteolysis.

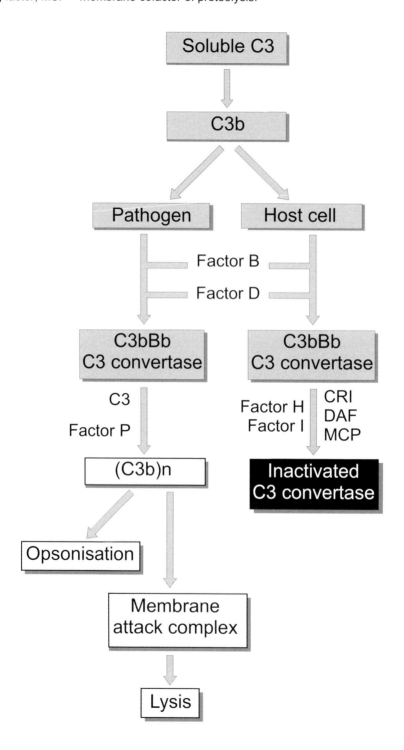

DAF, which has a similar structure to MCP, is attached to the epidermal basement membrane by a glycosylphosphatidylinositol (GPI) anchor; the protein is also found on elastic fibres in the dermis.

CD59 is a membrane-associated complement inhibitory protein, which is constitutively produced by KCs *in vitro*. Activation of CD59 expressed by KCs by its T cell ligand CD2 results in the production of the cytokines IL-1α, IL-6 and GM-CSF.

UVB light up-regulates the levels of MCP, DAF and CD59, but has no effect on C3 and factor B production. In contrast, various cytokines have no effect on expression of the complement regulatory proteins with the exception of TGF-β_1, -β_2 and -β_3, which, together with unknown additional factors, enhance MCP and CD59 levels.

In addition to acting as complement regulatory proteins, these membrane proteins are also used by microorganisms to gain entry into host cells. Thus CR2 on T and B cells has been shown to act as a receptor for Epstein Barr virus, and MCP and DAF act as receptors for the measles virus and echovirus. MCP expressed by KCs is also a receptor for the M proteins of group A streptococci.

2.2 Polyunsaturated fatty acid metabolites

2.2.1 Linoleic acid

The ability of the epidermis to act as a barrier to prevent water loss is attributed to the lipid bilayers or lamellae present in the intercellular spaces of the stratum corneum. The most abundant polyunsaturated fatty acid in human skin, which plays an essential role in the maintenance of this epidermal water barrier, is the 18-carbon polyunsaturated fatty acid, linoleic acid. However, deficiency of linoleic acid not only results in excessive water loss, but also in a characteristic scaly skin disorder implicating the fatty acid in regulation of epidermal proliferation. Epidermis contains the enzyme 15- lipoxygenase, which metabolises linoleic acid to 13-hydroxyoctadecadienoic acid (13-HODE), the major metabolite, and small amounts of 9-HODE [3] (Fig. 2.2). Normal skin epidermis is unique in that it preferentially metabolises linoleic acid to 13-HODE, as it is unable to transform it to γ-linolenic acid. 13-HODE is then substituted into diacylglycerol to give 1-acyl-2–13-HODE-glycerol, which selectively suppresses the β isoform of membrane-associated epidermal protein kinase C resulting in inhibition of epidermal hyperproliferation.

2.2.2 Arachidonic acid

The second most prominent polyunsaturated fatty acid in the skin is the 20-carbon fatty acid arachidonic acid, which comprises approximately 9% of the total fatty acids in epidermal phospholipids. Arachidonic acid is released from membrane phospholipids by the action of cytosolic phospholipase A2 present in the upper epidermal layers. This enzyme, which is induced by UV light, chemicals and other factors that injure the skin, is associated with various normal skin functions, such as cell proliferation and differentiation, wound healing and host defence against bacteria. Two different pathways can convert the liberated arachidonic acid to either prostaglandins or 15-HETE (15-hydroxyeicosatetraenoic acid) [3] (Fig. 2.2).

Figure 2.2 Metabolism of linoleic acid and arachidonic acid in the epidermis of skin. 13-HODE = 13-hydroxyoctadecadienoic acid; PKC-β = β isoform of protein kinase C; 15-HETE = 15-hydroxyeicosatetraenoic acid; COX-1 = cyclooxygenase-1; PG (E_2, F_{2a}, D_2) = prostaglandin (E_2, F_{2a}, D_2); LTB_4/A_4 = leukotriene B_4/A_4.

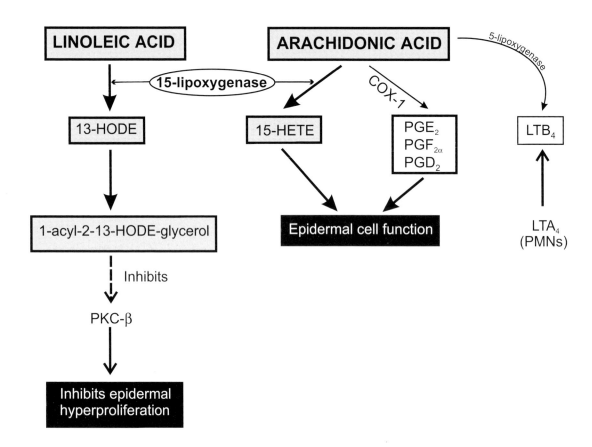

2.2.2.1 Prostaglandins

The first pathway converts arachidonic acid by enzymatic peroxidation and cyclooxygenation to the prostaglandins PGE_2, $PGF_{2\alpha}$ and PGD_2. Two isoforms of prostaglandin H synthase, also known as cyclooxygenase (COX), enzymes are involved in the pathway; COX-1 (constitutive) which maintains basal levels of prostaglandins necessary to maintain physiological epithelial function, and COX-2 (inducible) which is induced by proinflammatory stimuli and UV light, resulting in the production of high levels of the lipid mediators. COX-1 is constitutively expressed in KCs throughout the normal epidermis, in endothelial cells of small blood vessels, and in sweat gland epithelium. In contrast COX-2 expression is normally very low and restricted to a small number of suprabasal KCs in the epidermis. Altered levels of COX-2 are a characteristic feature of epithelial tumours including squamous cell carcinoma of the skin.

PGE$_2$ plays an important role in the skin, not only in homeostasis, but also in repair of the epidermis after wounding when levels are increased *in vivo* [4]. Furthermore, there is increased PGE$_2$ synthesis associated with high mitotic activity in non-confluent proliferating KCs in culture. These effects are mediated via specific G protein-coupled PGE receptors, of which there are 4 different subtypes, two of which are expressed in the epidermis by KCs and LCs [5].

2.2.2.2 15-HETE and Leukotrienes

The second pathway generates 15-hydroxyeicosatetraenoic acid (15-HETE), a mediator of basal epithelial function, from arachidonic acid. This process is catalysed by the 15-lipoxygenase enzyme, which has high activity in the epidermis. In contrast epidermal 5-lipoxygenase, which catalyses the conversion of arachidonic acid to the ether-linked phospholipid, leukotriene LTB$_4$, is normally present at only very low levels in KCs, although the enzyme can be up-regulated by culture of KCs under conditions that induce differentiation. However, levels of LTB$_4$ may be elevated in KCs due to its conversion from LTA$_4$ derived from activated leukocytes such as PMNs. This involves the enzyme LTA$_4$ hydrolase present in both basal and suprabasal KCs, which is subsequently inactivated. This process of transcellular LTB$_4$ synthesis may account, at least in part, for the elevated levels of this proinflammatory leukotriene in skin lesions of psoriasis. In addition to being a potent chemotactic factor for T lymphocytes and PMNs, LTB$_4$ exerts effects on vascular permeability and blood flow, and can stimulate DNA synthesis in cultured KCs.

2.3 Secretory immunoglobulins

The polymeric immunoglobulin receptor, secretory component has been detected in normal skin, either along the epidermal basement membrane or focally on the surface of KCs, and in sweat glands by immunostaining [6]. This suggests that KCs may be able to interact with IgA, which could be of relevance to certain skin diseases such as dermatitis herpetiformis in which IgA is deposited underneath the epidermal basement membrane.

Furthermore, immunostaining for IgA has been found in sebaceous glands and in various parts of the eccrine sweat glands in normal skin [7]. IgA was concentrated near the pilosebaceous duct opening in sebaceous glands, and all over the sweat ducts, whilst only scattered IgA-positive cells were seen in the secretory parts of the sweat gland. Immunoelectron microscopy further suggested that IgA was taken up by endocytosis into glandular cells and processed. These findings suggest that IgA present in sebum and sweat may play a role in the inactivation of invading microorganisms as part of the skin's defence mechanisms.

2.4 Cytokines and Chemokines

As discussed in Chapter 1, KCs are the major source of cytokines and chemokines in skin (summarised in Table 1.3). Many of these cytokines are constitutively expressed at low levels and are up-regulated in response to a variety of stimuli such as trauma, bacterial infections, UV irradiation and chemical irritants. The cytokines produced by KCs can be subdivided into various subclasses: proinflammatory, immunomodulatory, growth factors, colony stimulating factors and interferons [8] .

KC-derived cytokines can play autocrine and/or paracrine roles in the skin. In addition to activating the proliferation and differentiation of the cells that produce them, the main function of these cytokines is to regulate the function of other cell types such as LC and T cells in the epidermis, and endothelial cells and fibroblasts in the dermis (Fig. 2.3). These other skin cell types also produce their own repertoire of cytokines, which can, in turn, affect KC function (see Chapter 1). Furthermore, chemokines produced by KCs attract leukocytes into the epidermis from the circulation.

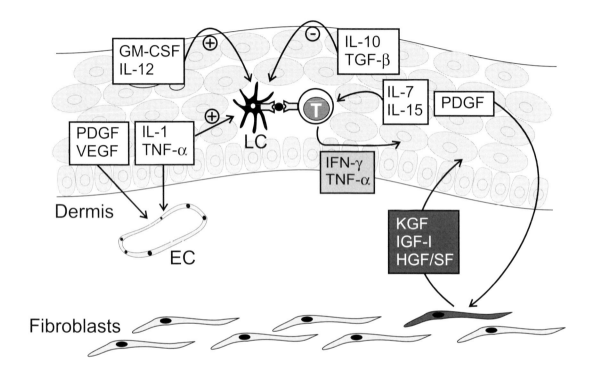

Figure 2.3 Cytokine-mediated interaction between KCs and other skin cells. KCs produce cytokines that have either a stimulatory (+) or inhibitory (-) effect on antigen presentation by LCs to T cells. T cells and fibroblasts also produce cytokines that affect KC function and growth. EC = endothelial cell.

2.4.1 Interaction between keratinocytes and Langerhans cells

LC function is regulated by various cytokines produced by KCs, particularly GM-CSF which is essential for LC viability and up-regulates costimulatory molecules B7-1 and B7-2 on the cell surface *in vitro*. Furthermore, the induction of dendritic cells from precursors isolated from the blood and bone-marrow has an absolute requirement for GM-CSF *in vitro*. In addition, IL-1 potentiates the antigen-presenting function of LCs, and IL-12 promotes their accessory cell function, augmenting IFN-γ production in responder T cells.

In contrast, the inhibitory cytokine IL-10 inhibits ICAM-1 expression on LCs thus decreasing their interaction with LFA-1-positive T cells. In addition, IL-10 prevents the up-regulation of CD80 on LCs, leading to inhibition of Th-1 cell responses. TGF-β_1 has also been shown to be inhibitory, at least in mice, for MHC Class II up-regulation on LCs by cytokines such as IL-1, TNF-α and GM-CSF. TGF-β_1 is also involved in the synthesis of Birbeck granules in dendritic cells induced in culture by GM-CSF and IL-4.

IL-1 and TNF-α produced by KCs play a key role in the emigration of LCs from the epidermis to lymph nodes. This is discussed in detail in Chapter 4.

2.4.2 Interaction between keratinocytes and T cells

KCs produce two cytokines that promote T cell growth and activity, IL-7 and IL-15, which bind to the β and/or γ chains of the IL-2 receptor. IL-7 induces cytokine production and expression of the IL-2 α-chain (CD25) receptor by T lymphocytes, and has been implicated in trafficking of T cells into the epidermis via its effects on their adhesion to laminin-5, a constituent of the basement membrane. IL-15, in common with IL-2, stimulates T cell proliferation and activates NK cells.

Conversely, IFN-γ produced by activated T cells in inflammatory skin stimulates KCs via specific receptors on their surface inducing HLA-DR and ICAM-1 expression. ICAM-1 can also be induced on KCs, to a lesser degree, by TNF-α. This allows interaction between T cells and KCs via LFA-1 and ICAM-1, respectively, mediating T cell infiltration into the epidermis.

2.4.3 Interaction between keratinocytes and endothelial cells

IL-1 and TNF-α produced by KCs induce various effects on dermal endothelial cell function, including the production of various cytokines (including IL-1 and IL-6) and of PGI_2, NO and PAF, and the up-regulation of ICAM- and VCAM-1 expression on the endothelial cell surface. The increased expression of adhesion molecules, and the vasodilatory effects of PGI_2 and NO facilitate the migration of T cells from the circulation into the skin during inflammation.

In addition, KCs synthesize VEGF, which induces proliferation of dermal endothelial cells via the two VEGF receptors, kdr and flt-1. Levels of VEGF are induced by hepatocyte growth factor/scatter factor (HGF/SF) produced by fibroblasts and smooth muscle cells, and by cytokines such as KC-derived TGF-α and EGF.

Homodimers and heterodimers of the A and B isoforms of PDGF synthesized by KCs stimulate proliferation of microvascular endothelial cells, and other dermal cells (see below).

2.4.4 Interaction between keratinocytes and fibroblasts

KC-derived PDGF stimulates proliferation of dermal cells such as fibroblasts, smooth muscle cells (and microvascular endothelial cells) and acts as a chemoattractant for fibroblasts, and PMNs, monocytes and smooth muscle cells, during wound healing. In turn, fibroblasts release growth factors for KCs, in particular KGF that exerts potent mitogenic effects, and also IGF-I, which regulates KC proliferation and differentiation in combination with EGF and EGF-like factors. Fibroblasts also synthesize HGF/SF, which induces VEGF production by KCs.

2.4.5 Leukocytes attracted by keratinocyte-derived chemokines

KCs are capable of producing a range of chemokines belonging to the CXC and CC subfamilies, which can attract various types of leukocytes into the epidermis [8].

Basal KCs constitutively synthesize CCL27 (CTACK) and CCL20 (MIP-3α), chemokines responsible for the trafficking of T cells and LCs, respectively, into the epidermis of both non-inflamed and inflamed skin [9,10]. CCL27 attracts T cells bearing CCR10, a CCL27 receptor, towards the epidermis along a chemotactic gradient and, during inflammation when CCL27 is up-regulated, some of these T cells enter the epidermis. On the other hand, CCL20 is largely responsible for recruitment of CCR6 receptor-positive LCs into the epidermis, whilst a lesser role is played by another chemokine, CXCL12 (SDF-1α), a weak chemoattractant produced by basal KCs that is recognised by LCs via their CXCR4 receptors.

In inflammatory skin diseases such as psoriasis, IFN-γ produced by Th-1 cells induces KCs to produce CXCL9 (Mig) and CXCL10 (IP-10) which are chemoattractants for CXCR3-positive activated Th-1 cells. IFN-γ and TNF-α also induce CCL5 (RANTES) and CCL2 (MCP-1) production by KCs which can attract not only activated T cells, but also monocytes, dendritic cells, NK cells, and in the case of CCL5, eosinophils providing that they express the corresponding receptors (CCR1, CCR3 or CCR5 for CCL5, and CCR2 for CCL2). PMNs expressing CXCR1 or CXCR2 receptors are also present in the epidermis of psoriatic skin lesions, drawn in from the circulation by increased levels (up-regulated by TNF-α) of epidermal CXCL1 (GRO-α) and CXCL8 (IL-8).

2.4.6 Cytokine inhibitors

The production or functions of cytokines in the skin are regulated in various ways. In the case of IL-1, inhibition of the cytokine can occur by binding to the IL-1RII receptor, which has no cytoplasmic domain and cannot therefore transduce a signal to the inside of the cell, or by binding to the soluble forms of the extracellular domains of the receptors released from the surface of the cell. In addition, IL-1ra acts as a competitive inhibitor of IL-1 by binding to IL-1RI without subsequent signal transduction.

Cytokines can also suppress the production of other cytokines, a good example of which is the reciprocal relationship between IFN-γ and IL-4. Thus IFN-γ inhibits the development of Th-2 cells producing IL-4, whilst conversely, IL-4 inhibits the development of Th-1 cells producing IFN-γ. Furthermore, the cytokine IL-10, also called cytokine synthesis and inhibitory factor, inhibits the synthesis of various cytokines, including IFN-γ by Th-1 cells.

Another mechanism by which the effects of cytokines are regulated is by inhibition of components of the cytokine-signalling pathway. Inhibition of signal transducers and activators of transcription (STAT) phosphorylation is mediated in KCs by two members of the SOCS/CIS family, SOCS-1 and SOCS-3, which are induced by cytokine or UVB stimulation of KCs [11]. SOCS-1 is induced by IFN-γ or IL-4 and is a crucial inhibitor of IFN-γ/STAT-1 and IL-4/STAT-6 signalling in KCs. SOCS-3 is induced by IFN-γ or IL-6, and regulates IFN-γ/STAT-1 and IL-6/STAT-3 signalling.

2.5 Neuropeptides

Neuropeptides are released from sensory or autonomic nerve fibres in the skin in response to stimuli such as physical, chemical or thermal injury, or UV irradiation. In addition to their well-defined functions within neurons, neuropeptides modulate the function of immunocompetent and inflammatory cells, and cutaneous cells through high affinity neuropeptide receptors or by direct activation of intracellular signalling pathways. These effects are terminated by degradation of neuropeptides by specific endopeptidases such as neutral endopeptidase, a member of a family of cell surface zinc metalloproteinases present in skin and other tissues. Furthermore, immunocompetent cells, and several epidermal as well as dermal cells can themselves synthesize a variety of neuropeptides including substance P, calcitonin gene-related peptide (CGRP), somatostatin, vasoactive intestinal peptide (VIP), pituitary adenylate cyclase-activating polypeptide (PACAP) and proopiomelanocortin (POMC)-derived peptides (Table 2.2)[12,13].

2.5.1 Substance P

Substance P is a member of the tachykinin peptide family, which also includes neurokinin A (NKA), neurokinin B (NKB), neuropeptide K and neuropeptide γ, and is derived from precursors α-preprotachykinin and β-preprotachykinin. NKA is also derived from the latter and shares common biological activities with substance P. There are three tachykinin (neurokinin) G-protein coupled receptors (NK1R, NK2R and NK3R), which preferentially bind substance P, NKA and NKB, respectively. In the skin, KCs, endothelial cells, mast cells, fibroblasts, Merkel cells and LCs all express tachykinin receptors.

2.5.1.1. Cutaneous neuroinflammation

Substance P is a potent vasodilator acting directly on vascular smooth muscle and enhancing NO production by endothelium. It also acts as an IgE-independent stimulator of histamine release from mast cells. These two actions may explain the cutaneous weal and flare response, respectively, in response to antidromic (in the opposite direction to normal) stimulation of sensory nerves. NKA is less potent than substance P in inducing flare and itch in human skin, which may be due to a poorer ability to stimulate histamine release.

Substance P can also modulate inflammation via its effects on proliferation of various skin cell types. Thus substance P, and also NKA, can stimulate the growth of KCs, fibroblasts, endothelial cells and arterial smooth muscle cells *in vitro*, although suppression of KC proliferation has also been demonstrated under certain culture conditions. Furthermore, substance P and NKA can directly induce NGF in KC. This may be relevant in the maintenance and regeneration of cutaneous nerve fibres in both normal skin and in inflammatory reactions and wound healing.

2.5.1.2 Modulation of immune cell function

Substance P, in common with other neuropeptides, modulates various immune and inflammatory functions such as the production of proinflammatory and immunomodulatory cytokines by various cell types including KCs, T and B cell proliferation, NK and mast cell activity, and expression

Table 2.2 Neuropeptides and their receptors

NP	NPR	Stimulatory effects	Inhibitory effects
Substance P	NKR1	Potent vasodilator IgE-independent mast cell histamine release Growth of epidermal and dermal cells KC cytokines and NGF production Mast cell activity ICAM-1, VCAM-1 on endothelial cells Promotes induction and elicitation of CHS to haptens	
CGRP	CLR (+ RAMP-1)	Vasodilator Induces hapten tolerance Melanocyte proliferation *Endothelial cells*: proliferation, IL-8 production and adhesion molecule expression	LC antigen-presentation (incr. IL-10, decr. B7-2) DTH and CHS induction
Neuropeptide Y	Y2R	Vasoconstrictor Sweat regulation?	Sweat regulation?
Somatostatin (14 AA)	SR-5 subtypes	Fibroblast proliferation	
VIP	VIPR	Vasodilator Induces vascular permeability IgE-independent mast cell histamine release KC proliferation Leukocyte chemotaxis, at low doses Increases B cell IgM production	DTH PLA_2 Thymocyte and mitogen-induced PBL proliferation PBMN and PMN migration, at high doses B cell IgA production NK activity ACD
PACAP-38	VPAC1 VPAC2	IgE-independent mast cell histamine release	CHS induction DTH elicitation LC antigen presentation (incr. IL-10, decr. B7-2)

NP	NPR	Stimulatory effects	Inhibitory effects
POMC-derived peptides	MC-1R (MC-5R)	Upregulates IL-10 Hapten tolerance B cell IgE production IL-1-induced endothelial IL-8 production Proliferation and melanin production by follicular melanocytes	Cytokine production by various cell types Macrophage NO production CHS B cell IgE production, at high doses Mast cell histamine release IL-1β-induced KC CXCL1 and CXCL8 expression LPS-induced endothelial adhesion molecule expression Monocyte and dendritic cell Class I, B7-2, CD40, ICAM-1
Protease-activated receptors	Protease-activated receptor-1	*KCs and fibroblasts*: Ca^{2+} influx, proliferation, IL-6 and/or GM-CSF production *Endothelial cells*: Ca^{2+} influx, von Willebrand factor, P-selectin, E-selectin, ICAM-1, VCAM-1, NO, PDGF, ET-1, VEGFR expression, proliferation, cell contraction, permeability	KC differentiation
	Protease-activated receptor-2	*KCs*: Ca^{2+} influx, IL-6, IL-8, GM-CSF, phagocytosis, melanosome uptake *Endothelial cells*: Ca^{2+}, IL-6, IL-8, NF-κB	*KCs*: proliferation, differentiation, TG-1 and involucrin expression
	Vanilloid receptor-1	KCs: Increases CXCL8, PGE$_2$ and COX-2	

of adhesion molecules ICAM-1 and VCAM-1 by endothelial cells. Furthermore, substance P has been shown to promote the induction and elicitation of contact hypersensitivity to haptens in skin (see Chapter 4). The latter was demonstrated in mice by genetic deletion of substance P-degrading neutral endopeptidase, which is normally present in KCs, dermal microvascular endothelial cells and hair follicles [14]. This resulted in a markedly augmented ear swelling response, probably due to the accumulation of proinflammatory substance P. In contrast, deletion of NK1R inhibited the proinflammatory effects of substance P, markedly reducing the contact hypersensitivity response [15]. These studies illustrate the involvement of the cutaneous nervous system in the inflammatory response to contact allergens.

Cytokines such as IL-1β enhance sympathetic neurone-derived substance P production, which has been detected by immunostaining in nerve fibres in lesional skin of patients with atopic dermatitis, psoriasis and other inflammatory skin diseases. In patients with atopic dermatitis, substance P regulates the proliferation and cytokine production of PBMC in response to house dust mite allergens [16].

2.5.2 Calcitonin gene-related peptide

The calcitonin peptide family consists of five members; calcitonin, amylin, adrenomedullin and two calcitonin gene-related peptides CGRP-α or CGRP-1 and CGRP-β or CGRP-2. The receptor for CGRP consists of the calcitonin-like receptor (CRLR) expressed with a receptor-activity modifying protein (RAMP)-1. (CRLR expressed with RAMP2/3 is specific for adrenomedullin). CGRP receptors are expressed on various inflammatory cell types including macrophages, mast cells and PMNs, and in the skin, on KCs, melanocytes, LCs and dermal microvascular endothelial cells.

2.5.2.1 Cutaneous neuroinflammation

CGRP released from efferent nerve fibres contributes to neuroinflammation by inducing vasodilation and plasma extravasation. However, unlike substance P, VIP and somatostatin, CGRP will only cause a weak weal and flare reaction and only at relatively high concentrations. Thus intradermally injected CGRP induces a gradually developing, but long-lasting and strong erythematous response that is not dependent upon histamine release by mast cells.

2.5.2.2 Modulation of immune cell function

Unmyelinated afferent sensory nerve fibres containing CGRP in the skin have been detected in association with either substance P or, more commonly, somatostatin (see below), in free epidermal nerve endings and in axons surrounding blood vessels in the dermis and dermal papillae. CGRP-positive sensory axons containing weak somatostatin-specific staining have also been detected in sweat glands. In the epidermis, CGRP-containing nerves have been shown in close association with LCs and, furthermore, CGRP has been observed on the surface of some of these cells. These findings are relevant in view of the inhibitory effects of the neuropeptide on the antigen-presenting function of LCs [17]. The exact mechanism is unknown but is believed to be via induction of IL-10 release by LCs, and down-regulation of costimulatory molecules such as B7-2 on the surface. In addition, CGRP inhibits the induction of delayed-type and contact hypersensitivity, and induces hapten-specific tolerance via the induction of IL-10 in animal models [18,19]. CGRP is up-regulated in skin after UV irradiation suggesting a role for this neuropeptide in UV-induced immunosuppression. CGRP has also been shown to stimulate melanocyte proliferation accompanied by accumulation of intracellular cAMP suggesting that the nervous system may be involved in the regulation of pigmentation of the skin [20].

In the dermis, CGRP stimulates proliferation and IL-8 production by endothelial cells and up-regulates their expression of adhesion molecules. These effects may be relevant in psoriasis and other inflammatory skin diseases such as vitiligo in which CGRP levels are up-regulated. Other immunomodulatory effects mediated by CGRP include the inhibition of mitogen/antigen-induced peripheral blood mononuclear cell proliferation and cytokine production, and the stimulation of T cell chemotaxis.

2.5.3 Neuropeptide Y

Neuropeptide Y is found in nerve fibres located around the cutaneous vasculature, and plays a role in regulation of skin blood flow via vasoconstrictive effects mediated by Y2 receptors. Neuropeptide Y is not only present in the wall of arteries, arterioles and veins, but also in nerve fibres in the basal layer of the epidermis, and in association with eccrine sweat glands (and to a lesser degree apocrine and sebaceous glands and hair follicles) suggesting a role in the regulation of sweat production. In atopic dermatitis, neuropeptide Y-like immunoreactivity has been found on LCs in the epidermis.

2.5.4.Somatostatin

Somatostatin (somatotropin release-inhibiting factor) occurs in two biologically active forms, consisting of either 14 or 28 amino acids. It is a ubiquitous peptide with inhibitory effects on several neuropeptides and hormones, and which possesses immunomodulatory properties, which has led to its use as a treatment for psoriasis.

In the skin, the 14 amino acid somatostatin is found in the epidermis and on the LC membrane. In addition, a subset of DDC is somatostatin-positive, and the neuropeptide is associated with Meissner corpuscles in the dermal papillae. Somatostatin, which is also produced by mast cells and PMNs, mediates its effects either indirectly through other molecules, or directly via receptors, of which there are 5 subtypes, on target cells. Blood vessels, smooth muscle, sweat glands and fibroblasts in the dermis express somatostatin receptors. Fibroblasts, which express subtype 2/3 receptors, are induced by somatostatin to proliferate but the effect is weak.

2.5.5 VIP

VIP and peptide histidine methionine (PHM) are two members of the glucagon-secretin family, which play a role in skin. Nerves secreting these peptides are found around the glandular cells, ducts and myoepithelial cells of the eccrine sweat glands, where they stimulate sweat production, around the arterial section of the superficial and deep vascular plexuses, and adjacent to hair follicles. PHM-secreting nerve fibres are also seen close to apocrine glands. Nerve fibres secreting VIP have been observed in psoriasis, atopic dermatitis and other inflammatory skin diseases.

VIP induces vasodilation, increases vascular permeability and regulates blood flow, and when released from sensory nerve endings or mast cells, can induce KC proliferation via specific VIP receptors by stimulating adenylate cyclase activity. In common with substance P, VIP induces histamine release by mast cells in an IgE-independent manner, but in contrast to that neuropeptide, VIP exerts anti-inflammatory effects, such as the suppression of experimental delayed hypersensitivity reactions [21] and inhibition of phospholipase A2. VIP is also inhibitory in its effects on various immune cell functions such as proliferation of thymocytes and of mitogen-induced peripheral blood lymphocytes, but preferentially induces chemotaxis of T lymphocytes. In addition, VIP decreases IgA and stimulates IgM production by B cells, and inhibits natural killer cell activity. Interestingly, VIP exerts an inhibitory effect on established allergic contact dermatitis, possibly in part by stimulating IFN-γ production by peripheral blood T cells.

2.5.6 PACAP

PACAP is a neuropeptide homologous with VIP, which occurs as two variants, PACAP-27 and C-terminally extended PACAP-38. In the skin, PACAP-38 is located predominantly in dermal nerve fibres close to the dermal-epidermal border, hair follicles, blood vessels and sweat glands, whilst the PACAP-27 variant is absent. The levels of PACAP-38 are elevated in psoriasis, as compared to those of normal skin, suggesting its involvement in the disease process. High affinity receptors for PACAP (VPAC1 and VPAC2) are present in skin on eccrine sweat and apocrine glands in the dermis and on LCs in the epidermis.

PACAP is an immunosuppressive neuropeptide which prevents induction of contact hypersensitivity, and inhibits the ability of LCs to elicit delayed hypersensitivity in previously immunized mice or present antigen to antigen-specific T cells *in vitro*, probably via induction of IL-10 production and down-regulation of B7-2 costimulator molecules [22]. PCAP also induces histamine release in skin mast cells, in common with VIP.

2.5.7 POMC-derived peptides

POMC is a neurohormone, produced not only in the pituitary gland but also by various cell types, which is synthesized as a large prohormone and subsequently cleaved by specific serine proteases called prohormone convertase (PC)1 and PC2. The active peptide hormones formed include melanocyte-stimulating hormones (α-, β-, and γ-MSH), adrenocorticotropic hormone (ACTH), corticotropin-like intermediate lobe peptide (CLIP), β-lipotropic hormone (β-LPH) and β-endorphin (β-EP). In the skin, POMC-peptides are constitutively present in KCs, melanocytes and LCs in the epidermis, and in fibroblasts and dermal microvascular endothelial cells in the dermis. Levels of the hormones are up-regulated by various stimuli such as IL-1, TNF-α, UVB irradiation and phorbol esters. Conversely, TGF-β has been shown to down-regulate mRNA specific for POMC in fibroblasts. In addition, POMC-peptides have been detected in various immune cells such as lymphocytes, macrophages and splenocytes.

POMC-peptides exert pleiotropic effects, which are mediated by five G-protein-coupled melanocortin (MC) receptors whose expression varies in different tissues and which have different affinities to individual POMC-peptides. The human MC-1R binds α-MSH with the highest affinity and is widely expressed by inflammatory (T and B cells), antigen-presenting (macrophages, dendritic cells), epidermal (KCs, melanocytes) and dermal (fibroblasts, endothelial) cells. MC-1R is also expressed by cutaneous adnexal structures including hair follicles, sweat glands and sebaceous glands. Expression of MC-1R can be up-regulated by IL-1β, UV irradiation and α-MSH itself. MC-2R binds specifically to ACTH, whilst MC-3R and MC-4R are mainly expressed within the central nervous system. MC-5R has been detected at a low level in cutaneous sebaceous glands and can be up-regulated by stimulation of sebocytes with α-MSH.

2.5.7.1 Modulation of immune cell function

POMC-peptides, particularly α-MSH, are potent modulators of inflammatory and immune cell responses [23]. α-MSH inhibits proinflammatory (IL-1, TNF-α, IL-6) and immunomodulatory (IFN-γ, IL-4, IL-13) cytokine production, but up-regulates the production of the anti-inflammatory cytokine, IL-10. The hormone also down-regulates the expression of MHC Class I, costimulatory CD86 and CD40 molecules and ICAM-1 on monocytes and dendritic cells, and inhibits macrophage production of the cytotoxic compound, NO. In addition, α-MSH inhibits the activation of the nuclear transcription factor NF-κB by various inflammatory agents including IL-1, TNF-α and LPS. These immunomodulatory and anti-inflammatory effects appear to be mediated by the C-terminal tripeptide of α-MSH.

In mouse models of contact hypersensitivity *in vivo*, systemic or topical application of α-MSH or its C-terminal tripeptide, prior to sensitisation with contact allergens, inhibits both the sensitisation and elicitation phases of contact hypersensitivity and induces hapten-specific tolerance via effects on dendritic cell function. These effects are mediated by the generation of IL-10-producing suppressor T cells expressing cytotoxic T lymphocyte-associated antigen-4 (CTLA-4), a B7-binding molecule which, when cross-linked, causes decreased T cell proliferation due to down-regulated IL-2 production.

α-MSH (and ACTH) also modulates IL-4 and anti-CD40-mediated release of IgE by B cells *in vitro*. This may result in an increase in antibody production when the neuropeptides are present at physiological concentrations, or, conversely, inhibition at higher peptide doses. In a mouse model of allergic airway inflammation, systemic treatment with α-MSH *in vivo* resulted in a marked reduction in allergen-specific IgE production, eosinophil influx and IL-5 production, which was mediated by IL-10 production.

α-MSH also inhibits histamine release and decreases mRNA specific for IL-1, TNF-α and lymphotactin (XCL1, a chemokine for T cells), in mast cells.

2.5.7.2 Modulation of cutaneous cell function

In the skin, the production of chemokines such as CXCL8 (IL-8) and CXCL1 (GRO-α) by KCs in response to stimulation by IL-1β is suppressed by α-MSH. Partial blockage of IL-1β-induced chemokine production by sebocytes has also been reported. In contrast, α-MSH synergises with IL-1β to stimulate dermal microvascular endothelial cells to secrete increased levels of CXCL8, but down-regulates the LPS-induced expression of adhesion molecules essential for leukocyte recruitment and extravasation across the vessel wall, such as ICAM-1, VCAM-1 and E-selectin.

α-MSH also plays an important role in pigmentation of hair, stimulating follicular melanocytes to proliferate and produce eumelanin (brown pigment) via the MC-1R receptor.

2.6 Proteinase-activated receptors

Proteinase-activated receptors (PARs) constitute a novel subset of seven-transmembrane, G-protein-coupled receptors with a unique mechanism of activation [reviewed in ref 24]. Instead of stimulation via binding of a ligand, activation of PAR is initiated by proteolytic cleavage of the N-terminus of the receptor by serine proteases exposing a tethered ligand that binds and autoactivates the receptor. Four PARs have been described, three of which (PAR-1, -3, -4) are sensitive to thrombin, a trypsin-like serine protease that mediates the formation of fibrin from fibrinogen in the coagulation cascade. In contrast, PAR-2 is sensitive to trypsin and tryptase, and other serine proteases that are tissue-specific. Both PAR-1 and PAR-2 have been described in skin and are involved in regulation of cutaneous inflammation.

2.6.1 PAR-1

PAR-1 is expressed by KCs in the epidermis, and fibroblasts, vascular smooth muscle and endothelial cells in the dermis. Thrombin stimulates Ca^{2+} influx, proliferation and IL-6 production, but inhibits differentiation of KCs via its effects on PAR-1. Similarly, PAR-1 activation of fibroblasts induces increased proliferation, IL-6 and GM-CSF production.

Activation of endothelial cells is an important part of the coagulation and wound healing processes. Thrombin, released from platelets, induces Ca^{2+} influx and stimulates the release of von Willebrand factor (an adhesive protein), the cell surface redistribution of P-selectin, and increased expression of ICAM-1, VCAM-1 and E-selectin. Thrombin also stimulates mitogenesis, cell contraction, and increased permeability of endothelial cells, and increases NO, PDGF and ET-1 production. The VEGF receptors, kdr and flt-1, on endothelial cells are also up-regulated.

2.6.2 PAR-2

KCs, endothelial cells, hair follicles, myoepithelial cells of sweat glands, DDC, and sensory afferent nerves in the skin all express PAR-2. The main endogenous activator of PAR-2 in skin is most likely tryptase, a chymotrypsin-like protease, which is abundant in mast cells. Although trypsinogen, the precursor of trypsin, is present in skin (produced by endothelial cells during inflammation), it has not been established whether specific enteropeptidases required for processing of trypsin are also available.

PAR-2 is expressed at higher levels in the more differentiated granular layer than in the basal and suprabasal KCs of the epidermis, but is up-regulated throughout the epidermis by UV irradiation. PAR-2 activation of KCs results in transient cytosolic Ca^{2+} mobilisation but, in contrast to PAR-1 stimulation, proliferation is inhibited even in the presence of growth factors. Differentiation of KCs, and calcium- or IFN-γ-induced transglutaminase type 1 and involucrin synthesis are also inhibited, whilst production of IL-6, IL-8 and GM-CSF are increased. In addition, activation of PAR-2 stimulates phagocytosis and melanosome uptake by KCs.

PAR-2 activation of endothelial cells by agonists such as tryptase induces Ca^{2+} mobilisation, increases IL-6 and IL-8 production, and activates NF-κB transcription factor.

In a mouse model of experimentally induced allergic and toxic contact dermatitis, functions such as ear swelling, plasma extravasation and leukocyte adherence were shown by gene deletion to be dependent upon PAR-2 expression, supporting a proinflammatory role for the receptor *in vivo* [25]. These effects were mediated by NO and did not involve NF-κB activation. Furthermore, intralesional injection of endogenous PAR-2 agonists induced enhanced and prolonged itch in patients with atopic dermatitis via stimulation of neuronal PAR-2 [26].

2.7 Vanilloid receptor-1

Vanilloid receptor-1 (VR-1) is a non-selective cation channel, which acts a polymodal receptor responding not only to vanilloids such as capsaicin (a pain inducer), but also to heat and protons (reduced pH), conditions present during tissue injury. In the skin, VR-1 is expressed on sensory nerve fibres and on various cell types such as KCs (predominately basal), mast cells, dermal blood vessels, hair follicles, differentiated sebocytes, sweat gland ducts and the secretory part of eccrine sweat glands [27].

Activation of VR-1 on KCs by capsaicin induces a dose-dependent influx of Ca^{2+}, and an increase in CXCL8 (IL-8), PGE_2 and COX-2 (see Section 3.2.2.1) production which can be attenuated by the VR-1 antagonist, capsazepine [28]. Thus activation of epidermal VR-1 may play a role in the induction of inflammation in response to noxious chemical stimuli.

Summary

The humoral components of the skin immune system consist of complement components, polyunsaturated fatty acid metabolites, secretory immunoglobulins, cytokines and chemokines, and neuropeptides.

- Complement components produced by KCs include C3 and B, which are involved in the alternative complement activation pathway. Simultaneous production of complement regulatory proteins ensures that the KCs are protected from complement-mediated damage.

- Linoleic acid and arachidonic acid are produced by KCs and metabolised in the epidermis to 13-HODE, and PGE_2 or 15-HETE, respectively. These metabolites are involved in regulation of epidermal cell function. Small amounts of LTB_4, which has various functions including acting as a chemoattractant for T cells and PMNs, are also produced from arachidonic acid.

- Secretory components (which bind IgA) and/or bound IgA, are present on KCs, and sweat and sebaceous glands forming part of the skin's defence system.

- Cytokines produced by KCs have paracrine effects on LCs, T cells, endothelial cells and fibroblasts, which may, in turn, exert reciprocal effects on KC function. Functional effects induced by KC-derived cytokines on target cells include modulation of viability, proliferation, cytokine production, expression of adhesion molecules and trafficking.

- KCs produce a range of CXC and CC chemokines, which attract T cells, LCs and other immune cells to the skin.

- Neuropeptides are released from sensory or autonomic nerve fibres in the skin, and by epidermal and dermal cells, and include substance P, CGRP, neuropeptide Y, somatostatin, VIP, PACAP, POMC-derived peptides, PAR and VR-1. Several cell types in the skin express specific receptors for these molecules, which can modulate various immune and inflammatory functions.

References

1. Pasch M.C., Van Den Bosch N.H., Daha M.R., Bos J.D., Asghar S.S. Synthesis of complement components C3 and factor B in human keratinocytes is differentially regulated by cytokines. J.Invest.Dermatol. 2000; **114:** 78-82.

2. Dovezenski N., Billetta R., Gigli I. Expression and localization of proteins of the complement system in human skin. J.Clin.Invest. 1992; **90:** 2000-12.

3. Ziboh V.A., Miller C.C., Cho Y. Metabolism of polyunsaturated fatty acids by skin epidermal enzymes: generation of antiinflammatory and antiproliferative metabolites. Am.J.Clin. Nutrition 2000; **71:** 361S-6S.

4. Kampfer H., Brautigam L., Geisslinger G., Pfeilschifter J., Frank S. Cyclooxygenase-1-coupled prostaglandin biosynthesis constitutes an essential prerequisite for skin repair. J.Invest.Dermatol. 2003; **120:** 880-90.

5. Kabashima K., Sakata D., Nagamachi M., Miyachi Y., Inaba K., Narumiya S. Prostaglandin E2-EP4 signalling initiates skin immune responses by promoting migration and maturation of Langerhans cells. Nat.Med. 2003; **9:** 744-9.

6. Huff J.C. Epithelial polymeric immunoglobulin receptors. J.Invest.Dermatol. 1990; **94(6 Suppl):** 74S-8S.

7. Metze D., Jurecka W., Gebhart W., Schmidt J., Mainitz M., Niebauer G. Immunohistochemical demonstration of immunoglobulin A in human sebaceous and sweat glands. J.Invest.Dermatol. 1989; **92:** 13-7.

8. Uchi H., Terao H., Koga T., Furue M. Cytokines and chemokines in the epidermis. J.Dermatol. Sci. 2000; **24 (Suppl 1):** S29-S38.

9. Homey B., Alenius H., Muller A. *et al.* CCL27-CCR10 interactions regulate T cell-mediated skin inflammation. Nat.Med. 2002; **8:** 157-65.

10. Dieu-Nosjean M.-C., Massacrier C., Homey B. *et al.* Macrophage inflammatory protein 3α is expressed at inflamed epithelial surfaces and is the most potent chemokine known in attracting Langerhans cell precursors. J.Exp.Med. 2000; **192:** 705-17.

11. Yamasaki K., Hanakawa Y., Tokumaru S. *et al.* Suppressor of cytokine signaling 1/JAB and suppressor of cytokine signalling 3/cytokine-inducible SH2 containing protein 3 negatively regulate the signal transducers and activators of transcription signalling pathway in normal human epidermal keratinocytes. J.Invest.Dermatol. 2003; **120:** 571-80.

12. Rossi R. & Johansson O. Cutaneous innervation and the role of neuronal peptides in cutaneous inflammation: a minireview. Eur.J.Dermatol. 1998; **8:** 299-306.

13. Luger T.A. Neuromediators - a crucial component of the skin immune system. J.Dermatol. Sci. 2002; **30:** 87-93.

14. Scholzen T.E., Steinhoff M., Bonaccorsi P. *et al.* Neutral endopeptidase terminates substance P-induced inflammation in allergic contact dermatitis. J. Immunol. 2001; **166:** 1285–91.

15. Scholzen T.E., Steinhoff M., Sindrilaru A. *et al.* Cutaneous allergic contact dermatitis responses are diminished in mice deficient in neurokinin 1 receptors and augmented by neurokinin 2 receptor blockage. FASEB J. 2004; **18:** 1007-9.

16. Yokote R., Yagi H., Furukawa F., Takigawa M. Regulation of peripheral blood mononuclear

cell responses to dermatophagoides farinae by substance P in patients with atopic dermatitis. Arch.Dermatol. Res. 1998; **290:** 191-7.

17. Torii H., Tamaki K., Granstein R.D. The effect of neuropeptides/hormones on Langerhans cells. J.Dermatol. Sci. 1998; **20:** 21-8.

18. Asahina A., Hosoi J., Beissert S., Stratigos A., Granstein R.D. Inhibition of the induction of delayed-type and contact hypersensitivity by calcitonin gene-related peptide. J.Immunol. 1995; **154:** 3056-61.

19. Kitazawa T. & Streilein J.W. Hapten-specific tolerance promoted by calcitonin gene-related peptide. J.Invest.Dermatol. 2000; **115:** 942-8.

20. Hara M., Toyoda M., Yaar M. *et al*. Innervation of melanocytes in human skin. J.Exp.Med. 1996; **184:** 1385-95.

21. Girolomoni G. & Tigelaar R.E. Peptidergic neurons and vasoactive intestinal peptide modulate experimental delayed-type hypersensitivity reactions. Ann.N.Y.Acad.Sci. 1992; **650:** 9-12.

22. Kodali S., Friedman I., Ding W., Seiffert K., Wagner J.A., Granstein R.D. Pituitary adenylate cyclase activating polypeptide inhibits cutaneous immune function. Eur.J. Immunol. 2003; **33:** 3070-9.

23. Luger T.A., Scholzen T.E., Brzoska T., Bohm M. New insights into the functions of alpha-MSH and related peptides in the immune system. Ann.N.Y.Acad.Sci. 2003; **994:**133-40.

24. Macfarlane S.R., Scatter M.J., Kanke T., Hunter G.D., Plevin R. Proteinase-activated receptors. Pharmacol. Rev. 2001; **53:** 245–82.

25. Seeliger S., Derian C.K., Vergnolle N. *et al*. Proinflammatory role of proteinase-activated receptor-2 in humans and mice during cutaneous inflammation in vivo. FASEB J. 2003; **17:** 1871- 85.

26. Steinhoff M., Neisius U., Ikoma A. *et al*. Proteinase-activated receptor-2 mediates itch: a novel pathway for pruritus in human skin. J.Neurosci. 2003; **23:** 6176-80.

27. Stander S., Moormann C., Schumacher M. *et al*. Expression of vanilloid receptor subtype 1 in cutaneous sensory nerve fibers, mast cells, and epithelial cells of appendage structures. Exp.Dermatol. 2004; **13:** 129-39.

28. Southall M.D., Li T., Gharibova L.S., Pei Y., Nicol G.D., Travers J.B. Activation of epidermal vanilloid receptor-1 induces release of proinflammatory mediators in human keratinocytes. J.Pharmacol.Exp.Ther. 2003; **304:** 217-22.

3

Skin Immune System: Innate Immunity

The innate immune system is an ancient form of the host defence against microorganisms, predating the adaptive immune response. All multicellular organisms have developed the ability to recognise and eliminate invading microorganisms using innate immune responses. Importantly, in most cases this involves the ability to distinguish between pathogens and self. Once a pathogenic bacterium has breached the physical barrier provided by the epithelial layers of the skin (and gastrointestinal, respiratory and urogenital tracts) and begins to replicate, the host brings into play a variety of cells, receptors and mediators as the first line of defence against the invader.

3.1 Alternative Complement Pathway

The alternative complement pathway differs from the classical complement pathway in that activation can occur on many microbial surfaces without the presence of antibody. This means that the response is immediate rather than, as for the classical pathway, requiring a delay of 5-7 days for antibody production to take place. The alternative complement pathway therefore represents an innate defence mechanism, whilst the classical pathway is classified as an acquired immune response to pathogens. Unlike the pattern recognition molecules described below, the alternative complement pathway does not need to recognise pathogens as being different from host cells, but instead host cells are protected from the effects of complement activation whilst foreign cells which lack complement control proteins are destroyed. The complement proteins produced in the skin, and the steps involved in the alternative complement pathway are described in Chapter 2 (Section 2.1 and Fig 2.1).

3.2 Components of Innate Immunity: PAMPs and PRRs

The molecules recognised must be shared by many pathogens and represent conserved molecular patterns (termed pathogen-associated molecular patterns, PAMPs), which are essential to the survival and/or pathogenicity of the organism. Examples of microbial stimulators of innate immune responses include lipopolysaccharides and peptidoglycan expressed by Gram-negative and Gram-positive bacteria respectively, unmethylated CpG motifs present in bacterial DNA, and mannans found in yeast cell walls. None of these structures are synthesised by the host organism.

To recognise PAMPs, the host organisms have developed a set of non-clonal receptors that can recognise a common molecular pattern expressed by different ligands and are therefore termed pattern-recognition receptors (PRRs). These receptors differ from the clonal antigen-specific receptors expressed by T and B lymphocytes because they are encoded in the germ line DNA; they have evolved due to selective pressure by pathogens, and do not require gene rearrangement. There are a variety of different PRRs, expressed on the cell surface or intracellularly, or secreted into the blood stream and tissue fluids. These belong to several different protein families such as the C-type lectins, pentraxins and leucine-rich proteins [1].

The recognition of pathogens by PRRs results in the activation of various types of innate immune responses including phagocytosis, opsonization, complement activation, production of cytokines and chemokines, and synthesis of anti-microbial peptides.

3.3 Phagocytic cells

The predominant phagocytic cells involved in the innate immune response are the macrophages and PMNs. Macrophages are white blood cells derived from circulating monocytes that mature and become resident in the connective tissue associated with the lungs, gastrointestinal tract and skin, and in blood vessels of the liver and spleen. PMNs are white blood cells with a very short lifespan that are produced in large numbers every day, and contain abundant cytoplasmic granules storing antibiotic substances and lytic enzymes. Both cell types engulf microorganisms after initial interaction between specific receptors on their surface and corresponding ligands on the surface of bacteria. The bacteria may (or may not) display complement components on their surface as a result of activation of the alternative complement pathway. This is a process called opsonisation, which involves the binding of substances (specific antibodies and/or complement) that enhance the subsequent uptake of microorganisms by phagocytes. Internalisation of microorganisms takes place by phagocytosis, a process that involves surrounding the foreign particle with plasma membrane and forming a vacuole called the phagosome. The phagosome matures to form a phagolysosome in which the microbes become exposed to an array of microbicidal agents, such as reactive oxygen derivatives generated locally, and the contents of the granules transported to the phagocytic vacuole. NADPH oxidase complexes are assembled and activated in the phagolysosomal membrane leading to the production of large amounts of superoxide anions (O^{2-}), hydrogen peroxide (H_2O_2) and, with the help of myeloperoxidase stored in PMN granules, other potent antimicrobial oxidants. The peroxidase-positive granules in PMNs also contain preformed antimicrobial peptides (see Section 3.6) and other proteolytic enzymes. Furthermore reactive nitrogen intermediates such as NO may be produced in macrophages, which can kill pathogens such as *Escherichia coli, Staphylococcus aureus* and *Candida albicans*.

3.4 Inflammatory Response

In addition to macrophages and PMNs, various cell types such as dendritic cells, mast cells, eosinophils and natural killer cells express PRRs and can become activated during an inflammatory response. Inflammation is an antigen non-specific reaction to infection which results in the differentiation of these activated cells into short-lived effector cells whose task is to eliminate the infection. This involves the production of cytokines, such as IL-1 and TNF-α which activate vascular endothelium, and of chemokines, a closely related family of proteins which act as chemoattractants recruiting monocytes, PMNs and other effector cells from the blood to the site of infection. In addition, inflammatory mediators that increase vascular permeability such as prostaglandins, leukotrienes, and PAF (see Section 2.2.2), and molecules toxic to the pathogen, including toxic oxygen radicals, peroxides and NO, are produced. The local effects produced by these mediators include heat and redness caused by increased local blood flow, and pain and swelling resulting from accumulation of fluid as the velocity of blood flow is decreased and vascular permeability is increased.

3.5 Pattern-Recognition Receptors in Normal Skin

The PRRs that have, so far, been reported on/in cells of normal skin include Toll-like receptors, CARD/Nod proteins, dectin-1, CD91, C-type lectin receptors and integrins (Table 3.1). Studies of PRRs in skin are at a relatively early stage and it is likely that the number and variety of receptors detected will expand as more research is applied to this area.

Table 3.1 Pattern-recognition receptors in skin

PRR Family	Specific receptor	Skin cell type
Toll-like receptor (TLR)	TLR1 and TLR2	Ubiquitously expressed on epidermal and dermal cells with some variation in levels of TLR2.
	TLR4	Constitutively expressed on dermal cells, but inconsistent detection on epidermal KCs and LCs
	TLR3	Fibroblasts
	TLR5	Basal KCs and endothelial cells
	TLR6	Mast cells (KCs negative)
CARD/Nod	CARD4/Nod1 CARD15/Nod2	KCs
Type II lectin receptor	Dectin-1	LCs
Hsp receptor	CD91	DDCs and fibroblasts (KCs and LCs negative)
C-type lectin receptors	Macrophage C-type lectin	Immature macrophages
	Macrophage mannose receptor (CD206)	KCs and endothelial cells (LCs negative)
	DEC-205 (CD205)	LCs (low levels)
Integrins	$\alpha_M\beta_2$	LCs
	Various integrins	KCs

3.5.1 Toll-like Receptors

Toll-like receptors (TLRs) are mammalian homologues of Toll, a type 1 transmembrane receptor first described in Drosophila whose activation in adult flies leads to a potent anti-fungal response. The first human homologue of Toll, now called TLR4, was reported in 1997 and was followed by the identification of 10 more structurally related members of the TLR family (TLR1-TLR11) [2,3].

3.5.1.1 TLR Structure and Signalling

The TLR structure is composed of an extracellular domain containing leucine-rich repeats, and a cytoplasmic domain, which shares significant homology with that of the IL-1 receptor (IL-1R) family and is therefore termed the Toll/IL-1R (TIR) region. Not surprisingly the signalling pathways triggered by the activation of the TLRs and IL-1R are therefore very similar and involve association, via their TIR domains, with a cytoplasmic adaptor molecule called MyD88 (Fig. 3.1). MyD88 links the receptors to a serine-threonine kinase named IL-1R-associated kinase (IRAK), which becomes phosphorylated, subsequently dissociates from the receptor complex and associates with another adaptor molecule, TNF receptor-activated factor 6 (TRAF6). This in turn activates two distinct signalling pathways, one involving c-Jun NH_2-terminal kinase (JNK) and the transcription factor, activator protein-1 (AP-1), and the other an inhibitor kappa B (IκB) kinase complex and Nuclear Factor-kappa B (NF-κB). This results in the activation of specific target genes including those coding for proinflammatory cytokines and chemokines.

Several studies in mice have demonstrated that MyD88 is essential for the inflammatory responses mediated by all the TLR family. However, the TLR3 and TLR4 signalling pathways also have a MyD88-independent pathway, which is mediated by the MyD88-like molecule TRIF (TIR-domain-containing adaptor inducing IFN-β) and stimulates the transcription factor IRF-3 (interferon response factor-3) [4].

3.5.1.2 TLR Ligands

Each TLR binds specific microbial ligands, but these have not yet been identified in all cases (Fig. 3.2). Although most TLR engage with their specific ligands at the cell membrane, TLR3 and TLRs 7-9 require their respective ligands to be internalised to the endosome where interaction subsequently takes place.

The major ligand for **TLR4 is** LPS, a predominant component of the cell wall of Gram-negative bacteria. This was identified when a point mutation in the TIR domain of TLR4 was found to be responsible for the inability of the C3H/HeJ mouse strain to respond to LPS [5,6]. Other receptors in addition to TLR4 are also required for LPS recognition. Thus LPS is transported in the serum by LPS-binding protein and the resulting complex initiates signals through CD14, a glycosyl-phosphatidylinositol-linked cell surface protein present on monocytes, and myeloid cells. A small protein called MD-2, which lacks a transmembrane anchor, is also required and becomes associated with the extracellular region of TLR4 potentially forming a complex of TLR4/MD-2/CD14, which is able to bind LPS.

In common with LPS, the innate immune response to the fusion protein of respiratory syncytial virus (RSV) is also mediated by TLR4 and CD14. RSV persists for longer periods in the lungs

Figure 3.1   The TLR/IL-1R intracellular signalling pathway. IRAK = IL-1R-associated kinase; TRAF6 = TNF receptor-activated factor 6; MKK = mitogen-activated protein kinase (MAPK) kinase; Jnk = Jun N-terminal kinase; AP-1 = activator protein-1; IκB = inhibitor kappa B; IKK = IκB kinase; NF-κB = nuclear factor kappa B.

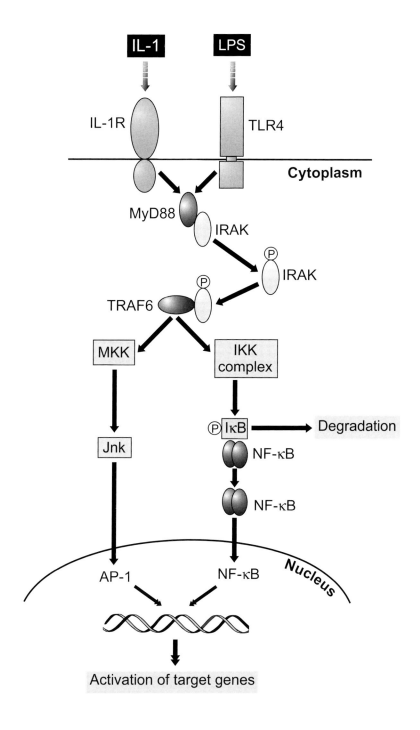

Figure 3.2   TLR microbial ligands

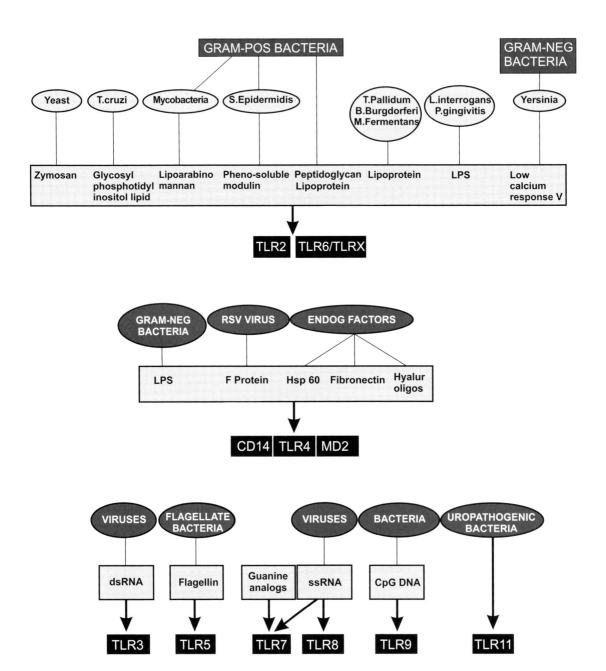

of infected TLR4-deficient mice than in normal mice supporting a role for TLR4 in the immune response to the virus.

In addition to microbial stimuli, three endogenous proteins, the heat shock protein (Hsp)60, fibronectin and hyaluronan have also been implicated as TLR4 ligands. Hsps are highly conserved immunogenic molecules, produced in high amounts in response to stress, which function as chaperones during protein folding assembly and in the transfer of proteins between cellular compartments. Fibronectin fragments and hyaluronan oligosaccharides are generated during an inflammatory response to injury when degradation of extracellular matrix components by proteases is increased. The ability to initiate an immune response in the absence of an infection is consistent with a hypothesis proposed by Matzinger that the key to triggering immunity is an association between an antigen and a "danger" signal [7]. Proteins released due to damage to tissue, in addition to molecules released by pathogens, could represent such danger signals.

TLR2 has a broad specificity and its ligands include yeast-derived zymosan, mycobacterial cell wall components, and a wide variety of microbial products from Gram-positive bacteria including peptidoglycan (although there is some evidence that contaminating lipoteichoic acid may be the true ligand) and lipoproteins (proteins containing lipid covalently linked to the NH_2-terminal cysteines). TLR2 also recognizes LPS from *Prophyromonas gingivitis* and *Leptospira interrogans*, but not from Gram-negative bacteria. This is explained by marked differences between the two groups of organisms in the relatively conserved lipid A structure of LPS, the part of the molecule responsible for the proinflammatory effects of LPS.

Recognition by TLR2 of some of these ligands requires cooperation with other TLRs. Thus TLR2-TLR6 heterodimers recognize peptidoglycan, but TLR2 detects bacterial lipopeptide without the involvement of TLR6. In addition, TRL6 enhances and TLR1 inhibits, the TLR2-mediated response to phenol-soluble modulin, a factor secreted by *Staphylococcus epidermidis*. Whether such cooperation is required for ligand recognition by other TLRs is not yet known; some of the TLRs (e.g. TLR4) probably function as homodimers.

TLR3 recognises double-stranded RNA (dsRNA), a molecular pattern indicative of a viral infection since most viruses produce it during replication. Activation of TLR3 by dsRNA induces the activation of NF-κB and the production of the type I interferons, IFN-α and IFN-β, which both inhibit viral replication and up-regulate the expression of TLR3.

TLR5 recognizes flagellin, a principle component of bacterial flagella in both Gram-positive and Gram-negative bacteria. The critical function of flagellin in bacterial motility means that the parts of the molecule important for its function are conserved and are, therefore, an ideal target for the innate immune system.

TLR7/8 recognise single-stranded RNA (ssRNA) motifs rich in uracil and guanosine. Guanine nucleoside analogues, a class of small molecules with immunostimulatory activity, and small anti-viral compounds such as various imidazoquinolines and imiquimod also activate TLR7.

TLR9 recognises unmethylated CpG motifs present in bacterial DNA, which have long been known for their immunostimulatory properties. In contrast to bacterial DNA, most of the mammalian genome is methylated and therefore not recognised.

TLR11, the most recently identified receptor, is necessary for an immune response to uropathogenic bacteria, but the molecule(s) involved have yet to be identified.

3.5.1.3 TLR Expression by Peripheral Blood Leukocytes

The expression of specific transcripts of TLRs 1-10 by peripheral blood leukocytes has been determined in different studies by the extraction of total RNA or mRNA from isolated subpopulations of T, B and NK cells, PMNs, eosinophils, monocytes, immature CD11c[+] dendritic and plasmacytoid pre-dendritic cells followed by Northern blotting or reverse transcriptase - polymerase chain reaction (RT-PCR), respectively [8,9]. (See summary in Table 3.2).

TLR1 is expressed on all the cell types; indeed, this appears to be the only TLR detected on T and NK cells, whilst B cells also express TLR9 and TLR10. (An exception to this is a subset of CD4[+] T cells termed "regulatory cells" whose function is to suppress immune responses and which selectively expresses TLR4). PMNs, eosinophils, plasmacytoid pre-dendritic cells and/or immature dendritic cells also express TLR9 and TLR10 at varying intensities.

TLRs 2, 4 and 5 are restricted to cells of myelomonocytic origin, that is PMNs, monocytes and/ or immature dendritic cells. However, TLR4 is also expressed by eosinophils. TLR7 is expressed by PMNs, eosinophils and plasmacytoid dendritic cells, whilst, in contrast, TLR3 is specific to immature dendritic cells and has not been detected on any of the other peripheral blood leukocyte

Table 3.2 TLR expression by peripheral blood leukocytes

TLR	T cells	B cells	NK cells	PMNs	Eosinophils	Monocytes	CD11c+ immature DCs	Plasmacytoid pre-DCs
1	✓	✓	✓	✓	✓	✓	✓	(✓)
2	✗	✗	✗	✓	✗	✓	✓	✗
3	✗	✗	✗	✗	✗	✗	✓	✗
4	✗	✗	✗	✓	✓	✓	✗	✗
5	✗	✗	✗	✓	✗	✓	(✓)	✗
6	✗	✗	NT	✓	✓	(✓)	(✓)	(✓)
7	✗	✗	NT	✓	✓	✗	✗	✓
8	✗	✗	NT	✓	✗	✓	(✓)	✗
9	✗	✓	NT	✓	✓	✗	✗	✓
10	✗	✓	NT	✓	✓	✗	(✓)	(✓)

Brackets denote weak expression; NT, not tested.

subpopulations.

TLRs 6 and 8 are variably expressed on PMNs, monocytes, immature dendritic and/or plasmacytoid dendritic cells.

In summary, cells with a myelomonocytic lineage (phagocytic or antigen-presenting), and eosinophils express a wider range of TLR family members than T, B and NK cells.

3.5.1.4 TLR Expression by Resident Skin Cells

Table 3.3 and Fig. 3.3 show the differential expression of TLRs (mRNA and/or protein) on various resident skin cell types [10,11].

In common with peripheral blood leukocytes, TLR1 is ubiquitously expressed on resident skin cells including KCs and LCs in the epidermis, and DDCs, endothelial and mast cells in the dermis, as shown by immunostaining. TLR2 is also commonly found on most skin cell types in the epidermis and dermis with some variation in intensity of staining. Thus TLR2 staining is strong on KCs

Table 3.3 TLR expression by resident skin cells

TLR	EPIDERMIS		DERMIS			
	KCs	LCs	DDCs	Fibroblasts	Endothelial cells	Mast cells
1	✓	✓	✓	NT	✓	✓
2	✓	✓	✓	NT	(✓)	✓
3	✗	✗	✗	✓	✓	NT
4	✓/✗*	✓/✗*	✓	✓	✓	✓
5	✓**	✗	✗	NT	✓	NT
6	✗	NT	NT	NT	NT	✓
7	✗	NT	NT	NT	NT	NT
8	✗	NT	NT	NT	NT	NT
9	✗	✗	✗	✗	NT	NT
10	✗	NT	NT	NT	NT	NT
CD14	✗	✗	✗	✗	NT	✓

* Positive or negative expression detected in different studies; ** Expressed on basal KCs.
 Brackets denote weak expression; NT, not tested.

throughout the epidermis, particularly in the basal layer (Fig. 3.4A, colour plate) whilst endothelial cells show only weak TLR2 expression. In contrast, TLR4 expression in the epidermis is somewhat inconsistent, being detected on KCs and LCs in some studies but not in others. This may suggest that TLR4 expression is not constitutive on these cell types (unlike various cell types in the dermis) but induced by local factors.

TLR3 is restricted to fibroblasts, whilst basal keratinocytes (Fig. 3.4B, colour plate) and endothelial cells selectively express TLR5. TLR9 was not detected on KCs, the two dendritic cell subsets (LCs and DDCs) or fibroblasts. KCs also do not appear to express TLRs 6, 7, 8 and 10 as shown by PCR analysis.

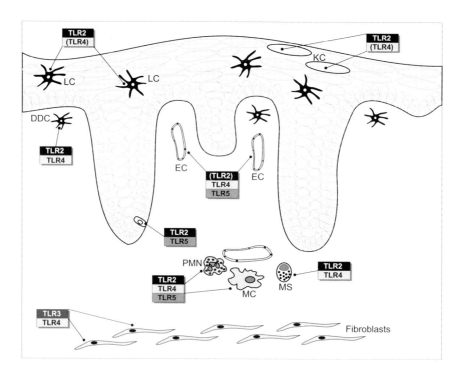

Figure 3.3   Differential expression of TLRs on resident skin cells. TLR2 is the predominant TLR expressed by epidermal LCs and KCs, whilst cells present in the dermis additionally express TLRs 3, 4 and/or 5. EC = endothelial cell; MC = macrophage; MS = mast cell.

3.5.1.5 Responses by Skin Cells to TLR Activation

Since each TLR (or pair of TLRs) binds a specific ligand, the combination of TLRs expressed by an individual cell type will determine its reactivity to different pathogens. KCs express TLRs 1, 2, 4 and 5 and can, therefore, be potentially activated by various Gram-positive components, fungi, LPS and bacterial flagellin. Indeed, KCs have been shown to functionally respond, via TLR2, to peptidoglycan and lipotechoic acid from *Staphylococcus aureus* by NF-κB translocation and increased transcription of the NF-κB controlled genes, iNOS (inducible nitric oxide synthase) and IL-8 [12]. Furthermore, KCs produce the anti-microbial peptide, β defensin-2 (see below) when stimulated by *C. albicans* (fungi), peptidoglycan (Gram-positive bacteria) or *Mycobacterium tuberculosis* via TLR2 [13].

As mentioned earlier (Section 3.5.1.2), TLR4 requires the involvement of the CD14 receptor to be activated by LPS. However, with the exception of mast cells (and infiltrating macrophages), CD14 has not been detected on the surface of resident skin cells. Studies of the response by KCs to LPS via TLR4 have produced conflicting results and may reflect differences in receptor expression and/or the requirement for other factors, which may or may not be present *in vivo*. This ability of KCs to respond more readily to TLR2 than to TLR4 ligands is consistent with the increased frequency of Gram-positive compared to Gram-negative infections of the skin.

LCs and DDCs express TLR1 and TLR2, but differ in their expression of TLR4 (constitutively expressed by DDCs and not by LCs). Both dendritic cell subsets lack TLRs 3, 5 and 9 required to recognise dsRNA, bacterial flagellin or bacterial CpG DNA motifs, respectively. Activation of dendritic cells (and macrophages) via TLRs results in the secretion of IL-12, which enhances differentiation of Th-1 cells, a subset of CD4+ T cells that produces IFN-γ, but not IL-4. IFN-γ plays an important role in bacterial defence by activating macrophages to kill pathogens, and up-regulating adhesion molecules on endothelial cells to enable the migration of other effector cells into the site of inflammation. IL-12 is produced (if at all) in very small amounts by cells such as KCs, which can phagocytose, process and present antigen, but do not express the costimulating molecules necessary for naive T cell activation and are therefore termed "non-professional" antigen-presenting cells. TLR activation also induces maturation of dendritic cells as shown by enhanced antigen processing, increased expression of MHC Class II, up-regulation of costimulatory molecules and expression of lymph node-homing chemokine receptors.

Fibroblasts express TLRs 3 and 4 and can recognise dsRNA and LPS, respectively. Interaction of dsRNA with TLR3 on fibroblasts (or immature dendritic cells) selectively induces production of IFN-α and IFN-β, type 1 interferons that inhibit viral replication. This is an example of a ligand-specific response to TLR activation, as type 1 interferons are not induced when bacterial ligands are recognised by their corresponding TLR classes.

Endothelial cells express higher levels of TLR4 than TLR2 and consequently respond to LPS, but not *M. tuberculosis* lipopeptide, as shown by NF-κB activation [14]. This TLR4-mediated response to LPS is inhibited by TLR1, which has also been shown to inhibit the TLR2-mediated response to phenol-soluble modulin, a factor secreted by *Staphylococcus epidermidis*.

Mast cells express TLRs 1, 2 4, and 6 enabling them to respond to Gram-positive and Gram-negative bacteria [15,16]. Activation of mast cell TLR2 by peptidoglycan, or TLR4 by LPS from *E. coli*, resulted in the production of TNF-α, IL-6 and Th-2-type cytokines such as IL-4, IL-5 and/or IL-13, depending upon the stimulus. Th-2 cytokines are induced by allergens and parasites and are involved in antibody production, particularly IgE, and eosinophil activation. Furthermore TLR2-but not TLR4-dependent mast cell stimulation resulted in cysteinyl leukotriene production, the release of histamine, degranulation and Ca^{2+} mobilization. Thus mast cells respond differentially to bacterial components that activate different TLR family members.

In summary, KCs and LCs in the epidermis of the skin can undergo TLR2-mediated activation by components of Gram-positive bacteria and yeasts, but may/may not respond to LPS from Gram-negative bacteria. In contrast, dendritic cells in the dermis together with fibroblasts, endothelial and mast cells express TLR4 and can respond to LPS (DDCs and mast cells also express TLR2). This may suggest that Gram-positive bacteria and yeast commonly (but not exclusively) enter the skin via breaks in the epidermis, which is consistent with the known location of these organisms on the surface of the skin. Gram-negative organisms, on the other hand, may enter from the circulation via the capillaries in the dermis and stimulate firstly the cells lining the vessels, and subsequently adjacent dendritic and mast cells. Fibroblasts may be important for recognising viruses as they are the only skin cell type currently known to express TLR3; these cells also express TLR4 which can recognise RSV fusion protein.

3.5.2 Nod proteins

Nod proteins are part of a protein family containing a caspase recruitment domain (CARD) linked to a nucleotide-binding oligomerization domain (Nod), which regulates apoptosis and/or NF-κB activation. Nod1 (CARD4) and Nod2 (CARD15), which show either broad or highly restricted tissue expression respectively, are intracellular molecules that function as cytosolic receptors for the recognition and response to pathogenic components of microorganisms. Furthermore, studies using CARD15-/- mice have shown that Nod2 signalling can modulate TLR2-driven activation of NF-κB [17]. Thus deficiencies of Nod2 or CARD15 mutations (as reported in Crohn's disease) increase TLR2-mediated NF-κB activation leading to enhanced Th-1 responses. Recent preliminary evidence suggests that Nod proteins may be present in normal KCs; augmentation of Nod1 and Nod2 expression, accompanied by IL-6 production, was reported after exposure of KCs to bacterial peptidoglycan [18].

3.5.3 Dectin-1

Dectin-1 is a type II lectin receptor for beta glucans found in zymosan (a cell wall preparation of *Saccharomyces cerevisiae*) and *C. albicans*, with a significant homology to type II lectin receptors expressed by natural killer cells. It is characterised by an immunoreceptor tyrosine-based signalling motif within the cytoplasmic domain that is tyrosine phosphorylated upon activation, generating intracellular signals that mediate phagocytosis and microbial killing. Dectin-1 is a 33kDa glycoprotein expressed at high levels on dendritic cells and low levels on macrophages, and selectively by epidermal LCs in the skin. Recently it has been shown that both dectin-1 and TLR2 are recruited to phagosomes containing zymosan, and that dectin-1 enhances the TLR2-mediated activation of NF-κB by beta-glucans present in the yeast particles [19]. Dectin-1 and TLR2 are synergistic in mediating the production of cytokines such as IL-12 and TNF-α, and, in addition, dectin-1 triggers production of reactive oxygen species, an inflammatory response that is primed by TLR activation. Thus the coexpression of dectin-1 and TLR2 enables epidermal LCs to recognise and respond effectively to fungi found on the surface of skin.

3.5.4 CD91

CD91 is one of the cell surface receptors for Hsps and has been detected on DDCs and fibroblasts, but not on KCs or LCs in the epidermis of the skin [11]. These CD91+ cells also express TLR4 and can functionally respond to Hsps, but there is some variation in the response depending on the Hsp tested. Thus the 27 kDa and 70 kDa Hsps (Hsp27 and Hsp70, respectively), but not Hsp60, triggered NF-κB activation in fibroblasts while only Hsp27 triggered substantial IL-12 production by dendritic cells, even though all three Hsps promoted dendritic cell maturation.

Unlike the cells capable of responding to Hsps, which are present in the dermis, the molecules themselves are located in the epidermis in the KC cytoplasm. Hsp27 is barely detectable, Hsp60 shows focal expression and Hsp70 is strongly and diffusely expressed. This differential pattern of expression between Hsps and the Hsp receptor may prevent inappropriate activation of the immune response by endogenous Hsps, but would still allow recognition of highly homologous bacterial Hsps entering the skin from the circulation.

3.5.5 C-type Lectin Receptors

The C-type lectins are calcium-dependent carbohydrate-binding proteins, which share a common carbohydrate recognition domain of 115-130 amino acids containing 14 invariant and 18 highly conserved amino acid residues. There are three C-type lectin receptors expressed on different cell types in normal skin; macrophage C-type lectin, macrophage mannose receptor and DEC-205.

3.5.5.1 Macrophage C-type Lectin

Macrophage C-type lectin is an endocytic receptor specific for galactose/N-acetylgalactosamine that is expressed in a subset of cells at an intermediate stage of differentiation from monocyte to macrophage, and induces macrophage tumoricidal activity [20]. The distribution of cells expressing this receptor in normal skin has been shown by immunostaining to be mainly in the upper dermis, at some distance from blood vessels. These cells also express CD68, a lysosomal glycoprotein that is present on monocytes, macrophages, neutrophils and basophils [20].

3.5.5.2 Macrophage Mannose Receptor (CD206)

The macrophage mannose receptor is found on macrophages and dendritic cells and binds to mannose present on glycoproteins derived from bacteria (Gram-positive, Gram-negative and mycobacteria), and fungi such as *Malassezia furfur* (previously called *Pityrosporum ovale*) and *C. albicans*, inducing phagocytosis. In addition to mannose, it is now evident that the receptor can also recognise fucose, N-acetylglucosamine and glucose, but not galactose. The expression of the mannose receptor CD206 has been regarded as a differentiation marker of immature dendritic cells as it is absent from monocytes and mature dendritic cells. Epidermal LCs also lack CD206, and fluorescein-dextran uptake by these cells is not effectively inhibited by mannose, an inhibitor for mannose receptor-mediated uptake. This suggests that LCs may have other, as yet to be identified, receptor(s) for carbohydrate-conjugated antigen uptake.

In contrast, KCs in the suprabasal epidermal layers do express the mannose receptor, as shown by immunostaining and confirmed by radioligand binding, which revealed a single class trypsin-sensitive receptor [21]. Furthermore, the killing of *C. albicans* by KCs can be inhibited with mannan (yeast mannose-rich polysaccharide) and mannosylated bovine serum albumin suggesting that the mannose receptor mediates this function.

Endothelium of the skin *in situ* and dermal microvascular endothelial cells *in vitro* also express the mannose receptor [22]. Endothelial cells have been shown to internalise dextran as well as *E. coli* via the receptor into acidic phagosomes demonstrating its functionality and suggesting a role for skin endothelium in antigen capture/clearing.

3.5.5.3 DEC-205 (CD205)

The DEC-205 receptor is a 205 kDa glycoprotein which is structurally similar to the mannose receptor, but shares only 27% overall amino acid similarity suggesting that the two receptors have distinct functions. The ligand specificity and function of the DEC-205 receptor is presently unknown but it is thought to act as an endocytic-phagocytic receptor for certain glycosylated molecules. The DEC-205 receptor is expressed broadly in lymphoid and non-lymphoid tissues and, in the skin, is present at low levels on LCs.

3.5.6 Integrins

Integrins are a family of heterodimeric membrane glycoproteins expressed on the cell surface and linked to the cytoskeleton, which act as adhesion molecules in cell-cell and cell-matrix interactions, and transmit signals both into and out from cells [23]. In addition, integrins are implicated in the innate immune response via their ability to bind to various bacteria, yeasts and viruses.

Each integrin consists of two non-covalently associated subunits, α and β. At least 14 different α and 8 β subunits have been identified; several α chains can associate with a single β chain and, to a lesser extent, the reverse is also true. The $\alpha_M\beta_2$ integrin (CD11b/CD18, also called Mac-1 or complement receptor 3) which is specific for myeloid cells has a binding site for yeast-derived β-glucans and bacterial LPS which is distinct from the region(s) which bind C3, fibrinogen and ICAM-1. This integrin, which recognises polymers containing mannose and N-acetylglucosamine as well as glucose-containing polysaccharides expressed by pathogenic organisms, is also expressed on the cell surface of LCs in the skin. Other integrins expressed by basal and/or suprabasal epidermal KCs ($\alpha_1\beta_1$, $\alpha_2\beta_1$, $\alpha_3\beta_1$, $\alpha_5\beta_1$, $\alpha_v\beta_5$, $\alpha_6\beta_4$) which bind collagen, laminin, fibronectin or vitronectin can also recognise viruses such as adenovirus and rotavirus, mycobacteria and various Gram-negative bacteria.

3.6 Antimicrobial molecules in skin

Antimicrobial peptides, proteins, molecules with enzyme or enzyme inhibitory activity and lipids present in skin are shown in Table 3.4.

3.6.1 Antimicrobial peptides

Members of the defensin and cathelicidin families are the major antimicrobial peptides present in skin [24]. These peptides act by associating on the bacterial membrane and forming pores. They have a positively charged domain, which allows binding to the negatively charged phospholipids on the bacterial membrane, and a hydrophobic domain that enables them to insert into the phospholipid

Table 3.4 Antimicrobial molecules in skin

Antimicrobial molecules	Constitutive /Induced (C/I)	Location
Antimicrobial peptides		
Defensins		
HBD-1	C	KCs and hair follicles
HBD-2	C/I	KCs and hair follicles
HBD-3	C/I	Stratum corneum
Cathelicidin		
hCAP18/LL-37	C	Mast cells, sweat glands
	I	KCs in psoriasis, contact dermatitis and SLE
Dermcidin	C	Sweat glands
Adrenomedullin	C/I	KCs, hair follicles, melanocytes, sweat, sebaceous gland
Antimicrobial proteins		
Bactericidal permeability-increasing protein (BPI)	C/I	Fibroblasts
Psoriasin (S100A7)	C/I	KCs
Calprotectin (S100A8/S100A9)	I	KCs in psoriasis
Antimicrobial molecules with enzyme/enzyme inhibitor activity		
RNase 7	C/I	KCs and stratum corneum
Anti-leukoprotease (secretory leukoprotease inhibitor)	C/I	KCs and stratum corneum
Elafin (skin-derived serine protease inhibitor)	C/I	KCs
Antimicrobial molecules with enzyme/enzyme inhibitor activity		
Palmitoleic acid	C	Sebum
Sphingosine	C	Upper stratum corneum

bilayer. Formation of multimeric complexes of the peptides constitutes a membrane pore with ion channel activity, which results in lysis and death of the microorganism. The antimicrobial peptides are generally more active against microorganisms than host cells as a result of differences in the composition of the phospholipids. Some peptides are inhibited by cholesterol, a component of host cell membranes, which is absent from those of microorganisms.

Dermcidin is a peptide with no homology to known antimicrobial peptides and is produced only in sweat glands. Adrenomedullin is a multifunctional peptide, which is widely synthesised in various tissues including skin.

3.6.1.1 Defensins

Defensins are small 3-4 kDa cationic peptides that form a β sheet structure with three disulphide bonds. The vertebrate defensins are divided into two types, α- and β-defensins which differ in their pairing of six conserved cysteines to form the disulphide bonds. Humans produce at least six different α-defensins and three β-defensins. The α-defensins, which were first identified in rabbits, are stored in the peroxidase-positive granules of PMNs (HNP-1, -2, -3, -4) and in the Paneth cells, specialised secretory epithelial cells at the base of crypts in the small intestine (HD-5, HD-6). In contrast, β-defensins (HBD-1, -2, -3) are not stored in granules but are synthesised and secreted in various epithelia. HBD-1 is found predominately (but not exclusively) in epithelia of the urogenital tract and kidney, HBD-2 in the respiratory tract and skin, and HBD-3 in the skin and tonsils. Unlike HBD-1, which is constitutively expressed, microorganisms and proinflammatory cytokines induce the production of HBD-2 and HBD-3. In keeping with this fact, the latter were initially isolated from extracts of lesional scales from patients with psoriasis, an inflammatory skin disease associated with streptococcal infections [25,26] (see Chapter 9). Defensins have a broad spectrum of antimicrobial activity against many bacteria, fungi and some viruses and are sensitive to increasing salt concentrations.

In normal skin, mRNA specific for HBD-1 is consistently expressed at various body sites whilst HBD-2 mRNA demonstrates a more variable expression. The presence of HBD-1 and HBD-2 in the Malpighian layer of the epidermis and/or stratum corneum and hair follicles, has been shown by immunostaining [27]. Furthermore, HBD-2 has been localised, by immunogold staining and electron microscopy, to the lamellar bodies of the KCs suggesting that it is released with the lipid contents into the extracellular space [28]. HBD-3 has been isolated from extracts of stratum corneum from normal skin although at markedly lower levels than from psoriatic scale.

The Gram-positive bacteria, *S. aureus* and *S. epidermidis,* and the Gram-negative *E. coli* and *Pseudomonas aeruginosa* can induce KC production of HBD-2, but strains of *Streptococcus pyogenes* are poor inducers. Both HBD-1 and HBD-2 show microbicidal activity against predominately Gram-negative organisms such as *E. coli* and *P. aeruginosa*, and yeasts, but are relatively ineffective against Gram-positive bacteria such as *S. aureus.* In contrast, HBD-3 is a more potent, broad-spectrum antibiotic that kills both Gram-positive and Gram-negative organisms and the yeast *C. albicans.*

Other functions have been described for β-defensins that could enhance the innate response of the epidermis, and provide a link between the innate immune response and acquired immunity. Thus HBD-2 can induce up-regulation of costimulatory molecules and the maturation of immature dendritic cells either by acting as an endogenous ligand and binding directly to TLR4, or possibly by delivering to the receptor minute amounts of LPS which would be insufficient by themselves to cause activation [29]. In addition, β-defensins can act as chemoattractants for immature dendritic cells and memory T lymphocytes via the chemokine receptor CCR6 [30].

3.6.1.2 Cathelicidins

Cathelicidins are a family of mammalian antimicrobial peptides and proteins (1-18 kDa) with approximately 40 members, multiples of which have been identified in the PMNs of cows, rabbits, and pigs [31]. They consist of a highly conserved cathelin-like N-terminal, named after a protein purified from porcine PMNs, and a variable C-terminal ranging from 12 to 100 amino acids long. With the exception of the rabbit p15 cathelicidins, the molecule is not antibacterially active until the C-terminal is separated from the cathelin-like domain. This involves, in most cases, the proteolytic enzyme elastase which is present in the azurophil granules of PMNs and comes in contact with the cathelicidins in the phagosome after phagocytosis of microorganisms. Some of the antibacterial C-terminal peptides form amphipathic α helices, whilst others form amphipathic β sheets as found in the defensins, but differ in having two disulphide bridges rather than three (protegrins).

The single human member of this family is known as hCAP18/LL-37 and has a C-terminal peptide of 37 amino acids in the form of a a helix. The hCAP18/LL-37 peptide is stored in neutrophils, but is also found in skin mast cells, sweat eccrine glands, and in lesional KCs in the skin of patients with psoriasis, nickel contact dermatitis and SLE [32]. It is, however, barely detectable in the epidermis of normal, uninflamed skin illustrating a requirement for induction of expression by inflammatory stimuli. In common with cathelicidins in general, the LL-37 peptide shows a wide spectrum of anti-microbial activity against Gram-positive and Gram-negative bacteria, and fungi. In addition, it exerts a range of other biological activities including acting as a chemoattractant for PMNs, monocytes, mast cells and T cells, inducing degranulation of mast cells and stimulating skin wound healing. Furthermore, recent work has suggested that the cathelin-like domain of hCAP18/LL-37, which shares homology with the cystatin family of cysteine protease inhibitors, can not only inhibit protease activity, but can also kill human pathogens including *E. coli* and *S. aureus* [33].

3.6.1.3 Dermcidin

Dermcidin is an antimicrobial peptide which is specifically and constitutively expressed in sweat glands in the dermis of skin, secreted into the sweat and transported in sweat to the epidermal surface [34]. Unlike hCAP18/LL-37, dermcidin is not present in sweat ductal epithelial cells. Although it has no amino acid sequence homology to known antimicrobial peptides, dermcidin is similarly produced as an inactive precursor protein that is cleaved to give an active C-terminal peptide. The C-terminal peptide of dermcidin, which consists of 47 amino acids, has a broad spectrum of activity against a variety of pathogenic microorganisms that is maintained over a broad pH range and in high salt concentrations.

3.6.1.4 Adrenomedullin

Adrenomedullin is a multifunctional peptide that exerts various effects including vasodilation, regulation of cell growth and antimicrobial activity. It is synthesised by a wide range of cells and tissues including skin, where it is present, together with its receptors, in KCs of the epidermis and hair follicle, epidermal melanocytes and in sweat and sebaceous glands. Adrenomedullin has antimicrobial activity against both Gram-positive and Gram-negative bacterial strains that form part of the skin, oral, respiratory and gastric microflora [35]. It does not, however, have any activity against *C. albicans*. Furthermore, interaction between epithelial cells and bacteria at these sites leads to an increase in adrenomedullin peptide and gene expression.

3.6.2 Antimicrobial proteins

3.6.2.1 Bactericidal permeability-increasing protein (BPI)

Bactericidal permeability-increasing protein (BPI) is a highly cationic 55-60 kDa protein with a positively charged N-terminal and a neutral but hydrophobic C-terminal connected by a proline-rich linker. It binds to LPS in the cell wall of Gram-negative bacteria with high affinity causing permeabilisation and death of the microorganisms. Initially, electrostatic attraction occurs between the cationic regions of BPI and the anionic regions of LPS. The insertion of BPI into the bacterial cell wall causes rearrangement of LPS and phospholipids and displacement of LPS-bound Mg^{2+} and Ca^{2+} resulting in increased permeability to hydrophobic molecules and inhibition of bacterial growth.

BPI, which is stored in the granules of PMNs, is structurally related to the LPS-binding protein in plasma. Because of its specificity for LPS, it has no effect on Gram-positive bacteria, which lack LPS in their cell wall. The N-terminal domain contains the bactericidal and LPS-neutralising activities of the molecule whilst the C-terminal part may facilitate phagocytosis of BPI-bacterial complexes. A recombinant form of the LPS-binding part of the protein is now in clinical use in patients with meningococcal and other Gram-negative bacteria-induced sepsis.

Recently it has been demonstrated that dermal fibroblasts constitutively produce BPI and the levels are increased by stimulation with IL-4 [36]. Epithelial cells of the oral, respiratory and gastrointestinal tracts also produce BPI, but KCs in skin have yet to be investigated for this protein.

3.6.2.2 Psoriasin (S100A7) and Calprotectin (S100A8/S100A9)

S100 is a multigenic family of Ca^{2+}-binding signalling proteins, which have intracellular and extracellular regulatory activities. Inside cells most S100 members are present as homodimers, or sometimes heterodimers, which have various functions including regulation of protein phosphorylation, Ca^{2+} homeostasis, cell proliferation and differentiation. Extracellular S100 proteins have regulatory effects on neuronal cell proliferation, differentiation and death, and the activity of inflammatory cells.

The S100 proteins, S100A7, S100A8, S100A9, S100A10 and S100A11 are all present in normal, healthy skin [37]. S100A7, also known as psoriasin because it was first identified in lesional skin from patients with psoriasis, is present in the nucleus and cytoplasm of basal KCs but is associated with the plasma membrane of differentiated keratinocytes in the spinous layer. The production of psoriasin by KCs can be induced by proinflammatory cytokines (TNF-α, IL-1 and IL-6), and by various microorganisms, particularly the mucoid form of *P. aeruginosa*. In addition to being chemotactic for CD4[+] T cells, preliminary evidence suggests that psoriasin is selectively bactericidal for *E. coli*, but has no effect on *P. aeruginosa*, *S. aureus* or *C. albicans* [38]. The mechanism by which psoriasin kills *E. coli* appears to be different from that of the β defensins as the bacterial membrane remains intact.

The S100A8 (myeloid-related protein (MRP)-8)/S100A9 (MRP-14) heterodimer, known collectively as calprotectin because of its calcium-binding properties and anti-microbial effects, is found at high concentrations in PMNs, activated macrophages, endothelial cells and the epidermis of psoriatic skin lesions. Levels of calprotectin are, however, absent or are expressed at minimal levels in normal epidermis. The C-terminal domain of the S100A8 chain is identical to the N-terminal sequence of peptides called neutrophil immobilizing factors suggesting that calprotectin can bring about the accumulation of PMNs in addition to its other functions, which include inhibition of macrophage activation and immunoglobulin synthesis by lymphocytes, propagation of inflammation, and antimicrobial activity. Calprotectin exerts inhibitory effects and, at higher concentrations, killing of *C. albicans* and of various Gram-positive and Gram-negative bacteria, possibly by depriving them of zinc [39].

3.6.3 Antimicrobial molecules with enzyme/enzyme inhibitor activity

3.6.3.1 RNase 7

The ribonuclease activity of human skin is partially attributed to a potent 14.5 kDa ribonuclease called RNase 7 isolated from the stratum corneum [40]. This enzyme, which is synthesized in KCs, exhibits broad-spectrum antimicrobial activity against many pathogenic microorganisms, with particular potent activity against a species of *Enterococcus faecium* with resistance to vancomycin. The levels of RNase 7 in KCs can be induced above constitutive levels by interaction with either cytokines, such as IL-1β and IFN-γ, or bacteria. RNase 7 is also constitutively expressed in epithelial tissues at other sites such as the respiratory and genitourinary tracts, and at low levels in the gut.

3.6.3.2 Antileukoprotease (ALP)

Antileukoprotease (ALP), also called secretory leukoprotease inhibitor or mucous protease inhibitor, is a 12 kDa cationic protein that can prevent proteolytic degradation of extracellular matrix proteins by PMN-derived serine proteases. This protease inhibitory activity is mediated by the C-terminal domain of ALP, whilst the N-terminal part of the molecule exerts antimicrobial activity against several skin-associated microorganisms such as *P. aeruginosa*, *S. aureus*, *S. epidermidis* and *C. albicans*. ALP is abundant in the secretions of respiratory and reproductive epithelia, and has also been found in KCs, stratum granulosum and stratum corneum of skin [41]. Up-regulation of ALP has been observed in lesional skin of psoriasis patients and in migrating KCs of healing wounds.

3.6.3.3 Elafin (skin-derived serine protease inhibitor)

Elafin (also known as skin-derived anti-leukoproteinase/trappin-2) is an epithelial serine protease inhibitor, which is only minimally expressed in normal skin, but is induced in KCs in inflamed skin conditions such as psoriasis, in epidermal skin tumours, and after wounding. Elafin helps to maintain the integrity of the epidermis by inhibiting the PMN enzyme elastase and also has antimicrobial activity against *P. aeruginosa*, the supernatants of which induce its expression [42]. In contrast, *E. coli* does not induce elafin and its growth is not inhibited by it.

3.6.4 Antimicrobial Lipids

3.6.4.1 Palmitoleic acid

Total lipids extracted from sebum inhibit the growth of various Gram-positive bacteria but are ineffective against most Gram-negative bacteria. The majority of the antimicrobial activity is accounted for by saturated (lauric acid) and unsaturated (palmitoleic acid) fatty acids. Palmitoleic acid is the most active sebum lipid fraction both against Gram-positive bacteria and in blocking the adherence of *C. albicans* to stratum corneum.

3.6.4.2 Sphingosine

The sphingolipid metabolite, sphingosine, produced by the action of ceramidases on ceramides, is present in the upper layers of the stratum corneum of the skin and exerts a potent antimicrobial effect on *S. aureus* at physiological levels. Low levels of sphingosine are associated with the increased numbers of bacteria, including *S. aureus*, which colonise the skin of patients with atopic dermatitis.

3.7 NK cells

Natural killer (NK) cells are large granular lymphocytes that lack surface markers expressed by T (TCR) or B (Ig) cells. They can kill tumour cells, healthy allogeneic (from an individual of different genetic makeup) and infected cells without prior activation or immunization and are therefore able to function as part of the innate immune response. For the NK cell to fulfil this role, it must be able to distinguish between an infected and uninfected cell. It achieves this by recognising alterations in the levels of MHC Class I molecules expressed on the target cell surface. MHC Class I expression, which is evident on most nucleated cells, is a sign of a healthy cell. In contrast, MHC Class I levels are down-regulated on infected cells which marks out the cell for killing by NK cells (the so-called "missing self model"). Killer cell inhibitory receptors that are specific for MHC Class I antigen regulate NK cell cytolytic activity by inhibiting the activation of killing by a variable array of stimulatory receptors. Thus the function of NK depends upon the balance between inhibitory and stimulatory receptor interactions with their corresponding target cell ligands [43].

In addition to being cytotoxic effector cells, NK cells are able to rapidly produce IFN-γ and other cytokines at the initial stages of certain infections with the subsequent generation of a protective Th-1 response. In this way, NK cells act as an important link between innate and acquired immunity.

It has been shown that 6% of natural killer cells in peripheral blood also express cutaneous lymphocyte antigen (CLA), a specific homing receptor for the skin, which binds to E-selectin, an adhesion molecule on the surface of endothelial cells [44]. Small numbers of NK cells are present in normal skin in which the majority of T lymphocytes also express CLA.

3.8 Interaction between Innate and Acquired Immunity

Dendritic cells are located at the interface between the innate and acquired immune systems. Thus when immature dendritic cells in the skin (and other peripheral tissues) encounter a pathogen, they undergo a process of maturation involving induction of costimulatory molecules (CD80 (B7-1), CD86 (B7-2) and CD40), increased MHC antigen expression, and the production of proinflammatory cytokines IL-12 and TNF-α. These mature dendritic cells have increased antigen processing and presenting ability, and migrate to lymph nodes where peptides derived from the pathogen are presented, bound to MHC molecules, to antigen-specific receptors on naïve T cells.

The dendritic cell senses the presence of the pathogen via stimulation of one or more PRRs, and the same cell processes and present peptides specific to the pathogen. In this way, both signals required for activation of a T cell (costimulation and specific MHC-bound peptide) will only be provided if the specific peptide originated from the same pathogen that initially induced the costimulatory activity [45]. Self-antigens, on the other hand, usually lack PAMPs and cannot therefore induce costimulatory activity so that T cells specific for self-antigens are not normally activated. In this way, activation of the acquired immune system occurs upon pathogen recognition by the innate immune receptors expressed by dendritic cells. Furthermore, stimulation of TLRs on dendritic cells by PAMPs usually results in Th-1 type responses, which are appropriate for the elimination of the microorganisms from which they are derived.

As mentioned above, HBD-2 can also act as a link between innate and acquired immunity by inducing up-regulation of costimulatory molecule expression and the maturation of dendritic cells, and acting as a chemoattractant for memory T lymphocytes and immature dendritic cells via the chemokine receptor CCR6. In addition, NK cells are able to rapidly produce IFN-γ and other cytokines at the initial stages of certain infections with the subsequent generation of a protective Th-1 response.

Thus the innate immune system provides an immediate, antigen non-specific inflammatory response to a pathogen and, in addition, alerts the acquired immune system via the initiation of dendritic cell maturation and the production of cytokines and chemokines. The clonal receptors of the acquired immune response can remember a previous encounter with a pathogen and can therefore mount a stronger antigen-specific response on second meeting. Thus the two immune systems complement each other and provide an optimal defensive response by the host against infection.

Summary

The skin provides not only a physical barrier to pathogens and other environmental dangers, but an effective innate immune response, which recognises and eliminates microorganisms that breach its defences. It achieves this via the alternative complement pathway, NK cells, a variety of PRR receptors that recognise conserved molecular patterns on pathogens, and by the production of antimicrobial molecules.

The PRR receptors expressed include TLRs, Nod proteins, dectin-1, CD91, C-type lectin receptors and integrins:

- Each skin cell type (resident and infiltrating immune cells) expresses a different combination of TLRs and a corresponding ability to respond to a particular set of microbial ligands.

- Nod1 and Nod2, intracellular receptors for pathogens, are also probably present in KCs. Nod2 negatively regulates TLR2 function ensuring modulation of NF-κB activation and suppression of immune responses.

- LCs in the epidermis selectively express dectin-1, which specifically recognises β-glucans in fungi. Dectin-1 enhances the TLR2-mediated activation of NF-κB by beta-glucans ensuring an effective response to fungi on the surface of the skin.

- CD91, a receptor for Hsps, is expressed by DDCs and fibroblasts, but not by epidermal cells that produce Hsps, thus preventing inappropriate activation by endogenous proteins.

- C-type lectin receptors specific for carbohydrates expressed by bacteria and fungi are present on KCs, endothelial cells and macrophages.

- KCs and LCs express integrins, which can bind various microorganisms.

A variety of antimicrobial molecules including β defensins and a cathelicidin, dermcidin, adrenomedullin, BPI, S100 proteins, RNase 7, ALP, elafin and lipids are produced predominately by KCs, and in some cases by sweat glands in the skin. Production in each case is constitutive and/or induced by microorganisms or proinflammatory cytokines.

References

1. Medzhitov R. & Janeway C.A. Jr. Innate immunity: impact on the adaptive immune response. Curr.Opin.Immunol. 1997; **9:** 4-9.

2. Janeway C.A. & Medzhitov R. Innate immune recognition. Ann.Rev.Immunol. 2002; **20:** 197-216.

3. Zhang D., Zhang G., Hayden M.S. *et al*. A toll-like receptor that prevents infection by uropathogenic bacteria. Science 2004; **303:** 1522-6.

4. Yamamoto M., Takeda K., Akira S. TIR domain-containing adaptors define the specificity of TLR signalling. Mol.Immunol. 2004; **40:** 861-8.

5. Poltorak A., He X., Smirnova L. *et al*. Defective LPS signalling in C3H/HeJ and C57BL/10ScCr mice: mutations in Tlr4 gene. Science 1998; **282:** 2085-8.

6. Qureshi S.T., Lariviere L., Leveque G. *et al*. Endotoxin-tolerant mice have mutations in Toll-like (Tlr4). J.Exp.Med. 1999; **189:** 615-25.

7. Matzinger P. Tolerance, danger and the extended family. Ann.Rev.Immunol. 1994; **12:** 991-1045.

8. Muzio M., Bosisio D., Polentarutti N. *et al*. Differential expression and regulation of Toll-like receptors (TLR) in human leukocytes: Selective expression of TLR3 in dendritic cells. J.Immunol. 2000; **164:** 5998-6004.

9. Kadowaki N., Ho S., Antonenko S. *et al*. Subsets of human dendritic cell precursors express different Toll-like receptors and respond to different microbial antigens. J.Exp.Med. 2001; **194:** 863-9.

10. Baker B.S., Ovigne J.-M., Powles A.V., Corcoran S., Fry L. Normal keratinocytes express Toll-like receptors (TLRs) 1, 2 and 5: modulation of TLR expression in chronic plaque psoriasis. Brit.J.Dermatol. 2003; **148:** 670-9.

11. Curry J.L., Qin J.-Z., Bonish B. *et al*. Innate immune-related receptors in normal and psoriatic skin. Arch.Pathol.Lab.Med. 2003; **127:** 178-86.

12. Mempel M., Voelcker V., Kollisch G. *et al*. Toll-like receptor expression in human keratinocytes: Nuclear factor kB controlled gene activation by *Staphylococcus aureus* is Toll-like receptor 2 but not Toll-like receptor 4 or platelet activating factor receptor dependent. J.Invest.Dermatol. 2003; **121:** 1389-96.

13. Pivarcsi A., Bodai L., Rethi B. *et al*. Expression and function of Toll-like receptors 2 and 4 in human keratinocytes. Int.Immunol. 2003; **15:** 721-30.

14. Faure E., Equils O., Sieling P.A. *et al*. Bacterial lipopolysaccharide activated NF-κB through Toll-like receptor 4 (TLR-4) in cultured human dermal endothelial cells. J.Biol.Chem. 2000; **275:** 11058-63.

15. Varadaradjalou S., Feger F., Thieblemont N. *et al*. Toll-like receptor 2 (TLR2) and TLR4 differentially activate human mast cells. Eur.J.Immunol. 2003; **33:** 899-906.

16. McCurdy J.D., Olynych T.J., Maher L.H., Marshall J.S. Cutting Edge: distinct Toll-like receptor 2 activators selectively induce different classes of mediator production from human mast cells. J.Immunol. 2003; **170:** 1625-9.

17. Watanabe T., Kitani A., Murray P.J., Strober W. NOD2 is a negative regulator of Toll-like receptor 2–mediated T helper type 1 responses. Nat.Immunol. 2004; **5:** 800–8.

18. Song P.I., Prado R., Kang Y., Kolot A., Armstrong C.A., Ansel J.C. Keratinocytes express nucleotide-binding oligomerization domain (NOD) 1 and 2: Implications for cutaneous innate immunity. J.Invest. Dermatol. 2004; **122:** A126 (Abstr).

19. Gantner B.N., Simmons R.M., Canavera S.J., Akira S., Underhill D.M. Collaborative induction of inflammatory responses by dectin-1 and Toll-like receptor 2. J.Exp.Med. 2003; **197:** 1107-17.

20. Higashi N., Morikawa A., Fujioka K. *et al*. Human macrophage lectin specific for galactose/ N-acetylgalactosamine is a marker for cells at an intermediate stage in their differentiation from monocytes into macrophages. Int.Immunol. 2002; **14:** 545-54.

21. Szolnoky G., Bata-Csorgo Z., Kenderessy A.S. *et al.* A mannose-binding receptor is expressed on human keratinocytes and mediates killing of *Candida albicans*. J.Invest.Dermatol. 2001; **117:** 205-13.

22. Groger M., Holnthoner W., Maurer D. *et al*. Dermal microvascular endothelial cells express the 180-kDa macrophage mannose receptor *in situ* and *in vitro*. J.Immunol. 2000; **165:** 5428-34.

23. Krissansen G.W. Integrins: Signalling and disease. Nature Encyclopedia of Life Sciences 2001; 1-9. (www.wls.net)

24. Gallo R.L., Murakami M., Ohtake T., Zaiou M. Biology and clinical relevance of naturally occurring antimicrobial peptides. J.Allergy Clin.Immunol. 2002; **110:** 823-31.

25. Schroder J.-M. & Harder J. Human beta-defensin-2. Int.J.Biochem & Cell Biol. 1999; **31:** 645-51.

26. Harder J., Bartels J., Christophers E., Schroder J.-M. Isolation and characterisation of human β-defensin-3, a novel human inducible peptide antibiotic. J.Biol.Chem. 2001; **276:** 5707-13.

27. Ali R.S., Falconer A., Ikram M., Bissett C.E., Cerio R., Quinn A.G. Expression of the peptide antibiotics human defensin-1 and human defensin-2 in normal human skin. J. Invest. Dermatol. 2001; **117:** 106-11.

28. Oren A., Ganz T., Liu L., Meerloo T. In human epidermis, beta-defensin 2 is packaged in lamellar bodies. Exp.Mol. Pathol. 2003; **74:** 180-2.

29. Biragyn A., Ruffini P.A., Leifer C.A. *et al*. Toll-like receptor 4-dependent activation of dendritic cells by β-defensin 2. Science 2002; **298:** 10255-9.

30. Yang D., Chertov O., Bykovskaia S.N. *et al*. Beta-defensins: linking innate and adaptive immunity through dendritic and T cell CCR6. Science. 1999; **286:** 525-8.

31. Zanetti M. Cathelicidins, multifunctional peptides of the innate immunity. J.Leuk. Biol. 2004; **75:** 39-48.

32. Frohm M., Agerberth B., Ahangari G. *et al*. The expression of the gene coding for the antibacterial peptide LL-37 is induced in human keratinocytes during inflammatory disorders. J.Biol.Chem. 1997; **272:** 15258-63.

33. Zaiou M., Nizet V., Gallo R.L. Antimicrobial and protease inhibitory functions of the human cathelicidin (hCAP18/LL-37) prosequence. J.Invest.Dermatol. 2003; **120:** 810-6.

34. Schittek B., Hipfel R., Sauer B. *et al*. Dermcidin: a novel human antibiotic peptide secreted by sweat glands. Nat.Immunol. 2001; **2**: 1133-7.

35. Allaker R.P. & Kapas S. Adrenomedullin and mucosal defence: interaction between host and microorganism. Regul. Pept. 2003; **112**: 147-52.

36. Reichel P.H., Seemann C., Csernok E. *et al*. Bactericidal/permeability-increasing protein is expressed by human dermal fibroblasts and upregulated by Interleukin 4. Clin.Diagn.Lab. Immunol. 2003; **10**: 473-5.

37. Eckert R.L., Broome A.-M., Ruse M., Robinson N., Ryan D., Lee K. S100 proteins in the epidermis. J.Invest.Dermatol. 2004; **123**: 23-33.

38. Gläser R., Harder J., Lange H, Bartels J., Christophers E., Schröder J.M. Antimicrobial psoriasin (S100A7) protects human skin from *Escherichia coli* infection. Nat.Immunol. 2005; **6**: 57-64 .

39. Brandtzaeg P., Gabrielsen T.O., Dale I., Muller F., Steinbakk M., Fagerhol M.K. The leucocyte protein L1 (calprotectin): a putative nonspecific defence factor at epithelial surfaces. Adv. Exp.Med.Biol. 1995; **371A**: 201-6.

40. Harder J. & Schroder J.M. RNase 7, a novel innate immune defense antimicrobial protein of healthy human skin. J.Biol.Chem. 2002; **277**: 46779-84.

41. Wiedow O., Harder J., Bartels J., Streit V., Christophers E. Antileukoprotease in human skin: an antibiotic peptide constitutively produced by keratinocytes. Biochem.Biophys.Res. Commun. 1998; **248**: 904-9.

42. Meyer-Hoffert U., Wichmann N., Schwichtenberg L., White P.C., Wiedow O. Supernatants of *Pseudomonas aeruginosa* induce the Pseudomonas-specific antibiotic elafin in human keratinocytes. Exp.Dermatol. 2003; **12**: 418-25.

43. McQueen K.L. & Parham P. Variable receptors controlling activation and inhibition of NK cells. Curr.Opin.Immunol. 2002; **14**: 615-21.

44. Chang S.E., Kim M.J., Lee W.S. *et al*. Natural killer cells in human peripheral blood and primary cutaneous natural killer cell lymphomas may express cutaneous lymphocyte antigen. Acta Dermatol.Venereol. 2003; **83**: 162-6.

45. Fearon D.T. & Locksley R.M. The instructive role of innate immunity in the acquired immune response. Science 1996; **272**: 50-3.

Acquired Immune Responses: Immunological Hypersensitivity Reactions

Immunological hypersensitivity reactions are immune responses that result in tissue damage and are designated as types I, II, III and IV depending upon the mechanism involved (Table 4.1). Subsequent to the original classification by Gell and Coombs, a fifth type of hypersensitivity reaction, which describes the stimulation of endocrine receptors by immune reactions, has now been included. However, the type V reaction is only observed in autoimmune diseases such as Graves' disease and, because it is not relevant to skin, has not been included here.

4.1 Type I Hypersensitivity

Type I hypersensitivity (immediate) reactions occur in individuals who have been previously sensitised to a specific allergen. The allergens come from a variety of sources including pollens, foods, chemical additives, drugs, animal dander and insect stings, and the allergic reaction induced can vary from a mild irritation to one that is life-threatening (anaphylaxis). In each case, the type I hypersensitivity reaction is mediated by immunoglobulin E (IgE) produced in response to an allergen, which would otherwise be an innocuous foreign substance.

4.1.1 Mechanism

The initial sensitisation of an individual to an allergen is dependent upon CD4$^+$ T cells. On stimulation, naïve CD4$^+$ T cells can potentially produce both Th-1 and Th-2 cytokines, but are polarised to either one of the cytokine patterns by the environment in which activation takes place. Thus in the presence of T cell-derived IFN-γ, and IL-12 from antigen-presenting cells, the T cells will develop a Th-1 phenotype. However, IL-4 released by mast cells will induce Th-2 cytokine expression. Furthermore, the two cytokine patterns are mutually exclusive with Th-1-inducing cytokines inhibiting Th-2 cytokine production, and vice versa.

4.1.1.1 Initial exposure to allergen

Antigen-presenting cells (APC) take up and process the allergen, and present it in the form of peptide-MHC Class II complexes to CD4$^+$ T cells expressing a TCR specific for the peptide (Fig. 4.1). Interaction between the TCR and peptide-MHC Class II complexes leads to further interactions between surface molecules on the T cell and APC resulting in activation of the allergen-specific T cells. In a susceptible individual, the activated T cells proliferate and produce Th-2 cytokines, including IL-4 or IL-13, which are essential for the production of IgE by B cells expressing the

Table 4.1 Characteristics of Hypersensitivity Reactions I - IV

Type	Speed of response	Antigens	Effectors	Mechanism	Examples/ Diseases
I	Immediate	Pollens, HDM, drugs, animal dander, insect venoms, fungi, foods - peanuts, egg milk, shellfish	IgE on mast cells (basophils) and/or Th-2 cells	Mast cell release of histamine and other mediators	Asthma, hayfever, urticaria, atopic dermatitis
II	Immediate	Glomerular basement membrane	Autoantibody ± complement	Lysis of target cells	Goodpasture's syndrome
		Conjunctival basement membrane			Occular cicatricial pemphigoid
		Acetylcholine receptor			Myasthenia gravis
		Red cell antigens			Autoimmune haemolytic anaemia
		Dsg 3, Dsg 1, BP 180			Bullous pemphigus/ pemphigoid
		ABO	Antibody ± complement		Acute haemolytic transfusion
		Rh-D			Haemolytic disease of the newborn
		MHC			Hyperacute transfusion reaction
		Drugs			Haemolysis, thrombocytopenia, agranulocytopenia

appropriate allergen-specific receptors. Two DNA rearrangement events are involved in the production of a functional IgE molecule by B cells; recombination of the variable (V), diversity (D) and joining (J) regions to give an allergen-specific binding site, and juxtapositioning of the VDJ region to an IgE constant (Fc) region.

The allergen-specific IgE then binds via its Fc region to high affinity IgE (FcεRI) receptors on the surface of mast cells (long-lived mononuclear cells in tissue), basophils (short-lived polymorphonuclear myeloid cells in blood), macrophages and other APCs. The IgE Fc receptors on mast cells and basophils consists of an α chain, to which the Fc part of IgE binds, a β chain and the two γ chains which transduce the signal for degranulation. However, the receptors on LCs and monocytes, which are probably involved in antigen presentation (see Chapter 7), lack the β chain. There is also a low affinity, type II IgE receptor present on about 25% of B cells that enhances

Type	Speed of response	Antigens	Effectors	Mechanism	Examples/ Diseases
III	Immediate	Intradermal: soluble antigens	Immune complexes, complement/ P-selectin, Mac-1	Recruited PMNs produce toxic substances causing tissue damage	Arthus reaction
		Intravenous: animal serum proteins			Serum sickness
		Inhaled: thermophilic moulds, mushroom spores, bird antigens			Extrinsic allergic alveolitis
		Autoantigens			SLE, rheumatoid arthritis, Sjögren syndrome
		? Autoantigens			Allergic vasculitis, erythema nodosum,
		Herpes simplex/ ?autoantigens			Erythema multiforme
IV	Delayed	Mycobacteria, bacteria, fungi, viruses, protozoans, autoantigens, grafts, certain insect bites	Th-1 cells, macrophages	Inflammation	Response to foreign and autoantigens
		Nickel, chromate, rubber, poison ivy, paraphenyldiamine, DNCB, DNFB, oxazolone			Allergic contact hypersensitivity
		HDM, food, parasites	Th-2 cells, eosinophils		Atopic dermatitis

antigen presentation; furthermore, proteolytic cleavage of the receptor releases soluble products that stimulate IgE synthesis, at least *in vitro*.

4.1.1.2 Subsequent exposure to allergen

After initial sensitisation, subsequent exposure to allergen results in activation of mast cells and basophils when allergen binds simultaneously to more than one molecule of IgE bound to the cell surface (Fig. 4.1). Cross-linking of surface-bound IgE molecules brings the receptors in close proximity, inducing activation of receptor-associated kinases and initiation of the second messenger cascade. This results in degranulation of the mast cells/basophils as secretory granules fuse with the

Figure 4.1 Mechanisms involved in a type I hypersensitivity reaction to allergen

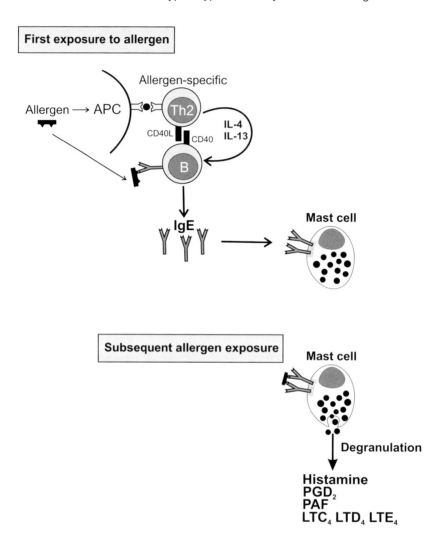

cell surface membrane, releasing high concentrations of stored histamine and several other potent mediators (see Chapter 1) into the extracellular space. It is these highly active mediators that are responsible for the clinical symptoms of allergy, asthma and anaphylaxis. Histamine is a vasoactive molecule that binds to specific receptors on vascular endothelial cells causing an increase in vascular permeability, and is responsible for the oedema and erythema observed in skin tests. In addition, histamine can cause the contraction of smooth muscle, which may account for the gastrointestinal symptoms associated with some allergic reactions. Other mediators released by mast cells include PGD_2 (a potent muscle constrictor), PAF, and LTC_4 and its metabolites LTD_4 and LTE_4, which comprise the activity that was previously termed "slow reacting substance of anaphylaxis" (see Chapter 2). Unlike mast cells, basophils do not produce prostaglandins at significant levels, and appear to synthesize only one cytokine, IL-4, whereas mast cells secrete a range of cytokines.

4.1.1.3 Late Reactions

The type I immediate reactions can be followed by late reactions, either as a flare 6-12 hours after a skin prick test, or as bronchoconstriction a few hours after the inhalation of allergen. The late reaction is mediated by activated mast cells, which release vasoactive mediators and various cytokines, including Th-2 cytokines. Infiltration is further promoted by stimulated epithelial and endothelial cells, and macrophages which release chemokines such as eotaxin (CCL11) and MCP (CCL2) in response to mast cell-derived cytokines, attracting macrophages, eosinophils and PMNs to the challenge site. Eosinophils contribute to the inflammatory process by producing highly toxic molecules such as the eosinophil cationic protein, which causes tissue damage. TNF-α, which is both stored in large quantities in the mast cell granules and is synthesized de novo in the cytoplasm, plays an important role in this process. Indeed, the late reaction can be largely inhibited by the administration of anti-TNF-α antibodies.

4.1.2 IgE detection and measurement

4.1.2.1 ELISA/RAST

Dilutions of serum to be tested are incubated with antigen adsorbed to the wells of a plastic microtitre plate to allow binding of IgE antibodies. The complex between the allergen and allergen-specific IgE is detected using an antibody specific for human IgE linked either to an enzyme such as alkaline phosphatase or peroxidase, as in the enzyme-linked immunosorbent assay (ELISA), or complexed to a radioisotope, usually ^{125}I, as in the radioallergosorbent test (RAST). A positive reaction in the ELISA is detected by the addition of a chromogenic substrate, which gives a coloured end product in the presence of enzyme, whereas in the RAST the amount of IgE bound is measured as radioactivity, which increases proportionally with allergen concentration until a plateau is reached.

4.1.2.2 Skin prick test

The skin prick test is used to demonstrate skin sensitivity to an allergen. An aqueous extract of the allergen, often suspended in 50% glycerol, is scratched into the skin on the volar aspect of the forearm or on the back using a lancet or small needle. Histamine, and buffer without allergen extract are included as positive and negative controls, respectively. The allergen binds to IgE antibodies bound to the surface of mast cells causing their activation and degranulation. After 10-20 minutes, the released mediators cause activation of blood vessels, nerves and skin cells. The diameter of the weal (area of oedema) obtained is measured and compared to that produced by the histamine positive control; a weal diameter exceeding 3mm is often considered positive. The response is dependent upon the degree of sensitivity, number of mast cells and potency of the allergen extract. Although very sensitive, the skin prick test has only 70-80% specificity with positive tests obtained in some individuals who are not clinically allergic, whilst a less pronounced response is observed in young children and the elderly.

4.1.3 Examples of type I hypersensitivities

4.1.3.1 Anaphylaxis

Anaphylaxis is the most severe form of immediate hypersensitivity, which results in oedema, bronchoconstriction and vascular collapse, and may eventually cause death. Insect stings, foods and drugs cause most of these severe allergic reactions. The allergens responsible for IgE production have been investigated and found to be low molecular weight soluble proteins or glycoproteins, which can rapidly penetrate mucous membranes. In the case of insect stings, the allergens have been identified as melittin, phospholipase A2 and hyaluronidase, major components of insect venom. Allergic reactions to an insect sting are mediated by IgE on mast cells and basophils and can range from extensive local reactions involving cellulitis to a more generalised urticaria (see Chapter 5) and anaphylaxis [1]. Treatment of the latter requires immediate subcutaneous or intramuscular administration of adrenaline (epinephrine) which rapidly helps to maintain blood pressure, reduces the undesirable effects caused by the released mediators, and inhibits the further release of more anaphylaxis-inducing factors.

4.1.3.2 Food allergy

Food allergy is an aberrant immune response to food and should be differentiated from food intolerance [2]. It commonly occurs to foods such as nuts (e.g. peanuts and brazil nuts), egg, milk, and shellfish resulting in diarrhoea, vomiting, and inflammatory skin diseases such as urticaria and eczema (see Chapter 7). These symptoms and skin conditions are mediated by IgE on mast cells and by allergen-specific Th-2 cells. Type I hypersensitivity reactions to food occur in about 6% of children and 1-2% of adults; the allergens involved are low molecular weight molecules resistant to digestion by proteases or denaturation by heat.

Although undigested protein fragments that gain access to gut-associated lymphoid tissue induce secretory IgA synthesis, this defence mechanism may not be sufficient to entirely remove the antigen, leaving small amounts available to initiate an immune response. Various factors may explain why food hypersensitivity develops, including the higher permeability of the intestine of very young children, and their early exposure to food antigens before the immune system has developed fully. In addition, down-regulation of the gut immune response or high levels of a particular food protein may play a role. Once an allergen has crossed the gastrointestinal barrier, a sequence of events mediated by T and B cells eventually leads to the production of IgE antibodies and a type I hypersensitivity reaction.

Peanuts are particularly allergenic causing a range of symptoms from hives to fatal anaphylaxis in sensitised individuals [3]. Often peanut sensitivity begins in very young children and persists into adulthood. To prevent sensitisation, the current recommendation is to delay introduction of peanuts to the diet until 3 years of age. There are three major peanut allergens found in the protein of the cotyledon, which, in common with other food allergens, have multiple IgE-binding epitopes. These regions comprise linear peptides of 6-15 amino acids in food allergens, but form conformational epitopes in many aeroallergens.

4.1.3.3 Asthma and Hayfever

A type I hypersensitivity reaction to *Dermatophagoides pteronyssinus* or house dust mite (HDM), animal dander, pollens or fungi produce symptoms such as bronchoconstriction, oedema, mucus production, inflammation and epithelial cell damage associated with asthma and hayfever. These symptoms are mediated by IgE on mast cells, and by Th-2 cells. IL-5 produced by the latter promotes the growth, activation and survival of eosinophils and can be detected in the airways of patients with asthma.

4.1.4 Treatment

Treatments for type I hypersensitivity reactions aim to either modulate the initial immune response to allergen, or to alleviate the clinical symptoms which are induced by subsequent exposure to allergen.

4.1.4.1 Modulation of the immune response to allergens

Immunotherapy was first tested as a means to desensitise individuals to a specific allergen as long ago as 1911, and involves the serial injection of increasing amounts of standardised extracts of the allergen [4]. This approach has been particularly successful in the case of insect venom hypersensitivity providing >95% protection against allergen-induced anaphylaxis. The doses of allergen administered are high and the injections are maintained over a 4-5 year period. This treatment regime prevents further type I hypersensitivity reactions to insect venom because it down-regulates the specific IgE response and the cellular response to allergen. However, immunotherapy has not proved to be suitable for food allergies as safety issues have compromised the use of this treatment in these patients, and, currently, the only effective approach for these patients is food avoidance.

Other potential ways of modulating the immune response to allergens include the use of allergen-specific, soluble TCRs to inhibit allergen presentation to T cells, peptides to compete with allergen-specific peptides for TCR binding, and antibodies to cytokines such as IL-4 and IL-13 to inhibit B cell production of IgE antibodies. Alternatively, altered peptide ligands could be used to induce T cell anergy or skew cytokine responses from the Th-2 to Th-1 phenotype.

4.1.4.2 Alleviation of clinical symptoms

The most straightforward way to alleviate clinical symptoms is by avoidance of the allergen. However this is not always feasible or practical, particularly in the case of peanuts, which are used in the preparation of a variety of foods and which can be ingested unknowingly leading to anaphylaxis and possible death in peanut allergic patients.

Alternatively, various drugs are used to inhibit symptoms, the most common being anti-histamines which block the binding of histamine to its receptors on different cell types. Other drugs used include corticosteroids, inhibitors of prostaglandin synthase, and anti-leukotrienes, but these provide limited effectiveness and may cause drowsiness.

4.2 Type II Hypersensitivity

Type II hypersensitivity reactions cause tissue damage when antibody binds to antigen on the surface of a target cell or tissue, and occurs without the direct involvement of lymphocytes. This results in the lysis of the target cell, hence its alternative name, antibody-mediated cytotoxic reaction.

4.2.1 Mechanism

Type II hypersensitivity reactions are initiated by the binding of antibody to antigen on a cell or on an extracellular component. The antibodies involved are present in the individual's blood prior to induction of the response. They may, for example, be produced in response to a viral infection but are cross-reactive with the target autoantigen. Alternatively, the antibodies may be part of the baseline antibody repertoire present at birth and bind to antigens on target cells introduced into the body during blood transfusion or organ transplantation.

4.2.1.1 Phagocytosis/Antibody-dependent cellular cytotoxicity

As in the normal immune response to bacteria, bound antibody may act as an opsonin, inducing phagocytosis of the target cell by macrophages and PMNs, and its destruction intracellularly by enzymes and oxygen free radicals (Fig. 4.2A).

Alternatively, the interaction between the effector cell and the Fc domain of the antibody bound to the target cell can lead directly to target cell lysis, a mechanism called antibody-dependent cellular cytotoxicity (ADCC) (Fig. 4.2B). Lysis is mediated by the release of superoxides, enzymes and vasoactive amines by activated effector cells expressing Fc receptors, such as macrophages, PMNs, monocytes and NK cells. NK cells may also use perforin, a protein that can insert itself into the target cell membrane and form a channel, to cause lysis. The subclass of Fc receptors that mediate ADCC varies in different cell types being FcγRIII in NK cells and FcγRI in macrophages and monocytes.

The lysis of antibody-coated erythrocytes and tumour cells by Fc receptor-expressing cells has been demonstrated *in vitro*; in addition, it has been proposed that ADCC may be the means by which cells are destroyed in autoimmune antibody-dependent diseases.

4.2.1.2 Complement-mediated cytotoxicity

Type II hypersensitivity reactions can also involve the binding of complement to target cells. C3b bound to a target cell, either with or without bound IgG, acts as an opsonin, mediating phagocytosis of the cell (Fig. 4.2A).

Binding of IgM or IgG antibody to antigen on the target cell can activate the classical complement pathway via binding of C1q, thus initiating a complement cascade resulting in the production of C8 and C9, the formation of a transmembrane channel and lysis of the cell (Fig. 4.3). In diseases where antibodies to extracellular matrix cause tissue damage, the activation of the complement pathway probably has an indirect effect via the release of cytokines and subsequent recruitment of monocytes and PMNs capable of producing destructive enzymes.

Figure 4.2 Mechanisms involved in a type II hypersensitivity reaction. Cells are destroyed by A) phagocytosis, and B) antibody-dependent cellular cytotoxicity

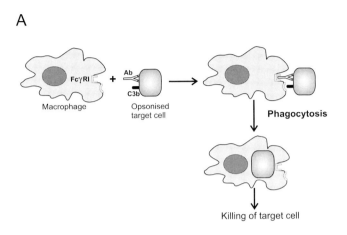

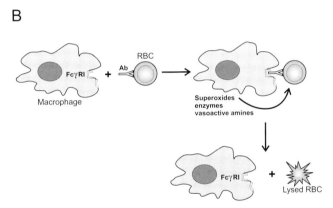

Figure 4.3 Type II hypersensitivity reaction mediated by complement activation

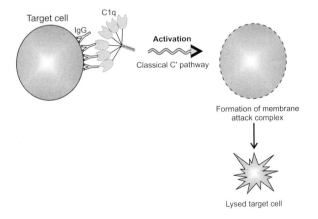

4.2.2 Examples of Type II hypersensitivity

4.2.2.1 Autoantibody-induced diseases

Goodpasture's syndrome, a progressive glomerulonephritis, is a classical example of a type II hypersensitivity reaction in which IgG autoantibodies and complement are deposited in a linear fashion along the basement membrane of the glomeruli [5]. These anti-basement membrane antibodies recognise an epitope situated in the non-collagenous region of the α3 chain at the C-terminal end of type IV basement collagen. (Type IV collagen is the major component of the basement membrane and consists of 6 different chains including α1, α2 and α3).

The stimulus for the production of autoantibodies in Goodpasture's syndrome is not known. However, a preceding history of an upper respiratory infection has been found in up to 60% of patients. Thus homology between an epitope expressed by the microorganism responsible for the infection and the autoantigen epitope on the basement membrane may exist, leading to cross-reaction. Alternatively, changes to the structure of the domain containing the pathogenic epitope may induce autoantibody production. The α3 non-collagenous domain occurs naturally as a hexamer, but will only induce the renal pathology of Goodpasture's syndrome in a rabbit when injected in the dimer form, suggesting that changes to the structure of this region must take place for the disease to be manifested. This may be achieved by environmental factors known to provoke the disease such as viral infection, exposure to hydrocarbons and smoking. Furthermore, the genetic element of the disease (suggested by its occurrence in twins and families) may include a predisposition to develop an autoimmune response to this modified region.

Other examples of type II hypersensitivity in which autoantibodies are directed against the basement membrane of the conjunctiva, acetylcholine receptors in the post-synaptic muscle membrane, or antigens on red blood cells include ocular cicatricial pemphigoid, myasthenia gravis and autoimmune haemolytic anaemia, respectively. Autoantibodies also bind to sites in the skin and cause tissue damage, as in the conditions bullous pemphigus and bullous pemphigoid. These will be described in detail in Chapter 5.

4.2.2.2 Natural antibody-induced transfusion reactions

Of 19 blood group systems described, the ABO system is the most significant. Each individual contains IgM antibodies in their serum that are specific for ABO antigens not expressed by their own red blood cells. These antibodies are naturally occurring and may be induced by bacterial antigens with homology to ABO glycoproteins. Acute haemolytic transfusion reaction occurs when an individual is transfused with an incompatible blood type, resulting in binding of IgM antibodies to the transfused red blood cells, complement activation and red cell lysis [6]. This causes a fall in blood pressure due to the release into the circulation of vasodilatory complement factors, C3a, C4a and C5a, and can result in renal failure and even death. Fortunately, with thorough screening of blood group types (transfusion reactions can potentially occur with any of the non-ABO blood groups), acute haemolytic transfusion reactions are rare.

4.2.2.3 Antibody-induced haemolytic reactions requiring previous sensitisation

When a mother who is negative for the D antigen of the Rh blood group gives birth to a D-positive child, she becomes sensitised and produces IgG antibody against the Rh-D antigen. This is not a problem until she becomes pregnant a second time with a Rh-positive child when the anti-Rh-D antibodies pass through the placenta, bind to foetal red blood cells and cause complement-mediated lysis. This condition is known as haemolytic disease of the newborn. Interestingly if the mother also produces an antibody to an ABO antigen expressed by the foetal red blood cells (e.g. mother is group A and baby is group B) sensitisation to D antigen is prevented because of the rapid destruction of the baby's red cells to which the mother is exposed during birth. It is now common practice to use prophylaxis (administration of anti-D immune globulin immediately after birth) to prevent sensitisation and subsequent damage to the baby's red cells [7].

Hyperacute transplant rejection is another example of an antibody-induced haemolytic reaction. This contrasts with acute and chronic rejection, which are mediated primarily by type IV reactions. Hyperacute rejection of grafts occurs in grafts that are revascularised straight after transplantation, such as liver or kidney, and involves pre-existing antibodies to MHC antigens, induced by previous transplantations or transfusions. These immediately bind to the graft and activate complement, resulting in destruction of the transplanted tissue. This type of reaction can be largely prevented by cross-matching blood from the donor and recipient prior to transfusion.

4.2.2.4 Drug-induced blood cell destruction

Certain drugs can induce IgG-mediated destruction of red blood cells when administered to individuals who have preformed drug-specific antibodies. Lysis occurs when the antibodies bind to the drug attached to red blood cells. Examples of such drugs are the antibiotics penicillin G, ampicillin and cephalosporins. Haemolysis can also occur when drugs attached to plasma proteins bind to the surface of red cells, and complement is activated. In addition, drugs such as methyldopa, levodopa and mefenamic acid can induce the development of IgG antibodies to red blood cells, presumably because of homology between the drug and red cell epitopes. In contrast to the mechanisms above, serum containing these antibodies can cause haemolysis in a normal recipient in the absence of the antibody-inducing drug.

Type II hypersensitivity reactions to drugs can also target white cells or platelets. Antibodies to quinidine, which is used to treat cardiac arrhythmias, can bind to the drug attached to platelets resulting in complement activation and thrombocytopenia. Other drugs such as sulphonamides and phenylbutazone have been associated with the destruction of white cells (agranulocytopenia).

4.2.3 Treatment

Corticosteroids are commonly used in the treatment of autoantibody-induced type II hypersensitivity reactions and are very effective in dampening down an acute immune response and preventing tissue damage. However, these drugs have many side effects, which limits both the concentrations used and the length of time that they can be administered. An alternative approach, which has been used effectively in Goodpasture's syndrome and in myasthenia gravis, is plasmapheresis, which can give almost immediate beneficial effects. Plasmapheresis involves the removal of antibodies from the blood and is most successful for IgM antibodies because they are predominately intravascular, whereas effective IgG removal may require the process to be repeated several times. Non-steroidal immunosuppressive drugs are also used to treat chronic antibody-mediated autoimmune diseases such as Goodpasture's syndrome and ocular cicatricial pemphigoid. Drugs such as methotrexate, cyclosporin, azathioprone and cyclophosphamide can be used effectively, but potential toxic effects on organs such as the liver and kidney make stringent and regular monitoring essential.

4.3 Type III Hypersensitivity

Type III hypersensitivity reactions are caused by the formation of immune complexes of IgG or IgM antibodies with soluble antigen, which are then deposited at sites of filtration such as lymph nodes, kidneys, synovial joints and skin. Alternatively antibody-antigen complexes may develop at sites of inoculation of antigen during immunisation. Subsequent unregulated activation of the classical complement pathway may ensue, leading to overproduction of inflammatory mediators and tissue damage.

4.3.1 Mechanisms for phagocyte recruitment

Overproduction of IgG and IgM antibodies to a particular antigen (autoantigen or foreign antigen) can lead to the formation of large amounts of circulating immune complexes which subsequently accumulate at various sites in the body. This leads to tissue damage, which is mediated by phagocytes that infiltrate the site and become activated. Recent data suggest that there are both complement-dependent and complement-independent mechanisms for recruiting phagocytes to sites of immune complex deposition.

4.3.1.1 Complement-dependent mechanisms

The detection and removal of immune complexes involves the classical complement pathway, which, if not regulated effectively, can lead to type III hypersensitivity reactions and tissue damage (Fig. 4.4). Complement can both inhibit the formation of large immune complex lattices by preventing Fc-Fc interactions, and solubilise those complexes that have already formed by the insertion of activated complement components, C3b, C3d and C4b into the lattice. This process occurs in healthy individuals as part of normal clearance physiological mechanisms.

Activation of the classical complement pathway involves the recognition by C1q of the immune complex [8] (Fig. 4.4). C1q consists of six globular heads at its C-terminus, which interact with the Fc regions of antibodies (CH2 or CH3 regions of IgG or IgM, respectively) associated with antigens. The C1q-immune complex then binds via the C1q N-terminal (collagen-like) triple helical stalk region to cells via Fc or C1q receptors. Several cell types, such as B cells, PMNs, erythrocytes and monocytes, express receptors for aggregated C1q. Various types of C1q receptors exist which may reflect differences in C1q function [9]. One of these receptors, CR1 (CD35, the C3b-C4b receptor), binds to immune complexes opsonized by C3b and C4b and removes them from the circulation, taking them to the liver and spleen for processing and removal. In addition, CR1 binds to the stalk

Figure 4.4 Complement-dependent type III hypersensitivity reaction

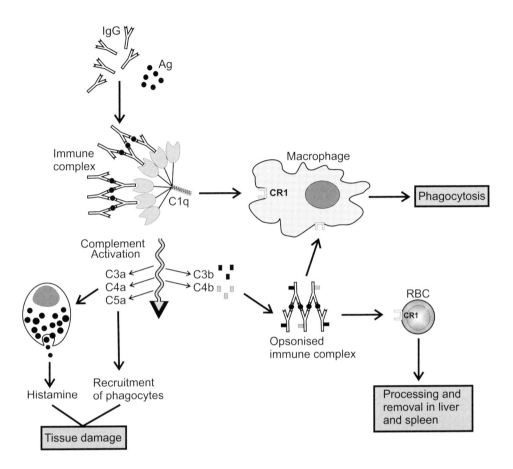

region of C1q and may mediate clearance of C1q-associated immune complexes.

In the autoimmune disease SLE, C1q deficiency is associated with increased levels of immune complexes (see Chapter 6). Thus, when complement levels are reduced (as in the case of an inherited deficiency) or complement activation is inhibited, large immune complexes accumulate in various tissues throughout the body illustrating the importance of complement activation during immune complex formation .

The activated complement components C3b, C4b and the chemoattractant C5a have, however, been implicated in the recruitment of phagocytes to the site of inflammation and subsequent hypersensitivity reaction with tissue damage. Gene knockout mice which lack the C5a receptor are unable to clear microorganisms or immune complexes from the lung, but PMN infiltration and tissue damage are absent suggesting that C5a-C5a receptor interactions are a necessary prerequisite for immune-complex-induced inflammation at this site [10]. In contrast, when mice that have had the genes for C3 or C4 deleted are challenged with pathogenic immune complexes, they produce a normal Arthus reaction, an inflammatory response characteristic of type III hypersensitivity (see below) [11]. This suggests that complement activation is not essential for inducing a type III hypersensitivity reaction and that other factors may also be involved in recruiting phagocytes to potential sites of inflammation. However, complement components do appear to be necessary for controlling the formation of immune complexes at the early stages of the inflammatory response.

4.3.1.2 Complement-independent mechanisms

Adhesion molecules such as P-selectin and Mac-1 may mediate PMN recruitment at sites of inflammation when complement components formed in the later stages of activation (C3 and C4) are absent (Fig. 4.5). P-selectin is expressed on the surface of activated platelets and endothelial cells during vascular injury and, together with L-selectin, mediates the rolling of PMNs on activated endothelial cells prior to their extravasation into inflammatory sites (see Chapter 1). Activation of endothelial cells may be induced by the deposition of immune complexes, histamine released by mast cells or by thrombin released from platelets. Evidence to support a role for P-selectin in PMN recruitment has been obtained in a model of the Arthus reaction [12]. Rats were treated with anti-P-selectin antibody before intradermal injection of antigen, resulting in abrogation of the type III hypersensitivity response. This suggests that complement in the absence of P-selectin is not sufficient to recruit PMNs to sites of immune complex deposition.

Mac-1 (CD11b/CD18), also known as complement receptor type 3 (CR3), is expressed on monocytes and PMNs and binds to the inactivatable C3b fragments (iC3b) found on immune complexes and other opsonized targets. The role of Mac-1 in immune complex-induced PMN recruitment in the kidney during glomerulonephritis appears to be secondary to the initial binding of PMNs to the immune complexes via interaction between cell surface FcγR and Fc [13]. Once PMNs have attached, Mac-1 is involved in the reorganisation of the actin cytoskeleton, encouraging spreading of the cells over the immune complexes and maintaining PMN attachment.

Substance P, a vasoactive neuropeptide released by nerve endings during inflammation (see Chapter 2), has been shown to play a role in the early stages of immune-complex-mediated hypersensitivity responses such as those present in asthma, lung injury and experimental arthritis. When immune complexes are deposited on endothelial cells lining blood vessels, substance P is released and triggers the release of proinflammatory mediators by postcapillary venule endothelial cells, and possibly also by macrophages and mast cells via interaction with specific receptors. In addition, the increased vascular permeability induced by substance P causes the leakage of complement components into the extravascular space, leading to the deposition of more antigen at the site of inflammation and enhancement of the immune response.

4.3.2 Phagocyte-induced tissue damage

Once recruited to the site where immune complexes are deposited, phagocytic PMNs and monocytes are responsible for the ensuing tissue damage [14]. This is mediated by a variety of toxic substances released by the cells during ingestion and removal of the immune complexes, and includes defensins, elastase, cathepsins, proteinases and reactive oxygen intermediates. The latter, which includes superoxide (O^{2-}), hydroxyl radical, and also hydrogen peroxide (H_2O_2), can cause damage to proteins, nucleic acids and lipids. Endothelial cells, due to their proximity, are particularly prone to damage during removal of immune complexes by phagocytes. The phagocytes also release a variety of proinflammatory cytokines such as IL-1, IL-6, TNF α and chemotactic CXCL8 (IL-8)

Figure 4.5 Complement-independent type III hypersensitivity reaction

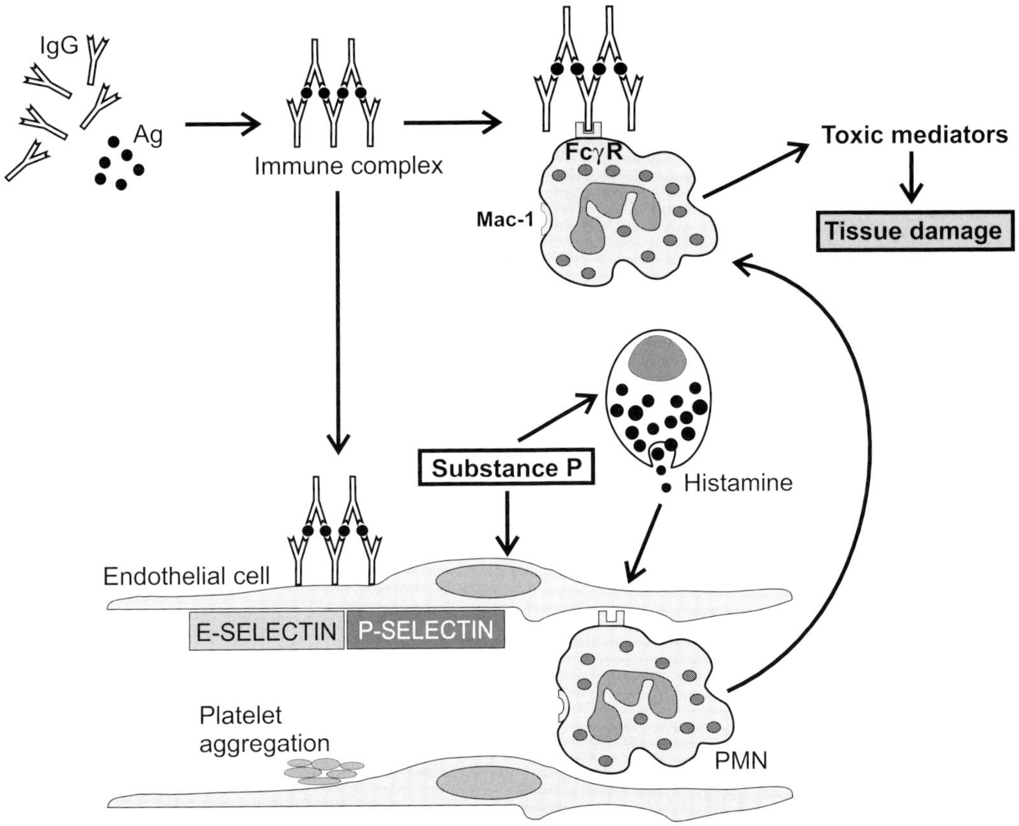

which contribute to the cell-mediated immune response.

Immune complex deposition also results in platelet aggregation and the release of vasoactive amines such as histamine and serotonin (5-hydroxytryptamine), which cause vascular permeability. Furthermore, platelets and PMN act in a synergistic manner enhancing each others' effects on endothelial cells at sites of immune complex deposition. Activated mast cells have also been implicated in subcutaneous tissue damage during an Arthus reaction. They exert these effects via FcγRIII, as shown by the restoration of the response in mast cell-deficient mice by administration of mast cells from wild type, but not FcγR-deficient mice [15].

4.3.3 Examples of type III hypersensitivity

Type III hypersensitivity reactions can be provoked by antigens introduced intradermally, systemically or by inhalation resulting in different clinical presentations. Intradermal injection of antigen results in the Arthus reaction, intravenous administration of animal serum induces serum sickness involving vasculitis, arthritis and nephritis, and inhaled avian and fungal antigens can lead to conditions known as farmer's lung or bird fancier's lung.

In addition, the formation of circulating immune complexes is an important component of the immunopathogenesis of various autoimmune diseases such as SLE, rheumatoid arthritis and Sjögren syndrome. In SLE the immune complexes themselves may drive the inflammatory process associated with the disease, which presents in various organs including the skin. There are also other type III hypersensitivity reactions that affect the skin such as allergic vasculitis, erythema nodosum and erythema multiforme. In these conditions, immune complexes are deposited in vessel walls of the dermis and subcutaneous fat, inducing inflammation. A detailed description of SLE will be given in Chapter 6.

4.3.3.1 Arthus reaction

The classical example of the type III hypersensitivity response is the experimentally induced Arthus reaction, named after the scientist who first observed the phenomenon. The Arthus reaction is induced by an intradermal or subcutaneous injection of soluble antigen into an animal that has already been stimulated to produce high levels of antibody by previous exposure to the antigen. Within hours, antigen binds to antibody from the blood forming immune complexes that bind to C1q, the first component of complement, triggering the activation of the complement cascade and subsequent recruitment of tissue damage-inducing phagocytes. This is manifested as erythema and oedema, which dissipates after 6-8 hours as immune complexes are cleared from the skin by phagocytes.

4.3.3.2 Serum sickness

Serum sickness is an example of a systemic type III hypersensitivity reaction induced by multiple injections of animal sera. Horse sera containing neutralising antibodies to pneumonia or diphtheria were used to treat humans suffering from these diseases in the era before antibiotics became available. Five to 10 days after injection, antibodies against the horse serum proteins developed and formed large immune complexes, which caused inflammation in the joints, skin and glomeruli of the kidneys. From 10 days onwards, clinical manifestations of immune complex deposition such as fever, tenderness of the joints and proteinuria became apparent, but these clinical effects were transient and disappeared once the antigens had been removed.

4.3.3.3 Farmer's lung/Bird fancier's lung

Allergic responses induced by the inhalation of antigens are commonly IgE-mediated type I hypersensitivity responses. However, certain allergens induce a predominately IgG response and the formation of immune complexes. In patients with so-called farmer's lung, antigens from the spores of thermophilic moulds such as *Micropolyspora faeni* and *Thermoactinomyces vulgaris*, which grow on silage and hay, induce antibody formation. In bird fancier's lung, antibodies to mucin in pigeon excreta and other bird-derived antigens are produced. On subsequent exposure to the antigens, immune complexes form and induce a granulomatous reaction in the lung characterised by an influx of T lymphocytes. These two conditions are examples of extrinsic allergic alveolitis that produces symptoms of breathlessness and flu-like symptoms at 4-8 hours after exposure. Surprisingly, the symptoms for either condition are less severe in smokers, possibly due to inefficient antibody production and consequently reduced immune complex formation.

There are various other sources of avian and fungal antigens that can cause extrinsic allergic alveolitis, which are indicated by the names of the diseases, such as budgerigar's lungs, maple stripper's lungs (caused by exposure to mould in stored maple tree bark) and mushroom worker's lung (induced by mushroom spores).

4.3.4 Treatment

The main treatments for type III hypersensitivity are either immunosuppressive or immunomodulatory.

4.3.4.1. Immunosuppressive drugs

Acute serum sickness caused by, for example, anti-toxins or anti-venoms administered for snakebites is usually mild and self-limiting and does not require medication. However, severe serum sickness, induced by long-term injection of foreign material in chronic conditions, may require anti-inflammatory treatment to suppress symptoms. Anti-histamines are used to treat urticarial lesions, whilst salicylates or non-steroidal anti-inflammatory drugs (NSAIDs) are used to decrease fever and minor muscular pain. In SLE, in addition to NSAIDs, anti-malaria drugs (prednisone, hydroxychloroquine and mepacrine) are administered to treat skin rashes, arthralgia, fever and general malaise. For severe disease flare and maintenance, corticosteroids and other immunosuppressive drugs such as chlorambucil, cyclophosphamide and azathioprine are used.

4.3.4.2 Immunomodulation

There are several potential therapeutic targets in the development of a type III hypersensitivity reaction. The early stages of complement activation are protective, as binding of C1q to immune complexes limits their size and C3b helps to solubilise them. However, release from cells of intracellular substances such as calreticulin, decorin and proteochondroitin sulphate can inhibit complement activation by competing with immune complexes for C1q binding. Thus blocking the action of these intracellular proteins could be beneficial. Current experimental efforts are, however, aimed at a later stage of the complement cascade, the prevention of C5 activation (using anti-C5 antibodies) in order to inhibit recruitment of inflammatory cells to sites of immune complex deposition. This has proved to be a successful approach in the mouse model of SLE and has led to phase 1 trials in SLE patients.

The presence of immune complexes leads to local up-regulation of P-selectin on endothelial cells, and increased expression of Fc receptors and Mac-1 on inflammatory cells. One possible approach would be to use anti-P-selectin antibody to prevent PMN rolling and extravasation into tissues. Alternatively, preventing the interaction between immune complexes and Fc receptors on inflammatory cells could be used to inhibit inflammation. This could be achieved using soluble Fc receptor peptides or monoclonal antibodies to Fc receptors. Mac-1 could also be targeted as it cooperates with FcγR on the surface of PMNs to maintain cell attachment and spreading of the cells over immune complexes. However, since antibodies may induce type III hypersensitivity reactions, their use in treatment may not be feasible.

4.4 Type IV Hypersensitivity

Type IV hypersensitivity depends upon the interaction of antigen with T lymphocytes and is referred to as delayed-type hypersensitivity because of the time taken for the reaction to develop. This type of reaction is induced by several different stimuli, most commonly as a response to antigens from various microorganisms and to certain chemical substances, but is also involved in response to proteins in insect bites, rejection of transplants from a genetically different (allogeneic) donor and in certain autoimmune diseases.

4.4.1 Generation of a cell-mediated immune response

Unlike the other types of immunological hypersensitivity, type IV hypersensitivity can be transferred by T lymphocytes, but not serum, from one genetically identical host to another. The delayed-type response is initiated when a sensitised individual is re-exposed to antigen and T cells become activated (Fig. 4.6). Antigen is processed by antigen-presenting cells including resident LCs, vascular endothelial cells and monocytes, and presented as peptide fragments bound to MHC molecules. $CD4^+$ T cells are the main effector cells in delayed-type responses, but $CD8^+$ T cells also play a role. $CD4^+$ T cells in turn activate macrophages; both cell types mediate the hypersensitivity response via the secretion of cytokines.

4.4.1.1 Th-1 cytokine response

Type IV hypersensitivity responses to microbial and contact antigens (see below) are mediated by $CD4^+$ (and $CD8^+$) T cells, which produce a Th-1 (Tc-1) type cytokine profile. Cytokines are secreted in sequence, with IL-2 detected first at about 12 hours after antigen exposure and peaking at 24 hours, at which time TNF-α and IFN-γ first appear [16]. The latter two cytokines stimulate monocytes, and also epithelial and endothelial cells, to produce more TNF-α and other proinflammatory cytokines such as IL-1 and IL-6 which, in turn, induce chemokine production by various cell types. Chemokines such as CCL2 (MCP-1) and CCL3 (MIP-1α) are produced and recruit other T cells, macrophages and/or PMNs to the lesion. In addition, the adhesion molecules E-selectin and ICAM-1 are up-regulated on endothelial cells facilitating this cellular recruitment.

The importance of cytokines in the manifestation of delayed hypersensitivity has been shown by inhibition of the skin response with injection of the inhibitory cytokine, IL-10 [17]. Conversely, injection of supernatants containing a mixture of cytokines produced by peripheral blood lymphocytes stimulated *in vitro*, or of the cytokines themselves, enhances the immune response.

4.4.1.2 Th-2 cytokine response

Immunisation of an animal in the absence of Freund's adjuvant results in a T cell-mediated hypersensitivity reaction with a faster onset and resolution time. This is referred to as the Jones-Mote reaction or chronic basophil hypersensitivity because of its' characteristic basophilic infiltrate. This different presentation is explained by the production of Th-2 type cytokines including IL-5, which together with the chemokine CCL5 (RANTES), recruits, activates and maintains the viability of eosinophils and basophils at the inflammatory site. A Th-2 cytokine-mediated response is an

Figure 4.6 Mechanism involved in a type IV hypersensitivity reaction

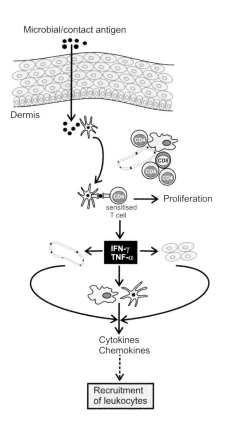

important part of the late reaction in immediate hypersensitivity (see above), which causes damage to the lungs in asthma, and is also involved in the response to parasites. In atopic dermatitis, the T cell-mediated hypersensitivity response is mediated predominately by Th-2 cytokines, but Th-1 cytokines also play a role in the later stages. The immunopathogenesis of atopic dermatitis will be discussed in detail in Chapter 8.

4.4.2 Response to microorganisms

4.4.2.1 Microbial stimuli

Repeated exposure to a variety of different microorganisms, or to antigens derived from them, can induce a delayed hypersensitivity response. The most well known example of this is the reaction induced by intradermal injection of tuberculin protein into the skin of animals infected with *Mycobacterium tuberculosis*, the causative agent of tuberculosis. Purified protein derivative (PPD) is commonly used to test for a delayed hypersensitivity response in tuberculosis. Injection of an attenuated strain of *M. bovis*, Bacille Calmette-Guérin (BCG), can also induce a subsequent delayed response to PPD. Furthermore, mycobacteria have a strong adjuvant activity for induction of type IV hypersensitivity. This has led to the practice of immunising animals with protein antigen suspended in Freund's complete adjuvant (killed mycobacteria emulsified in mineral oil) in order to enhance the immune response.

Infection with a variety of fungi including *Cryptococcus neoformans*, *Trichophyton* and *Candida* species, and certain viral infections such as smallpox, measles and Herpes simplex are associated with a type IV hypersensitivity reaction. In addition, injection of antigens from *Chlamydia trachomatis* induces a delayed hypersensitivity response called the Frei test in patients with lymphogranularum venereum. Furthermore, several protozoal diseases, such as those caused by *Leishmania* and *Schistosoma* species, also involve a T cell-mediated immune response.

4.4.2.2 Histology of reaction

The initial histological response, at 4 hours, to intradermal injection of microbial antigens is an infiltration of PMNs around postcapillary venules. This response is replaced, after about 12 hours, by a perivascular accumulation of T lymphocytes and monocytes and enlargement of endothelial cells lining the venules. The endothelial cells become leaky, allowing fibrinogen to be released into the surrounding tissue where it is converted into fibrin. The combined presence of mononuclear cells and fibrin cause induration at the site of antigen exposure, a characteristic feature of delayed-type hypersensitivity.

These histological changes are apparent clinically as erythema and oedema within the first 12 hours after injection of antigen, whilst induration develops gradually reaching a maximum at 24-72 hours. This slower rate of development contrasts with the Arthus reaction (see above) in which marked inflammation occurs at the site of repeated injections of antigen within hours.

4.4.2.3 Granuloma formation

If antigen persists at the site of exposure for several weeks due to inefficient removal by macrophages, a granulomatous reaction may ensue. A chronic granulomatous response to *M.tuberculosis* is responsible for the lung disease in tuberculosis. In sarcoidosis, the antigenic trigger that induces the formation of granulomas is unknown. Furthermore, a non-immunological granuloma can be induced by non-antigenic particles such as talcum powder.

The granuloma forms when epithelioid cells (probably macrophage-derived, large flattened cells) and macrophages surround the infectious agent. Multinucleated or giant cells, which are probably derived from the fusion of macrophages or epithelioid cells, are also present, surrounded by a cuff of lymphocytes. Collagenous capsules may also develop around some pathogens due to proliferation of fibroblasts.

4.4.3 Contact hypersensitivity

Contact hypersensitivity (or allergic contact dermatitis) presents as an eczematous skin reaction in sensitised individuals, and is the most common clinical presentation of type IV hypersensitivity. Allergens that induce contact sensitivity are too small in size to act as antigens alone, and become immunogenic only when presented as a conjugate with normal host proteins or peptides. Examples of common contact allergens include nickel (jewellery and fasteners), potassium dichromate (scissors and coins) and paraphenyldiamine (permanent hair dye) (Table 4.2), and plants such as poison ivy and poison oak, which are prevalent in North America. Patch testing may be required to determine the identity of the contact allergen responsible for the skin reaction (see below). For experimental induction of contact hypersensitivity, the chemical agents dinitrofluorobenzene (DNFB), dinitrochlorobenzene (DNCB) and oxazolone are used. These contact sensitisers have the advantage of being able to cause hypersensitivity after only one exposure and are sensitising in nearly all immunocompetent individuals.

During sensitisation, LCs take up the immunogenic complexes and migrate to the skin-draining lymph nodes where they present processed peptide antigen bound to MHC Class II (or class I) molecules to naïve $CD4^+$ ($CD8^+$) T cells. On subsequent exposure to allergen, sensitised T cells return to the skin, produce cytokines and attract in various cell types to produce an infiltrate. A more detailed description of the sensitisation and elicitation stages of allergic contact dermatitis is given in Chapter 7.

4.4.4 *In vivo* tests for type IV hypersensitivity

4.4.4.1 Detection of infection

The delayed hypersensitivity reaction can be used to determine whether an individual is, or has been, infected with a particular microorganism. However, a positive reaction gives no indication as to how recent that infection may have been or whether it induced clinical symptoms. Furthermore, a negative reaction may be observed in a patient whose immune system is suppressed as a result of infection.

Testing for a delayed hypersensitivity response is most commonly used in the diagnosis of tuberculosis and involves the injection of 0.1ml of 5 TU (tuberculin units) of PPD intradermally in to the forearm (Mantoux test). The test is usually read after 48 hours, but may continue to develop up to 72 hours after injection, and the degree of response is assessed by measurement of the extent of induration. The extent of induration considered to give a positive response to PPD will vary with factors such as the presence of immunosuppression, and the degree of exposure to the infecting microorganism. Thus, in patients with HIV infection and in other similarly immunosuppressed individuals, a reaction of $\geq$ 5mm is considered positive. In contrast, $\geq$ 10mm induration is taken as a positive result in individuals living in areas of high prevalence of disease and who are therefore at risk of contracting tuberculosis. For an individual without any risk of contracting tuberculosis, a diameter of $\geq$ 15mm induration is necessary for a positive reaction to be recorded.

4.4.4.2 Function of the immune system

Another use of the delayed hypersensitivity test is to assess the function of an individual's cellular immune system. A lack of response to antigens to which an individual is, or has been, exposed to is termed anergy. This may be specific for a particular organism, or, as in patients infected with HIV, be a generalised failure to respond to antigens from commonly encountered microorganisms such as *Trichophyton, Candida* and mumps virus.

Table 4.2 Standard panel for contact dermatitis testing

Substance	Source	Substance	Source
Potassium dichromate	Leather, cement etc.	Nickel	Metal clasps, earrings, coins etc.
Neomycin	Antibiotic	Methylchloroisothiazolinone, Methylisothiazolinone	Biocide
Thiuram mix	Rubber additive	Mercaptobenzothiazole	Rubber additive
Paraphenyldiamine	Permanent hair dye	Primin	Primula
Cobalt	Metal	Sesquiterpene lactone mix	Compositae plane allergy
Caine mix	Local anaesthetic	Chlorocresol	Preservative
Formaldehyde	Biocide	2-bromo-2-nitropropane-1,3-diol	Biocide
Rosin	Colophony, resin from spruce trees	Cetearyl alcohol	Whitening agent in creams
Quinoline mix	Antiseptic	Fucidic acid	Antibiotic
Balsam of Peru	Fragrance	Tixocortol pivalate	Hydrocortisone allergy
Isopropylphenylparaphenylenediamine	Industrial rubber additive	Budesonide	Steroid allergy
Wood alcohols	Lanolin	Imidazolidinyl urea	Biocide
Mercapto mix	Rubber additive	Diazolidinyl urea	Biocide
Epoxy resin	Two-part adhesive	Methyldibromoglutaronitrile	Biocide
Paraben mix	Preservative	Ethylenediamine	Stabiliser, emulsifier
Paratertiarybutylphenol-formaldehyde resin	Adhesives	PCMX	Antiseptic in Dettol
Fragrance mix	Fragrance	Carba mix	Rubber additive
Quaternium-15	Biocide		

4.4.4.3 Patch testing

A standardised collection of the commonest known allergens is used to carry out patch testing (Table 4.2). The allergens are prepared at appropriate concentrations in a white soft paraffin base, with the exception of nickel which is in aqueous solution, and are applied to a healthy area of skin on the back using inert metal discs (Finn chambers) attached to a square piece of sticky plastic. Sets of allergen-coated discs are commercially available, and several sets can be stuck onto a patient's back at the same time. The Finn chambers are removed after 48 hours and a preliminary reading of erythema and induration taken (Fig. 4.7, colour plate). A second reading is taken after a further 48 hours. Care needs to be taken when reading patch test results as a well-demarcated, red raised area may be due to an irritant reaction rather than an allergic contact dermatitis. In addition, adverse side effects may also be experienced such as sensitisation to substances not previously met, the development of a Koebner reaction in patients with psoriasis or lichen planus, and in rare cases, induction of anaphylaxis. Positive reactions may be observed for more than one allergen and should be interpreted in conjunction with the patient's history of exposure. It should also be remembered that approximately 9% of normal, healthy people without skin disease have unexpectedly positive patch tests.

4.4.5 *In vitro* tests for type IV hypersensitivity

4.4.5.1 Macrophage migration inhibition assay

Macrophage migration inhibition factor (MIF) amplifies inflammatory responses to antigen, but its other function, the ability to inhibit the random migration of macrophages, forms the basis of the assay. Originally, unstimulated peripheral blood mononuclear cells (PBMC) were placed in capillary tubes within chambers containing supernatant from stimulated cells, and MIF measured as the inhibition of migration of cells out of the capillary tubes. The assay is now performed in two chemotaxis chambers separated by a 5mm pore filter. The number of cells that migrate from the top chamber onto the filter after incubation is dependent upon the concentration of MIF in the bottom chamber, which is determined by comparison with control samples.

4.4.5.2 Lymphocyte transformation assay

This test is based upon the increase in DNA synthesis observed in T lymphocytes stimulated by antigen, and is commonly assessed as the incorporation of radioactively labelled thymidine. PBMC are incubated with antigen, in triplicate, at 37°C for 5-7 days including an 18-hour pulse with tritiated thymidine at the end of the incubation period. The cells are then harvested onto filter paper and excess radioactive label washed away. The filter papers, placed in scintillation fluid, are counted in a β scintillation counter and the mean counts per minute (cpm) in the absence of antigen subtracted from the mean cpm in the presence of antigen. Alternatively, the results can be expressed as a stimulation index consisting of the mean cpm of the cells incubated in the presence of antigen divided by the mean cpm of the cells incubated without antigen.

4.4.5.3 Cytokine assays

The production of cytokines by PBMC stimulated with antigen is another means of measuring an antigen-specific T cell response. It is now possible to assay for a vast array of cytokines in addition to the commonly measured cytokines IL-2, IFN-γ and TNF-α associated with delayed hypersensitivity. ELISAs (see above) and ELISPOTS (the measurement of cytokine production by single cells rather than in supernatants) are generally used to measure individual cytokine levels. However, novel multiplex fluorescent bead and antibody microarray methods now exist which allow the simultaneous measurement of several cytokines in the same sample.

4.4.6 Treatment

Skin testing for delayed hypersensitivity, or patch testing for contact dermatitis is unlikely to cause any more than a mild local irritation. In the event that the effects are more marked, topical corticosteroids may be used. In the case of inflammatory skin diseases such as allergic contact dermatitis or atopic dermatitis and psoriasis, various topical and systemic treatments may be used. These will be discussed in Chapters 7, 8 and 9, respectively.

4.4.7 Overlap of hypersensitivity types in an immune response

Although hypersensitivity reactions fall into clearly defined types with different characteristics, their mechanisms overlap and it is more common than not that more than one type of reaction occurs during an immune response. A good example of this are the hypersensitivity responses induced by Th-2 cells. The Th-2 type cytokines IL-4 and IL-13 induce production of IgE antibodies which mediate type I immediate hypersensitivity reactions, whilst IL-5 (which is dependent upon IL-4) induces eosinophilia which is part of a delayed type IV hypersensitivity response. In addition, activated mast cells not only mediate type I responses, but also late inflammatory reactions (type IV reactions) via TNF-α, which triggers a chemokine cascade, and the influx of inflammatory cells.

Summary

There are four main types of hypersensitivity response, which can be defined as:

- Type I, an immediate response to allergens involving specific IgE bound to mast cells/basophils and resulting in mast cell degranulation and the release of histamine and other potent mediators that induce the clinical symptoms of allergy, asthma and anaphylaxis.

- Type II, an immediate response to auto-antigens, foreign blood group antigens or drugs by specific antibodies, in the presence or absence of complement activation, which results in lysis of target cells.

- Type III, an immediate response involving the formation of immune complexes between specific antibodies and soluble antigens (foreign or auto-antigens), which trigger complement activation and subsequent recruitment of tissue damage-inducing phagocytic cells.

- Type IV, a delayed response to microorganisms, autoantigens and allergens by antigen-specific T cells leading to cytokine/chemokine production, leukocyte recruitment and inflammation.

References

1. Moffitt J.E. Allergic reactions to insect stings and bites South Med.J. 2003; **96:** 1073-9.
2. Burks W. Food allergens. Clin. Allergy Immunol. 2004; **18:** 319-37.
3. Burks W. Peanut allergy: a growing phenomenon. J.Clin.Invest. 2003; **111:** 950-2.
4. Varga E.M., Nouri-Aria K., Till S.J., Durham S.R. Immunomodulatory treatment strategies for allergic diseases. Curr. Drug Targets Inflamm. Allergy. 2003; **2:** 31-46.
5. Bolton W.K. Goodpasture's syndrome. Kidney Int. 1996; **50:** 1753-66.
6. Jeter E.K. & Spivey M.A. Noninfectious complications of blood transfusion. Haematology/ Oncology Clin. North Am. 1995; **9:** 187-204.
7. Hartwell E.A. Use of Rh immune globulin: ASCP practice parameter. American Society of Clinical Pathologists. Am.J.Clin.Pathol. 1998; **110:** 281-92.
8. Eggleton P., Reid K.B., Tennor A.J. C1q – how many functions? How many receptors? Trends Cell. Biol. 1998; **8:** 428-31.
9. McGreal E. & Gasque P. Structure-function studies of the receptors for complement C1q. Biochem. Soc .Trans. 2002; **30:** 1010-4.
10. Kohl J. & Gessner J.E. On the role of complement and Fc gamma-receptors in the Arthus reaction. Mol. Immunol. 1999; **36:** 893-903.
11. Sylvestre D., Clynes R., Ma M., Warren H., Carroll M.C., Ravetch J.V. Immunoglobulin G-mediated inflammatory responses develop normally in complement-deficient mice. J.Exp. Med. 1996; **184:** 2385-92.
12. Santos L.L., Huang X.R., Berndt M.C., Holdsworth S.R. P-selectin requirement for neutrophil accumulation and injury in the direct passive Arthus reaction. Clin.Exp.Immunol. 1998; **112:** 281-6.
13. Tang T., Rosenkranz A., Assmann K.J.M. *et al*. A role for Mac-1 (CD11b/CD18) in immune complex-stimulated neutrophil function *in vivo*: Mac-1 deficiency abrogates sustained Fcγ receptor-dependent neutrophil adhesion and complement-dependent proteinuria in acute glomerulonephritis. J.Exp.Med. 1997; **186:** 1853-63.
14. Ricevuti G. Host tissue damage by phagocytes. Ann.N.Y.Acad.Sci. 1997; **832:** 426-48.
15. Sylvestre D.L. & Ravetch J.V. A dominant role for mast cell Fc receptors in the Arthus reaction. Immunity 1996; **5:** 387-90.
16. Buchanan K.L. & Murphy J.W. Kinetics of cellular infiltration and cytokine production during the efferent phase of a delayed-type hypersensitivity reaction. Immunol. 1997; **90:** 189-97.
17. Li L., Elliott J.F., Mosmann T.R. IL-10 inhibits cytokine production, vascular leakage, and swelling during T helper 1 cell-induced delayed-type hypersensitivity. J.Immunol. 1994; **153:** 3967-78.

Further Reading

1. Janeway C.A., Travers P., Walport M., Shlomchik M. Immunobiology. The immune system in health and disease 2004; Garland Publishing, New York.

2. Roitt I.M. & Delves P.J. Roitt's Essential Immunology 2001; 10th Edition, Blackwell Science, Oxford, UK.

3. Kay A.B. Allergy and allergic diseases. First of two parts. N.Engl.J.Med. 2001; **344:** 30-7.

4. Gerard N.P. & Gerard C. Complement in allergy and asthma. Curr.Opin.Immunol. 2002; **14:** 705-8.

5. Abbas A.K., Lichtman A.H., Pober J.S. Cellular and Molecular Immunology 2000; 4th Edition, Saunders, Philadelphia, PA.

6. Turk J.L. Delayed Hypersensitivity 1980; 3rd Edition, Elsevier/North Holland Biomedical Press, Amsterdam.

PART III: Immunological Mechanisms of Skin Disease

$$\boxed{5}$$

Antibody-Mediated Skin Diseases

This chapter describes three examples of antibody-mediated skin diseases, urticaria (type I hypersensitivity), and the autoimmune bullous skin diseases, pemphigus and bullous pemphigoid (type II hypersensitivity). In urticaria, mast cells are induced to undergo degranulation by the binding of either IgE antibodies specific for food allergens or drugs, or IgG autoantibodies, resulting in the formation of short-lived, itchy weals. In pemphigus and bullous pemphigoid, IgG antibodies target specific proteins in desmosomes or hemidesmosomes, resulting in intraepidermal or subepidermal blistering, respectively. Autoreactive T cells, with the same antigen specificity as pathogenic B cells, facilitate autoantibody production in each case.

5.1 Urticaria

The term urticaria covers a heterogenous group of skin disorders that can be triggered by various stimuli but which result in a final common pathway involving mast cell degranulation and the formation of short-lived, erythematous, raised and itchy areas of oedema or weals [1] (Fig. 5.1, colour plate). Individual lesions can vary in size and morphology, and usually (with one exception) last only 24 hours.

Urticaria is often associated with angioedema, which is characterised by swelling caused by oedema of the deeper tissues of the skin and mucous membranes. Swelling starts suddenly and may extend over several cm in diameter, but is generally short-lived and disappears after 24-72 hours. Patients with urticaria may also have associated systemic symptoms such as headache, dizziness, wheezing, vomiting or diarrhoea.

Possible reasons for the development of urticaria include defects in the normal response to stimuli such as a lower threshold for mast cell activation, an exaggerated response to stimuli and/or a lack of down-regulation of the response.

5.1.1 Acute and chronic forms

Urticaria is commonly referred to as acute or chronic depending upon the duration of the lesions. Acute urticaria is arbitrarily considered to have a duration of less than 6 weeks, whilst chronic urticaria includes those of more than 6 –12 weeks duration. Approximately a quarter of patients with urticaria will develop the chronic form at some stage in their disease.

Acute urticaria occurs more commonly in atopic patients and is more likely to be caused by food allergy than chronic urticaria in which foods are implicated in only 1-2% of patients. The majority of patients have the chronic form of urticaria, of which approximately one-third have evidence of autoimmune mechanisms.

5.1.2. Pathogenesis of urticaria

5.1.2.1 Causes of urticaria

Urticaria may be triggered by a variety of different factors although in some cases, such as urticarial vasculitis, the causes are unknown (Table 5.1).

Allergic mechanisms are not involved in all types of urticaria, but are commoner in atopic patients. Substances that cause IgE-mediated urticarial skin lesions are those that are implicated in other IgE-mediated reactions and include insect stings, various foods, and penicillin.

Certain chemicals can cause so-called pseudo-allergic or non-immunological urticarial reactions, notably aspirin and other cyclooxygenase inhibitors. Substances that induce mast cells to degranulate such as C3a and C5a, neuropeptides, cytokines, and the drugs, codeine and morphine can also cause non-immunological reactions.

Contact urticaria can be induced by exposure to foods (immunological) or chemicals (non-immunological); animal or plant products, metals or fragrances can also be involved.

Various physical stimuli, such as mechanical trauma, temperature change, light and water can also cause the formation of urticarial skin lesions.

Viral infections can provoke cold urticaria, but more commonly viral infections exacerbate pre-existing urticarial skin lesions, possibly via interferon, which may act by enhancing mediator release by mast cells or by decreasing the number of T suppressor lymphocytes.

5.1.2.2 Histology of skin lesions

Urticarial lesions are characterised by dermal oedema, which in the case of angioedema extends deeper into the subcutaneous tissue, and a variable perivascular inflammatory cell infiltrate consisting of mainly lymphocytes, with PMNs, eosinophils and degranulating mast cells (Fig. 5.2, colour plate).

In contrast in the urticarial vasculitis syndrome, a disorder that presents clinically as an urticarial eruption (see below), a histological picture of vasculitis is observed. There is a predominately PMN cell infiltrate, together with variable numbers of eosinophils and mononuclear cells in the walls of blood vessels. The latter appear abnormal due to oedema and the deposition of variable amounts of fibrin and nuclear fragments (nuclear dust).

The presence of PMNs in blood vessel walls is more common in patients with physical urticarias, particularly dermographism (response to mechanical stimuli), and also in cold and cholinergic urticaria. Patients with delayed pressure urticaria have an unusually long time period of several hours between elicitation and response. PMNs and eosinophils predominate during the first five hours, with activated CD4[+] T lymphocytes and eosinophils present in the later lesions. Activated CD4[+] T cells also predominate in chronic idiopathic urticaria (see below).

Table 5.1 Types of urticarias and their common triggers

Types of Urticaria	Triggers
Acute idiopathic	Unknown
Acute allergic	Foods - fish, shellfish, milk nuts, etc. Wasp and bee stings Penicillin
Pseudo-allergic	Cyclooxygenase inhibitors including aspirin Radiocontrast media Local anaesthetics Dextran Food preservatives and colourings C3a, C5a, neuropeptides, cytokines Codeine, morphine, turbocurarine
Contact: Immunological	Foods - fish, shellfish, milk, nuts etc. Metals, fragrances, drugs, animal and plant substances
Contact: Non-Immunological	Ammonium persulphate, dimethyl sulphoxide, cinnamic aldehyde, benzoic acid Metals, preservatives, disinfectants, plant substances
Physical	Mechanical trauma, temperature change, light, water
Chronic idiopathic	Autoantibodies to FcεRI and/or IgE
Hereditary angioedema	Autosomal dominant inheritance
Acquired C1 inhibitor deficiency	Associated with B cell lymphoproliferative or autoimmune disease
Urticarial vasculitis	Unknown
Urticarial pigmentosa/mastocytosis	Rubbing the skin

5.1.2.3 Mast cell mediators

When mast cells undergo degranulation, preformed mediators stored in granules and newly formed mediators generated from membrane phospholipids are released (see Chapter 1). In urticaria, the effects of these mediators are amplified by activation of complement and kinins, and additional mediators are released by infiltrating cells that contribute to the inflammatory response.

Of the preformed mediators, histamine plays a central role in the urticarial response (Fig. 5.3). This is shown by the production of a transient, red, raised and itchy weal by injection of histamine alone, and by the beneficial effects exerted by H_1 antihistamines in the treatment of physical urticarias. Histamine is also responsible for the systemic effects experienced by patients suffering a severe

Figure 5.3   Role of histamine in urticaria. EC = endothelial cell; C' = complement.

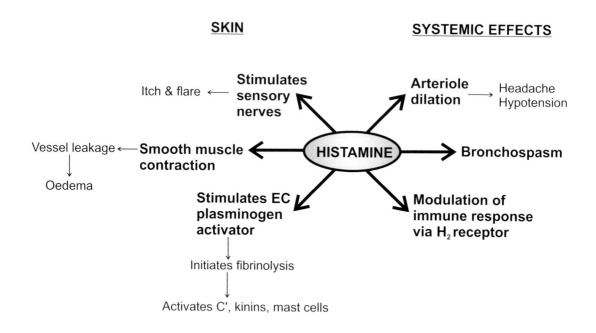

reaction, such as bronchospasm in cholinergic urticaria and headaches due to arteriole dilatation in cold urticaria.

Prostaglandin D_2 is synthesised in small quantities by mast cells and is subsequently rapidly metabolised making it unlikely that it plays a significant part in the formation of the urticarial lesion. The involvement of leukotrienes is also yet to be demonstrated. However, LTE_4 (metabolised from LTC_4), PAF-like activity and platelet clumping have been detected in cold urticaria.

Evidence for the involvement of the mast cell derived proteases, tryptase, chymase and carboxypeptidase in the urticarial response is indirect. However, these enzymes could amplify the response by enhancing mast cell degranulation and activating complement, kinins and the Hageman factor (coagulation factor XII). In addition, they could partially digest collagen and extracellular matrix allowing phagocytes to migrate through the skin more easily and increasing vascular permeability.

5.1.2.4 Kinins

Kinins are oligopeptides produced from high molecular weight kininogen by the action of kallikrein or kinogenases (Fig. 5.4). There are three kinins present in man, bradykinin, kallidin and methionyl-lysyl bradykinin, which are potent vasodilators and are associated with the coagulation and fibrinolytic systems. Kallikrein is activated by Hageman factor, whose activation is, in turn, enhanced by high molecular weight kininogen.

Bradykinin and kallidin are partially inactivated by the action of angiotensin converting enzyme

Figure 5.4   Production of bradykinin from kininogen by kallikrein. ACE = angiotensin converting enzyme

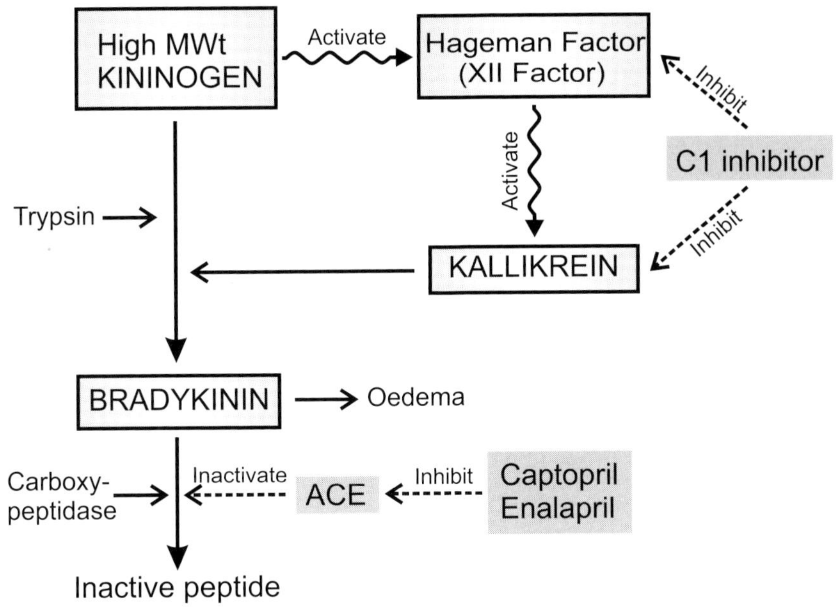

(ACE). Inhibitors of this enzyme (captopril and enalapril) induce angioedema, which is accompanied by increased levels of bradykinin. Further up the pathway, C1 esterase inhibitor, which inhibits activated Hageman factor and kallikrein, is deficient in hereditary angioedema implicating the kinins in the pathogenesis of this disorder. Kinin release has also been demonstrated in dermographism.

5.1.2.5 Complement activation

Classical or alternative complement activation has been described in urticaria [2]. In urticarial vasculitis, and possibly in other forms of urticaria, IgG and IgM in immune complexes activate complement via the classical pathway. Classical or alternative complement pathway activation has also been reported in a proportion of patients with chronic idiopathic urticaria. In the occasional case of localized, heat-induced urticaria, decreases in C3 and B levels have been detected indicating activation of the alternative pathway. In addition, trypsin released by mast cells can split C3 into C3a and C3b.

After activation of complement, the C3a, C4a and C5a anaphylatoxins produced can stimulate mast cells to release histamine, thus contributing to the pathogenesis of urticaria. Furthermore, C5a is a potent PMN chemotaxin. Intradermal injection of these complement peptides induces a weal and flare reaction and pruritus supporting their role as mediators of the response.

5.1.2.6 Neuropeptides

Neuropeptides released by sensory nerves in the skin include substance P, CGRP and NKA (see Chapter 2). Following firm stroking of the skin (dermographism), or injection of histamine, mast cell-derived mediators induce an axon reflex flare with release of neuropeptides. Substance P activates mast cells to release histamine, causing erythema, and all three neuropeptides act directly on blood vessels inducing vasodilation and subsequently oedema. In addition, the metabolites of CGRP are chemotactic for eosinophils.

Both substance P and the related peptide VIP are increased in the lesional and non-lesional skin of patients with cold urticaria and dermographism compared to controls [3]. Furthermore, pre-treatment of patients with cold and localised heat urticaria with topical capsaicin, which depletes nerves of neuropeptides, blocked the urticarial response supporting a role for neuropeptides in the formation of skin lesions [4]. Neuropeptides, particularly VIP, are also implicated in cholinergic urticaria in which the stimulus is neurogenic. In a further link between the nervous system and the skin, the endogenous opioid peptides, dynorphin, β-endorphin and α-neoendorphin can all induce histamine release at low concentrations in a non-immunological manner.

5.1.2.7 Protease inhibitors

To terminate the urticarial response, the mediators must be destroyed and secondary complement and kinin activation pathways inhibited. Mediators can be inactivated by binding to heparin, are removed by macrophages and granulocytes, or are metabolised. As mentioned above, proteases released by mast cells and leukocytes can amplify the response by enhancing mast cell degranulation and activating the complement, kinin, clotting and fibrinolytic pathways. Inhibitors, including α1-antitrypsin, α1-antichymotrypsin, inter-α-trypsin inhibitor, α2 macroglobulin, antithrombin III, and C1 esterase inhibitor, regulate the activity of these proteases by binding to them to form soluble complexes which are subsequently removed. Decreases in levels of protease inhibitors have been demonstrated in patients with cold, cholinergic or chronic urticaria or angioedema [5,6]. Although it is not known whether these variations represent cause or effect, treatment with protease inhibitors has been shown to be beneficial in some patients. For example, Trasylol, an active inhibitor of tissue kallikrein, was effective in patients with chronic urticaria, and danazol (an attenuated androgen) gave good results in patients with cholinergic urticaria, associated with significant elevations in several protease inhibitors particularly α1-antichymotrypsin [7].

5.1.2.8 Other cell types

PMNs, eosinophils and macrophages are attracted into the lesion in response to chemoattractants such as PAF and leukotrienes released by mast cells. Chemotactic factors for PMNs have been demonstrated in cold, heat, solar and cholinergic urticaria, and eosinophil chemotactic factors after challenge testing of cold urticaria. These cells, in turn, secrete mediators that recruit more cells and prolong the reaction. T lymphocytes are also attracted into urticarial lesions and appear to play an active role via the production of IL-3 (a mast cell growth factor) and histamine-releasing factors which induce degranulation of mast cells/basophils.

5.1.3 Types of urticaria

5.1.3.1 Acute idiopathic urticaria

In acute idiopathic urticaria, the weals can vary in diameter from only 2-5mm up to 30cm or more, are very often itchy, and are present for less than 24 hours. In about half of the patients there is accompanying angioedema affecting the eyelids, lips and/or tongue, and less commonly other parts of the body such as the hands, feet and trunk. The cause of this type of urticaria is unknown.

Table 5.2 Chemicals that trigger pseudo-allergic urticarial reactions

Urticaria-inducing chemicals
Cyclooxygenase inhibitors:
Aspirin (acetylsalicyclic acid)
Diclofenac
Fenoprofen
Ibuprofen
Indomethacin
Ketoprofen
Mefenamic acid
Metamizol
Naproxen
Paracetamol (acetominophen)
Phenylbutazone
Tolmetin
Preservatives:
Benzoic acid
Salicyclates
Ascorbic acid
Parabens
Sulphites
Antioxidants
Tartrazine
Radiocontrast media
Plasma expanders (dextran)
Local anaesthetics

5.1.3.2 Acute allergic urticaria

The classical model for urticaria is the IgE-mediated type I hypersensitivity response in which allergen cross-links antigen-specific IgE bound to Fc receptors on the surface of mast cells, resulting in mast cell activation and degranulation and the release of mediators (see Chapter 4). A modest IgE-mediated reaction to various foods such as fish, shellfish milk, nuts and certain vegetables can result in acute allergic urticaria which accounts for about 2-5% of the total number of cases of urticaria seen in a dermatology clinic. Other causes include wasp and bee stings and drug reactions. A more severe reaction may result in the more serious condition, systemic anaphylaxis. Although the measurement of total IgE levels is unhelpful in the diagnosis of allergic urticaria, determination of allergen-specific IgE by RAST may be useful in some individuals.

5.1.3.3 Pseudo-allergic (Non-immunological) urticaria

Pseudo allergic or non-immunological urticarial reactions are provoked on first exposure to a variety of chemicals [8] (Table 5.2). The response is not substance-specific and unrelated chemicals can induce a similar response in the same individual. The degree of response is dose-dependent, and removal of the drug results in resolution of skin lesions. The most common cause of pseudo-allergic urticaria is aspirin and other cyclooxygenase inhibitors, suggesting an alteration in the arachidonic acid pathway. Other chemicals that can provoke an urticarial response include radiocontrast media, local anaesthetics, dextran, and food preservatives or colourings. The mechanisms by which these chemicals induce histamine release are presently unknown.

Non-immunological reactions can also be caused by substances that induce mast cells to release histamine such as the anaphylatoxins C3a and C5a, neuropeptides (e.g. substance P), cytokines, and drugs (codeine, morphine and turbocurarine).

The angiotensin converting enzyme inhibitors, captopril and enalapril, can also induce angioedema and urticaria in susceptible individuals, a few days after the start of therapy. This reaction is probably due to the inhibition of proteases, which normally regulate levels of bradykinin (Fig. 5.4).

Skin prick testing does not correlate well with exacerbating factors of non-immunological reactions, and thus oral provocation tests may be used instead. This can involve placing the patient on a restrictive diet in hospital and administering the test substances in gelatin capsules at specific time points over a 24-hour period. Alternatively, the tests can be carried out on an outpatient basis, with the patients on a normal diet and taking low dose anti-histamine therapy to prevent severe reactions. Positive reactions occur within 24 hours of challenge and any further testing is suspended until the reaction dissipates. However, elimination of substances that give a positive oral test does not necessarily prevent urticarial reactions; furthermore, placebo may also induce a response making interpretation difficult.

5.1.3.4 Contact urticaria

Contact reactions are immediate, occurring during the first hour after exposure and resolving within 24 hours. The degree of response can vary from erythema with itching, tingling or burning, through the classical weal and flare, to the severest reaction, which is characterised by generalised urticaria with systemic symptoms (contact urticaria syndrome).

Contact urticaria can be either immunological or non-immunological. The immunological type is more common in atopic individuals and occurs in response to the same foods as those associated with allergic urticaria. Initial sensitisation usually takes place in the gastrointestinal or respiratory tracts, although it may also occur through the skin. On subsequent exposure, swelling of the lips or buccal mucous membranes, or sometimes itching and oedema of the oropharynx can occur. Other substances that can cause immunological contact urticaria include metals, fragrances, drugs, and animal and plant derivatives.

The non-immunological form of contact urticaria is more common and can occur in healthy individuals with no history of previous sensitisation. Substances that trigger this reaction include ammonia, persulphate, dimethyl sulphoxide, cinnamic aldehyde and benzoic acid. In addition, metals, preservatives, disinfectants and plants such as nettles and primula can also induce non-immunological contact urticaria.

To diagnose contact urticaria, simple skin tests such as the "rub test" or the "use test" can be employed together with a full contact history. The "rub test", as the name implies, involves gentle rubbing of the suspect substance on to normal skin and looking for signs of a reaction after 60 minutes. The "use test" similarly involves handling of the substance in the same way as when symptoms were induced. Patch skin tests can also be used to aid diagnosis. The open patch test involves spreading 0.1 ml of the test substance on to an area of 3 x 3cm unaffected skin on the back or upper arm; a positive weal and flare reaction or pinpoint vesicles will appear within 15 to 60 minutes. Alternatively, treated skin can be occluded (covered to keep in moisture) for 15 to 20 minutes; positive reactions appear 45 minutes after application. Scratch-patch testing may also be used; the substance is scratched into the skin and covered with a Finn chamber for 15 minutes. The chamber is then removed and the skin observed for a weal and flare reaction after 5 minutes.

5.1.3.5 Physical urticarias

Physical urticaria in which a weal and flare response occurs to a specific physical stimulus can be subdivided into various types [9] (Table 5.3). However, there is heterogeneity within each type and overlap between them, as two or more types are frequently present in a single individual. Physical urticarias account for approximately one-fifth of all cases of urticaria referred to dermatology clinics. The weals triggered by physical stimuli are short-lived (except in the case of delayed pressure urticaria) and, in some cases, their development appears to involve recognition by IgE of a molecule released or altered by the physical stimulus.

The different types of physical stimuli that induce urticaria are mechanical trauma, temperature change, light and water.

Mechanical trauma

The types of urticaria caused by mechanical trauma include dermographism, delayed pressure and, the rarely observed, vibratory angioedema.

In simple dermographism, stroking of the skin with moderate pressure induces a weal and flare reaction without itching. This is probably a physiological response as it occurs in about 5% of the normal population. In contrast, in symptomatic dermographism, pronounced itching accompanies the weal and flare response at sites where friction is experienced such as around collars and cuffs, or on the trunk after drying with a towel. A calibrated dermographometer, consisting of a stylus attached to a spring, can be used to determine the pressure required to induce a weal and flare response. The stylus is stroked longitudinally on the back with the dermographometer set at different pressures; a positive response at a pressure of $3.6g/mm^2$ or less confirms the diagnosis of symptomatic dermographism. The same instrument is used to confirm the diagnosis of delayed pressure urticaria (see below).

Symptomatic dermographism is, in most cases, IgE-mediated (as shown by passive transfer) with weal formation induced by mast cell-derived histamine and a substance P-induced flare. It is possible that, in the absence of IgE, mast cells may be directly activated by mechanical trauma.

In delayed pressure urticaria, constant pressure exerted by bra straps, belts, watches etc., causes delayed erythema, dermal and subcutaneous oedema. In addition, after manual activity or walking and jogging, swelling of the hands and/or feet may occur which closely resembles that of chronic idiopathic angioedema. In contrast to other types of urticaria, the reaction develops slowly, only becoming apparent between 30 minutes and 9 hours after the pressure has been applied. To confirm the diagnosis, the dermographometer is set at a pressure of 20.4 g/mm^2 and held firmly in a perpendicular position against the skin of the patient's back for varying numbers of seconds. A positive response is indicated by the appearance of a palpable lesion, which takes at least 30 minutes to appear and is read at 6 hours.

Table 5.3 Types of physical urticaria and their mediators

Urticaria	Stimulus	Mediators	IgE-mediated
Mechanical trauma			
Simple dermographism	Moderate stroking	Physiological	No
Symptomatic dermographism	Friction	Histamine, kinins, substance P	Yes
Delayed pressure	Constant pressure	Histamine, kinins, (LTB_4, LTC_4)	No
Vibratory	High frequency vibration	Histamine	No
Temperature change			
Cholinergic	Nervous stimulus to sweating	Histamine, eosinophil and PMN chemotactic factors	No
Idiopathic acquired cold contact	Cold contact	Histamine, eosinophil and PMN chemotactic factors, PGD_2, PAF, LTE_4	Yes
Localised heat	Heat contact (38-49°C)	Histamine, PMN chemotactic factors	Possibly
Solar	UVA, UVB	Histamine, eosinophil and PMN chemotactic factors	Yes
Aquagenic	Water	Histamine	Unknown

Although mast cell degranulation is necessary for the induction of delayed pressure urticaria, histamine does not appear to play a central role as shown by the ineffectiveness of anti-histamines in this disorder. Other mediators present include kinins and the leukotrienes LTB_4, LTC_4, LTD_4 and LTE_4, but the delay in the development of the response suggests that mediators produced by PMNs, eosinophils and/or T cells recruited to the skin may be more relevant.

Vibratory angioedema is a rare condition in which repeated stretching of the skin by high frequency vibration causes erythema and oedema of the dermis and subcutaneous tissues. Susceptibility to vibration-induced angioedema is usually inherited as an autosomal dominant trait, but sporadic cases do sometimes occur.

Temperature change

Types of urticarial reactions induced by change in temperature include cholinergic, cold and localised heat urticaria

In cholinergic urticaria, the response is not triggered by heat itself, but by the nervous stimulus to sweating. Thus extensive wealing occurs after exercise, a hot bath or shower, or after an intense emotional episode. Individual skin lesions, which are tiny and surrounded by a red flare, are mostly found on the upper part of the body and may merge to form larger weals. To confirm the diagnosis, the skin eruption is reproduced by energetic exercise sufficient to cause sweating, or by passively increasing the body temperature in a bath kept at 42°C for 10-15 minutes.

Acetylcholine released by nerves is an important mediator in the cholinergic urticarial response, but histamine and chemotactic factors that cause PMN recruitment are probably also involved. However, this type of response does not appear to be IgE-mediated. A decrease in the levels of the protease inhibitor α1-antichymotryptase (see above) has been reported; treatment of this deficiency appears to be beneficial suggesting that regulatory dysfunction is an important factor in this condition.

Idiopathic acquired immediate cold contact urticaria is the most common form of cold urticaria. Symptoms such as itching, burning, and development of weals occurs on rewarming of the skin after exposure to cold such as wintry wind or rain, or when touching frozen food. If the cold stimulus is sufficiently severe, systemic effects may also be experienced due to high histamine levels in the blood. To confirm the diagnosis, a melting ice cube is fixed to the patient's forearm with tape for 20 minutes. A positive response can be detected within 10 minutes of removal of the ice cube in a patient with active disease. Furthermore, high levels of histamine can be detected in blood taken from a patient's forearm immersed in cold water.

In 25-50% of cases the response is IgE-mediated and transferable, although, rarely, it can be mediated by cryoglobulins and cryofibrinogen. As in cholinergic urticaria, protease inhibitors may be decreased; furthermore, in some patients complement may be activated or there may be an associated vasculitis. The onset of cold urticaria can, in some patients, be associated with a previous infection such as syphilis, or an allergy to an antibiotic such as penicillin. Interestingly, repeated exposure to the cold may lead to a state of tolerance suggesting that mast cells become unresponsive, perhaps due to blocking of receptors or depletion of the cold-induced antigen.

Localised heat urticaria is a rare condition in which local application of heat (38-49°C) to the skin causes erythema and oedema for up to 2 hours.

Solar urticaria

Solar urticaria may have several initiating factors, including porphyria, SLE and drugs. It is characterised by diffuse erythema and itchy, tingling weals in response to UVA or UVB, particularly in areas of the body not normally exposed to light. The reaction occurs very rapidly (between 30 seconds and 3 minutes), disappearing again within an hour, and is confined to the area of exposure. More extensive exposure may result in accompanying systemic symptoms. A solar simulator may be used to confirm the diagnosis; an immediate response distinguishes solar urticaria from the more common polymorphic light eruption in which a response would not be observed for several hours.

In patients with solar urticaria, exposure to light causes the conversion of a precursor to an antigenic photoproduct, which triggers IgE-mediated mast cell degranulation. The antigen may be unique to the patients with solar urticaria or, alternatively, may also be present in normal irradiated skin but only induces a reaction in the patients. The precursor can be altered by irradiation with different wavelengths of light; this may affect its subsequent activity. Furthermore, removal of the precursor from the patient's serum by plasma exchange can prevent the development of skin lesions.

<u>**Aquagenic urticaria**</u>

Aquagenic urticaria is a rare type of physical urticaria in which itchy weals develop at the sites of contact with water, independent of its temperature. The lesions, which are found mostly on the upper part of the body, take 30 minutes to develop their maximum size and intensity, and then subside after 30-60 minutes. The pattern of the skin rash is similar to that of cholinergic urticaria, and can usually be reproduced by a 15-minute lukewarm shower to confirm the diagnosis.

5.1.3.6 Chronic Idiopathic Urticaria

Chronic urticaria has a similar presentation to that of acute urticaria, except that the urticaria or angioedema persists, continuously or episodically, for more than an arbitrary 6-12 weeks. Chronic idiopathic urticaria (chronic is synonymous with idiopathic in this context) accounts for 70% of all urticaria cases seen at dermatology clinics, and is often associated with physical urticarias, particularly delayed pressure urticaria.

A subset of 30-50% of patients with chronic idiopathic urticaria has been classified as autoimmune on the basis that they produce IgG autoantibodies to the alpha chain of the high affinity IgE receptor (FcεR1) and/or against IgE [10]. These patients cosegregate with chronic idiopathic urticaria patients who have an increased frequency of anti-thyroid autoantibodies specific for thyroglobulin or a microsomal-derived antigen, peroxidase [11]. There is an increased frequency of Hashimoto's thyroiditis in chronic idiopathic urticaria patients, but no evidence that the anti-thyroid antibodies are pathogenic in the urticarial reaction.

Autoantibodies against the high affinity IgE receptor and/or IgE are believed to be causative of chronic urticaria since an urticarial reaction can be induced by intradermal injection of anti-FcεR1

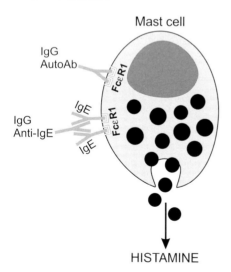

Figure 5.5 IgG autoantibodies present in chronic idiopathic urticaria

IgG into the skin of healthy volunteers [12]. However, there is no animal model at present to prove this theory conclusively. These antibodies, which are of the IgG_1 and IgG_3 subclasses and effectively fix complement, bind to the IgE receptor on mast cells and basophils and induce degranulation and the release of histamine (Fig. 5.5). In some patients, autoantibodies that do not have histamine-releasing activity are present. Such non-functional autoantibodies, which are of the IgG_2 and IgG_4 subclasses and do not fix complement, are also found in the sera of patients with physical urticarias and with autoimmune connective tissue and bullous diseases. In addition, there is also a minority of patients that lack these autoantibodies but produce an unidentified serum factor that can cause degranulation of basophils. Natural anti-FcεR1 antibodies are also present in healthy individuals and bind to the IgE receptor triggering histamine release, but only if IgE is previously removed from the receptor. This suggests that there may be a difference in the epitope recognised by the autoantibodies in healthy individuals compared to that in chronic idiopathic urticaria patients. Currently, the best methods for detection of functional autoantibodies are the autologous serum skin test and the basophil histamine release assay (see below).

The skin lesions from patients with chronic idiopathic urticaria contain an infiltration of eosinophils, basophils, PMNs, monocytes and T cells, and resemble that of a late allergen-induced reaction [13]. Both CD4$^+$ and CD8$^+$ T cells are present and some of the T cells are activated as shown by their expression of CD25 antigen (IL-2 receptor). However, in contrast to the late allergen-induced reaction, which has a Th-2 cytokine profile, the cytokines present include IL-4, IL-5 and IFN-γ (Th-0). Expression of the adhesion molecules, ICAM-1, VCAM-1 and E-selectin, which facilitate the recruitment of leukocytes into the skin are also up-regulated.

Autologous serum skin test

The autologous skin test involves the intradermal injection of 0.05ml of a patient's serum, collected during an active phase of the disease, into the same patient's uninvolved forearm skin. Equal volumes of saline and histamine (10 μg/ml) are injected into adjacent sites as negative and positive controls, respectively. The test is read 30 minutes later; if the diameter of the serum-induced weal is 1.5 mm greater than that of the bleb at the saline-injected site, a positive response is recorded. The induction of a weal and flare response is indicative of the presence of autoantibodies to the high affinity IgE receptor and/or IgE in the patient's serum.

Basophil histamine release assay

This assay analyses the histamine released by peripheral blood basophils from normal individuals after incubation with test sera. Alternatively dermal mast cells obtained from normal skin removed during surgery can be used. Histamine levels are determined using a radioimmunoassay and can be semi-quantified by comparing with a known concentration of allergen extract that induces the release of a known amount of released histamine. Both the sensitivity and specificity of this test are similar to those of the RAST technique (see Chapter 4).

5.1.3.7 Hereditary Angioedema

Hereditary angioedema is characterised by painless swellings, mostly on the peripheries and face, which are neither erythematous nor itchy. They are triggered by local trauma such as dental extraction, or anxiety, and persist for 2 to 3 days after which they dissipate. Commonly the gastrointestinal and upper respiratory tracts are involved, and in severe cases, swellings at these sites may be life threatening. This condition is inherited as an autosomal dominant trait and, in 80-85% of cases, involves a quantitative deficiency of C1 esterase inhibitor due to both decreased synthesis and increased metabolism (type I) [14]. A small proportion of patients have a second form of the disease (type II) in which the inhibitor is present in normal amounts but is functionally impaired due to point mutations that vary between different families. In both cases, the lack of functional inhibitor results in unrestrained protease action and potentiation of the complement (increased activated C1), kinin (increased bradykinin, Fig. 5.4), fibrinolytic and coagulation pathways. Bradykinin probably plays a major role in increasing vascular permeability, which leads to oedema and swelling.

To diagnose the disease, immunological assays are used to measure the level of C1 esterase inhibitor; a level of <100 mg/ml indicates type I disease. In addition, C4 and C2 levels are reduced in both types of the disease.

There are also two acquired forms of angioedema in which patients have the same clinical presentation, but no family history. One includes patients with B cell lymphoproliferative disease in whom metabolism of C1 esterase inhibitor is increased. In the second, more rare form, autoantibodies to the inhibitor cause cleavage of the protein.

5.1.3.8 Urticarial vasculitis

In urticarial vasculitis [15], the skin lesions are prolonged compared to other forms of urticaria, sometimes persisting for as long as three to seven days, and are sometimes painful. On resolution, the lesions may leave pigmentation, scaling or purpura. Systemic manifestations of urticarial vasculitis are common and similar to those of systemic vasculitis. Arthralgia is the most frequently experienced, but renal, gastrointestinal, pulmonary or ophthalmic involvement occurs in a proportion of patients. A raised ESR (erythrocyte sedimentation rate) is a common finding in these patients, and occasionally they may have low titres of antinuclear antibodies, presence of cryoglobulins, raised immunoglobulins or a positive rheumatoid factor.

The pathogenesis of urticarial vasculitis is that of an immune complex vasculitis similar to the Arthus reaction (see Chapter 4). PMNs infiltrate the blood vessel cell walls and there is evidence of complement activation via the classical, or sometimes the alternative, pathway. Complement factors C1, C3, C4 and properdin, together with IgG, IgM and fibrin are present in blood vessel walls and along the basement membrane as shown by direct immunofluorescence. Complement activation results in the release of C3a and C5a, which attract PMNs to the site and induce mast cell degranulation. In addition, circulating immune complexes have been demonstrated in many patients with urticarial vasculitis. It is not clear, however, whether these immune complexes initiate the reaction, or are secondary and accumulate due to tissue damage or inefficient clearance. An identical clinical presentation has been reported in some cases of SLE, serum sickness and hepatitis B infection implicating a variety of antigens in the disease process.

5.1.3.9 Urticaria Pigmentosa/Mastocytosis

This condition is characterised by the accumulation of mast cells in different organs of the body, and ranges from a single mastocytoma, to the spontaneously resolving lesions of childhood urticaria pigmentosa and then the more progressive adult form, to a rare mast cell leukaemia. The skin is virtually always involved and, when rubbed, wealing is induced (Darier's sign). Where wealing is extensive, blood histamine and PGD_2 levels are increased and exacerbate symptoms such as flushing, wheezing, headache and diarrhoea.

Mast cells in mastocytosis are larger than normal with larger granules and nuclei, but function normally. Mast cell-derived heparin and glycosaminoglycans chronically stimulate melanocytes resulting in the increased melanin pigmentation observed in skin lesions of patients with this condition, and which gives it its name.

5.1.4 Treatment

5.1.4.1. H$_1$-antihistamines

The first line treatment for urticaria is the H$_1$-antihistamines, which, in most cases, are effective in inhibiting the disease process. Tolerance to the drugs can occur, but sensitivity can be restored by temporary cessation of treatment. During this period, salbutamol or terbutaline (β-adrenoceptor stimulants) can be administered instead, but are less efficient. The response by patients with cholinergic, aquagenic or solar urticaria to H$_1$-antihistamines is, however, variable and may not adequately control the disease. In severe cases of cholinergic urticaria an attenuated androgen, danazol may be used, but side effects such as impaired hepatic function may restrict its use. A tricyclic antidepressant drug with H$_1$ and H$_2$ antihistamine activity, such as doxepin, may be given to patients whose disease is difficult to control. Drugs that block H$_2$ receptors are not effective on their own, and dermographism is the only type of urticaria in which these drugs add to the effects exerted by H$_1$ antihistamines. In those cases where alternative drugs are not available or suitable, potent non-sedatory H$_1$-antihistamines such as terfenadine, cetirizine or loratidine may give better efficacy than the traditional antihistamines.

5.1.4.2 Other treatments

If antihistamines do not control urticarial symptoms, short-term corticosteroid therapy or leukotriene receptor antagonists, such as montelukast and zafirlukast, can be used [16]. In a few patients that require high-dose corticosteroid therapy for long periods, low-dose cyclosporin may be an alternative option, but its use requires careful monitoring.

Urticarial vasculitis responds poorly to H$_1$-antihistamines and variably to non-steroidal anti-inflammatory drugs. Various drugs such as hydroxychloroquine, dapsone, colchicine, sulphasalazine and gold have been found to be effective in some patients.

In the case of a severe anaphylactic reaction, immediate treatment with subcutaneous adrenaline, intramuscular or intravenous H$_1$-antihistamines and intravenous hydrocortisone is imperative. In addition, systemic corticosteroids may be used in conjunction with antihistamines to treat serum sickness and severe cases of delayed pressure urticaria.

Acute attacks of hereditary angioedema are treated with C1 esterase inhibitor concentrate, which can be administered by the patient and acts within one hour of administration, or alternatively, with fresh frozen plasma, which is less immediate as it has to be given in hospital. Tranexamic acid may also be used to treat an acute attack, and oropharyngeal swelling can be reduced with ephedrine spray or subcutaneous adrenaline. Prophylactic treatment for patients with repeated severe attacks of angioedema involves raising the circulating levels of C1 esterase inhibitor with danazol or stanozolol.

5.2 Pemphigus

Autoimmune blistering skin diseases are subdivided into two major types on the basis of whether the blistering is epidermal (pemphigus) or subepidermal (pemphigoid) [17].

Pemphigus can be further subdivided into three subsets; pemphigus vulgaris, pemphigus foliaceous, and paraneoplastic pemphigus. All three types have in common the presence of pathogenic IgG autoantibodies against desmosomal proteins, the loss of keratinocyte-keratinocyte adhesion (acantholysis), and blistering and ulceration of the skin, mucous membranes or both. In addition, autoreactive T lymphocytes play an important role in the induction of autoantibody production. The disease subsets can be differentiated on the basis of particular clinical and immunopathological characteristics (Table 5.4).

5.2.1 Pemphigus vulgaris

5.2.1.1 Clinical features

Pemphigus vulgaris (PV) is the most common form of pemphigus but is a rare disease occurring in only 0.1 to 0.5 per 10,000 of the population. It occurs most commonly in middle age, affecting both sexes equally, and invariably presents with persistent painful oral ulcerations, or oral lesions develop early in the disease. These oral ulcers very often occur on the posterior buccal mucosae and gingivae, but can be found on any mucous membrane covered by stratified squamous epithelia. In many patients, mucous membranes are the only site of disease involvement. In those cases where the skin is also affected, fragile vesiculobullous lesions, without surrounding erythema, are frequently found on the scalp and neck and commonly on the trunk (Fig. 5.6A, colour plate). In severe cases, the blisters can extend to cover the whole body. The condition is chronic and progressive with sepsis a common cause of death within five years of onset.

PV is associated with several HLA Class I and class II alleles, some of which (DRB1*0402 and DQB1*0503) are rare in the general population [18]. The disease is over-represented in Jews and people of Mediterranean origin. In Jewish patients, the haplotype HLA-B38 (or HLA-B35), DRB1*0402, DQB1*0302 is increased. Another haplotype, DRB1*1401, DQB1*0503 is also found more frequently in PV patients. Other Class I alleles reported to be increased are HLA-B15 in Japanese patients, and HLA-B35, HLA-B44 and Cw4 in Turkish patients. Decreases in frequencies of DRB1*11, DRB1*07, DQ7 (DQA1*0501, DQB1*0301) and/or DQ2 (DQA1*0501, DQB1*02) in patients of different ethnic groups suggest that these Class II alleles may be protective.

5.2.1.2 Autoantibodies to desmoglein 3

Patients with active disease invariably have circulating IgG autoantibodies that bind specifically to stratified squamous epithelium. Using direct immunofluorescence these autoantibodies can be consistently demonstrated in skin (or mucosa), together with variable amounts of C3, on the surface of keratinocytes (but not on the basement membrane) (Fig. 5.7A, colour plate). In the epidermis, there is a loss of cell-to-cell attachment with rounding of keratinocytes resulting in the formation of a fragile intraepithelial blister. An inflammatory infiltrate is usually present and eosinophils may

Table 5.4 Characteristic features of pemphigus and bullous pemphigoid

Clinical features	Pemphigus vulgaris	Pemphigus foliaceous	Paraneoplastic pemphigus	Bullous pemphigoid
Age of onset	Any age, usually middle-age	Middle age	Any age	Old age
Clinical presentation	Oral ulcerations ± vesicobullous skin lesions	Erythematous, scaling plaques or superficial blisters on skin only	Painful ulcerations of several mucosae and polymorphic skin lesions. Respiratory epithelium can be involved leading to respiratory failure.	Infrequent, mild transient mucosal lesions. Itchy, erythematous, urticarial plaques developing into tense blisters and bullae on skin.
HLA association	DRB1*0402, *1401, *1404 DQB1*0302; *0503 HLA-B15, B35, B38, B44, Cw4	DRB1*1401 DQB1*0503 Endemic PV: DRB1*0404, *1402, *1406,*01, *1601	DRB1*03	Caucasians: DQB1*0301 Japanese: DRB1*0403, *0406, *1101 DQB1*0302
Antibody specificities	Desmoglein 3 ± Desmoglein 1 (Cholinergic receptors)	Desmoglein 1 (Cholinergic receptors)	Desmoglein 3, Desmoglein 1 (Plakins, 170 kDa antigen)	BP 180 (BP 230, laminin, β_4 integrin)
Antibody subclass	Active: IgG_4 Chronic: IgG_1	IgG_4 (IgG_1)	IgG_1, IgG_2 (Dsg 3)	Active: IgG_4 Chronic: IgG_1
Inflammatory events required for blister formation	No	No	No	Yes
Site of blister	Intraepidermal	Intraepidermal	Intraepidermal	Subepidermal
Disease association	None	None	B cell lympho-proliferative disease	None

predominate.

The autoantibodies in PV are pathogenic. This has been demonstrated by injecting neonatal mice with IgG fractions of PV sera, which results in the formation of skin lesions characteristic of the disease [19]. Furthermore, neonates born to mothers with active disease may transiently exhibit pemphigus lesions as a result of transfer of IgG autoantibodies via the placenta. In addition, the level of circulating autoantibodies correlates approximately with disease activity in individual patients.

The major target antigen of the autoantibodies in PV is desmoglein 3 (Dsg 3), a 130 kDa protein belonging to the cadherin superfamily of calcium-dependent adhesion proteins present in desmosomes (Fig. 5.8). Autoantibodies specific for Dsg 3 cause acantholysis, either by blocking Dsg 3 function or by down-regulating its expression, and, in addition, can also cause activation of complement and of plasminogen activator. However, these latter activating effects do not appear to be necessary for the formation of blisters (Fig. 5.9). Thus mice injected with pemphigus antibodies will present with blistering skin lesions even if they are complement-deficient, or if they have been treated with high doses of corticosteroids to abolish plasminogen activator activity [20].

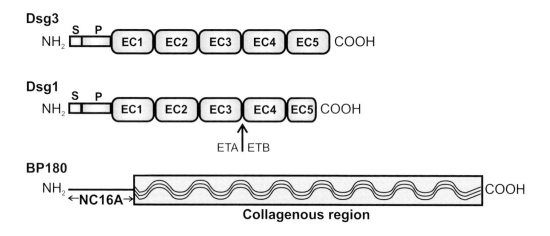

Figure 5.8   Structure of extracellular domains of autoantigens Dsg3, Dsg1 and BP 180.
Dsg3/Dsg1 = desmoglein 3/desmoglein 1; BP 180 = bullous pemphigoid 180kD antigen; S = signal sequence; P = propeptide; EC1-5 = extracellular subdomains 1-5; ETA and ETB = *S. aureus* exfoliatoxins A and B.

In active disease, anti-Dsg 3 autoantibodies are predominately of the IgG_4 subclass, but IgG_1, and to a much lesser extent, IgA and IgE subclasses are also produced [21]. The production of these isotypes, except for IgG_1, is driven by Th-2 cytokines (see below). Patients in remission, healthy unaffected relatives and some MHC Class II-matched normal individuals also have low levels of autoantibodies to Dsg 3, but these are of the IgG_1 subclass only [21]. IgG_1 antibodies, unlike the other immunoglobulin subclasses, are produced by B cells stimulated with Th-1 cytokines.

The specificity of anti-Dsg 3 autoantibodies has been studied further using peptides of 30 amino acids that span the extracellular domain of the Dsg 3 molecule. In active disease, patients with PV have high levels of IgG_1 and IgG_4 antibodies specific for two peptides, Bos (Boston) 1 (amino acids 50-79) and Bos 6 (amino acids 200-229) [21]. In prolonged remission, both subclasses of Bos 6-specific autoantibodies disappear, but IgG_4 and IgG_1 autoantibodies specific for Bos 1 persist at low levels. In healthy, unaffected relatives and in unrelated normal controls, only IgG_1 Bos 1-specific autoantibodies are present. Bos 6-specific IgG antibodies are more efficient than Bos 1-specific IgG

Figure 5.9   Complement activation is required for the formation of blisters in BP, but not in PV

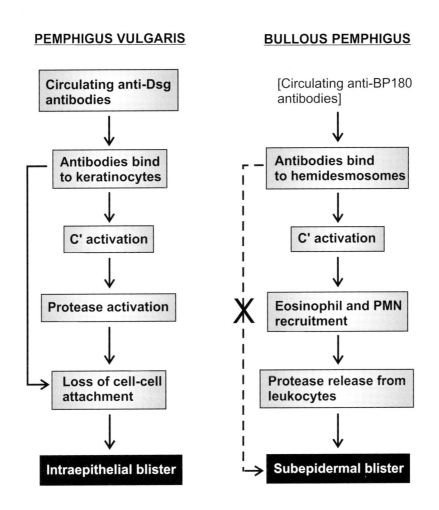

antibodies in the induction of acantholysis in human skin explants *in vitro* and are, therefore, more likely to play a central role, with Bos 1-specific autoantibodies acting perhaps as facilitators or enhancers of the disease process.

5.2.1.3 Autoantibodies to desmoglein 1

Targeted disruption of Dsg 3 in mice caused loss of keratinocyte adhesion and the formation of intraoral lesions with characteristics typical of PV. However, the Dsg 3 knockout mice did not develop skin lesions suggesting that autoantibodies against other antigen(s) may be involved in the disease process in the skin. Patients at an early stage of the disease or at a time when mucosal involvement is dominant have circulating autoantibodies exclusively against Dsg 3. However, non-cross-reactive antibodies to another desmoglein molecule, desmoglein 1 (Dsg 1) (Fig. 5.8) develop later in association with the development of skin lesions. Autoantibodies to Dsg 1, which has a different distribution to Dsg 3 in the epidermal layers of the skin and is poorly expressed in oral mucosa, are characteristic of another pemphigus subtype, pemphigus foliaceous (see below). Thus whilst autoantibody-mediated Dsg 3 dysfunction is sufficient for the induction of oral acantholysis, the formation of blisters in the skin requires that both Dsg 3 and Dsg 1 are disrupted.

5.2.1.4 Autoantibodies to other keratinocyte surface molecules

Autoantibodies to keratinocyte cell-surface molecules other than Dsg 1 and Dsg 3 have also been shown to induce clinical features of PV. Possible target antigens for pathological autoantibodies are the keratinocyte cholinergic receptors, which control keratinocyte adhesion and motility. Their inactivation by autoantibodies could trigger intracellular signals that cause disassembly of desmosomes, leading to acantholysis and blistering. Interestingly, patients with PV produce IgG antibodies that precipitate radiolabelled cholinergic receptors implicating these autoantibodies in the pathogenesis of PV [22].

5.2.1.5 T cell autoreactivity to Dsg 3 in PV patients

Antibody production by B cells usually requires T cell help. T cell recognition of epitopes of Dsg3 may therefore be necessary for the initiation and maintenance of Dsg 3 autoantibody production in patients with PV. Indeed, a requirement of Dsg 3-reactive CD4$^+$ T cells for anti-Dsg 3 autoantibody production by B cells in PV has been established *in vitro* using peripheral blood lymphocytes from PV patients, and, *in vivo*, in genetically engineered mice.

Peripheral blood CD4$^+$ T cells from patients with PV have been shown, in several different studies, to proliferate in response to the extracellular domain of Dsg 3 (and Dsg 1). Furthermore, Dsg 3-specific T cells were not restricted to one cytokine-producing type, since both Th-1 and Th-2 Dsg 3-reactive cells were detected in patients with acute onset (developing new lesions), chronic active (expansion/persistence of lesions) or remittent (no new lesions for at least six months) PV [23]. However, whilst the Dsg-reactive Th-2 cells were constantly present at the different stages of disease, the Dsg-reactive Th-1 cells were detected at a higher frequency in chronic active PV. Furthermore, T cells with a Th-2-like cytokine pattern have been demonstrated in skin lesions of pemphigus [24]. The levels of autoantibodies to Dsg 3 in patients with PV correlated with the ratio of autoreactive Th-1/Th-2 cells rather than with either T cell subset individually. These findings are consistent with a role for both Th-1 and Th-2 cells in the regulation of IgG$_1$ and IgG$_4$ subclasses of anti-Dsg 3 autoantibodies, respectively.

CD8$^+$ T cells responsive to Dsg 3 and with a Tc-1 cytokine profile have also been occasionally detected in patients with active PV. Their potential role in the disease has yet to be investigated.

5.2.1.6 MHC restriction/antigen specificity/TCR usage of autoreactive CD4$^+$ T cells

A T cell response to an antigen is described as being MHC restricted when there is a requirement for the antigenic peptide to be presented by a particular MHC allele(s). The suitability of a MHC allele for presentation of a particular peptide is determined by the structure of its peptide binding groove. Thus APCs expressing MHC Class II alleles that cannot accommodate the peptide in their binding groove are unable to induce activation of T cells specific for that peptide.

The T cell response to Dsg 3 is restricted by the alleles DRB1*0402, DRB1*1401 and/or DQB1*0503 prevalent in PV patients. However, other non-PV-associated MHC Class II alleles can also present Dsg 3 peptides to antigen-specific CD4+ T cells, including several DR11 alleles and DQB1*0301, due to homology to DRB1*0402 or DQB1*0503 respectively, in the third hypervariable region which binds the antigenic peptide [25].

The fine antigen specificity of the T cell response to Dsg 3 in PV patients has been further investigated in various studies using overlapping synthetic peptides spanning the extracellular domain (EC1-5) [26]. Several peptides from different regions have been shown to induce a response in PV Th-1 and/ or Th-2 cells in the context of PV-associated MHC Class II alleles indicating a polyclonal response to the protein. For example, three peptides from the EC2 domain of Dsg 3, two restricted by the DRB1*0401 allele, and one by DRB1*1102, have been identified as stimulatory for Dsg 3-reactive CD4+ T cells. In addition, the amino acid sequence of one of these T cell peptides overlaps with an immunodominant epitope for autoantibody production in patients with PV. Furthermore, in another study T cell clones specific for three different peptide sequences were shown to have restricted TCR Vβ and/or Vα expression with identical Vβ sequences specific for each peptide [27]. These findings suggest that the polyclonal T cell response can be subdivided into individual clones expressing particular TCR Vβ sequences that recognise individual Dsg 3 epitopes.

5.2.1.7 T cell autoreactivity to Dsg 3 in normal individuals

Healthy carriers of MHC alleles prevalent in PV (DRB1*0402, DQB1*0503) can also mount Dsg 3-specific T cell responses, which are similarly restricted to presentation by these MHC alleles. Unlike PV patients, Dsg 3-specific T cells in healthy individuals are restricted to the Th-1 type, which is consistent with their inability to produce anti-Dsg 3 autoantibodies of the IgG_4 subclass [23]. Furthermore, a recent study has shown that such healthy carriers have circulating Dsg 3-responsive regulatory T cells (Tr1 cells) that inhibit the proliferative response of Dsg 3-responsive CD4+ T cell clones in an antigen-specific and cell number dependent manner [28]. Dsg 3-activated Tr1 cells exert their suppressive effects via the production of IL-10 and TGF-β, but do not proliferate in response to antigen. In contrast, Dsg 3-responsive Tr1 cells were rarely detected in the blood of PV patients suggesting that the breakdown in tolerance to Dsg 3 in this disease may, at least in part, be due to a lack of T cell regulation.

A model for the immunopathogenesis of PV, encompassing the findings described above, is presented in Fig. 5.10.

5.2.2 Pemphigus foliaceous

5.2.2.1 Clinical features

Pemphigus foliaceous (PF) can be differentiated from PV by various characteristics (Table 5.4). PF, which unlike PV is not over-represented in the Jewish population, commonly presents in middle age, and the morbidity associated with it is usually considerably less than that of PV. Patients do not have mucosal involvement, and the skin lesions are characteristically erythematous, scaling

Figure 5.1   Model of the immunopathogenesis of PV

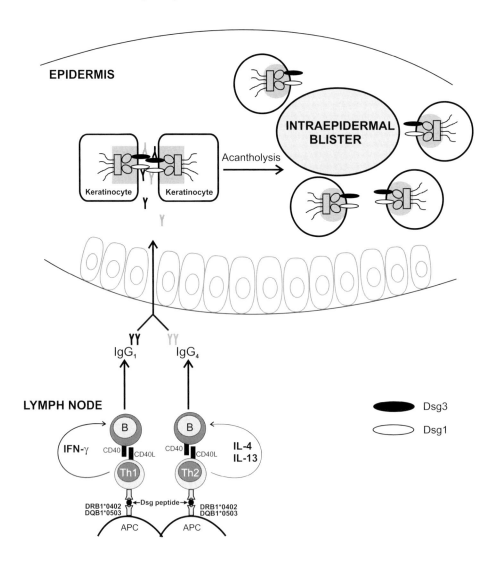

plaques or superficial blisters present on the trunk or central face. If skin involvement is extensive, an exfoliative erythroderma may develop which is difficult to differentiate from erythroderma of other causes. The HLA susceptibility alleles associated with PF are DRB1*1401 and DQB1*0503, two of the alleles associated with PV [18].

   An endemic form of PF called fogo selvagem, found in high frequency in Brazil and Columbia, has identical immunopathological features to that of PF in North America and Europe. However, both children and adults in the same family can be affected, and an environmental cause is suspected. In Brazil, the disease occurs in rural river valleys in which the black fly species, *Simulium nigrimanum* is prevalent, implicating the fly in the spread of a factor that triggers the disease in susceptible individuals. Endemic PF is associated with DRB1*0404, DRB1*1402, DRB1*1406 and various alleles of DRB1*01 in different Brazilian populations. These alleles share an amino acid sequence in the third hypervariable region suggesting that inheritance of this sequence is involved in susceptibility to PF [29]. Other DRB1*04 alleles and DRB1*1601 have also been reported to be increased in PF patients.

Certain drugs, most commonly penicillamine, can also trigger PF. However, this form of pemphigus does not usually resolve on withdrawal of the drug, but, once induced, behaves like sporadic PF.

5.2.2.2 Autoantibodies to desmoglein 1

The target for autoantibodies in PF is the 160 kDa desmosomal cadherin, desmoglein 1 (Dsg 1) (Fig. 5.8) which is expressed in the upper epidermis where Dsg 3 is absent. The location of the autoantigen explains the superficiality of the blisters in PF as acantholysis occurs only high up in the epidermis, just underneath the stratum corneum. This contrasts with PV in which both Dsg 1 and Dsg 3 are targeted by autoantibodies, and the blisters consequently extend more deeply into the epidermis. Histological analysis of PF lesions shows a separation immediately below the stratum corneum and a variable, sometimes scant, inflammatory infiltrate.

Anti-Dsg 1 antibodies cause PF lesions by binding to Dsg 1 and disrupting cell-cell adhesion. This may occur via inhibition of Dsg 1 function or alternatively by decreasing Dsg 1 expression. Support for such a mechanism has been provided by the discovery that the *S. aureus* exfoliatoxins A and B which cause bullous impetigo, and its more generalised form, staphylococcal scalded skin syndrome, are serine proteases that specifically degrade Dsg 1, but not Dsg 3 [30]. Furthermore, the toxin-induced superficial blisters present under the stratum corneum in these conditions are identical to those present in PV.

Anti-Dsg 1 autoantibodies of the IgG_4 subclass are present in high titres in PF patients and react with a conformational epitope on the ectodomain of Dsg 1 [31]. IgG_1 anti-Dsg 1 antibodies are also present but at lower levels and recognise a linear epitope. Both subclasses bind to monkey oesophagus and adult human skin, but the IgG_1 anti-Dsg 1 antibodies do not react with mouse skin which probably explains why they do not induce PF-like skin lesions in the passive transfer animal model.

Both IgG_1 and IgG_4 autoantibodies to Dsg 1 show clonal restriction as shown by oligoclonal banding on isoelectric focusing after probing with extracts of human epidermis [32]. However, whilst the IgG_4 banding is widely distributed over the pH range, the IgG_1 bands are concentrated in the more basic region suggesting that they have undergone selective somatic mutation by a negatively charged autoantigen. Similar findings have been reported for pathogenic DNA autoantibodies associated with SLE.

In common with PV, patients with PF also produce IgG antibodies that precipitate radiolabeled cholinergic receptors and which may be relevant to pathogenesis.

5.2.2.3 T cell autoreactivity to Dsg 1 in PF patients

The majority of patients with endemic PF tested showed circulating proliferative T cell responses to the extracellular domain of Dsg 1. Isolated Dsg 1-reactive T cell clones were memory CD4+ T cells which produced the Th-2 cytokines IL-4 and IL-5, but no IFN-γ, and whose responses were restricted to PF-associated DRB1 alleles. Further, it has been demonstrated that some Dsg 1 peptides can be presented to T cells by DRB1*0102, DQB1*0404 or DRB1*14 suggesting that the structure of the peptide binding pockets of these alleles are very similar. A study of the TCR Vβ gene usage of 17 Dsg 1-reactive T cell clones revealed ten different Vβ families and nine Jβ gene segments, but all showed oligoclonality [33]. Although there was preferential usage of Vβ 5.1 by five clones, three further clones with the same peptide specificity did not show the same Vβ usage. This contrasts with the T cell responses to Dsg 3 in PV, which show a restricted utilization of TCR Vβ by T cell clones responding to a particular Dsg 3 peptide.

5.2.3 Paraneoplastic pemphigus

5.2.3.1 Clinical features

Paraneoplastic pemphigus (PNP) is a rare form of pemphigus that develops exclusively in the context of a known or suspected neoplasm, most frequently a B cell lymphoproliferative disorder such as non-Hodgkin lymphoma, chronic lymphocytic leukaemia or Castleman's disease. Patients present clinically with painful ulcerations involving several mucosal surfaces, and polymorphic skin lesions. The disease course is progressive and, in association with a malignant tumour, will often prove fatal within two years. Once the disease has started, the progress of the autoimmune process is independent of the tumour; reduction of the tumour with chemotherapy does not affect disease activity. However, if PNP is associated with a benign tumour such as a benign thymoma or localized Castleman's disease, and the tumour is completely removed, remission of the autoimmune disease can occur in 6-12 months.

PNP differs from the other two forms of pemphigus in that the respiratory epithelium can be involved, causing death due to respiratory failure in about 30% of patients. Furthermore, PNP has a significant association with the HLA-DRB1*03 allele, whereas DRB1*04 and DRB1*14 (associated with PV and/or PF) appear not to be involved in PNP susceptibility [34].

5.2.3.2 Autoantibodies to desmogleins and plakins

Direct immunofluorescence of PNP lesions shows autoantibodies bound to the surface of keratinocytes, and C3 associated with the basement membrane zone. In addition, histological examination of PNP lesions shows an intense band-like lymphocytic infiltrate.

Autoantibodies specific for Dsg 3 and Dsg 1, which cause blisters when injected into neonatal mice in passive transfer experiments, are present in the circulation of patients with PNP. In addition, PNP patients have autoantibodies to a family of intracellular desmosomal plaque proteins called plakins, and an unidentified 170 kDa antigen. Plakin proteins connect the intermediate filaments of the cytoskeleton with transmembrane desmosomal and hemidesmosomal proteins (Fig. 5.11). The plakin proteins include desmoplakins I and II, the bullous pemphigoid antigen 1 (see below), envoplakin, periplakin and plectin. Antibodies from PNP sera purified with plectin linked to glutathione-S-transferase recognized fusion proteins of periplakin, envoplakin, and desmoplakin, in addition to that of plectin, demonstrating the presence of shared antigenic epitopes [35].

The pathogenicity of the plakin autoantibodies, which are not found in the other two forms of

Figure 5.11 Schematic diagram of proteins associated with desmosomes. Dsg 1/Dsg 3 = desmoglein 1/desmoglein 3; PG = plakoglobin; DP = desmoplakin.

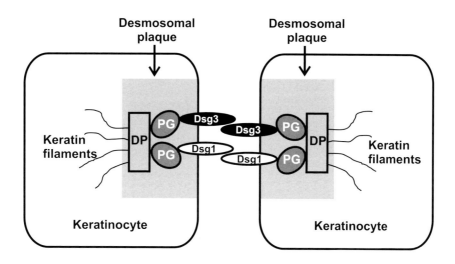

pemphigus, has yet to be established. Antibodies that bind to respiratory epithelia (probably specific for members of the plakin family) have also been detected in the sera of PNP patients, and bound to bronchial epithelial cell surfaces *in situ* where they are accompanied by acantholysis of the respiratory epithelium.

5.2.4 Treatment

Current treatment of PV is targeted at decreasing autoantibody synthesis, either with systemic corticosteroids (prednisolone) alone, or in combination with other immunosuppressive drugs such as the non-alkylating agents, azathioprine or mycophenolic acid, or the alkylating agents, cyclophosphamide or chlorambucil. Plasmapheresis may also be used for immediate disease control. The efficacy and extent of side effects of azathioprine use appear to be dependent upon the activity of an enzyme, thiopurine methyltransferase. Individuals with higher enzyme levels need higher doses of azathioprine to achieve a therapeutic effect, whilst low enzyme levels result in high effective concentrations of the drug and the risk of severe cytopenia.

Other immunosuppressive or immunomodulatory treatments such as cyclosporin, methotrexate, intravenous γ globulin or gold may also be used. Cyclosporin and methotrexate predominately target activated T lymphocytes and may therefore prevent autoantibody production by inhibiting autoreactive T cells.

Since the side effects of existing treatments contribute to the poor prognosis of PV, there is a requirement for future treatments to be more specific. Induction of regulatory T cells, by immunisation with immunodominant epitope-containing peptides or autoreactive T cells as currently being investigated in asthma and multiple sclerosis, respectively, may be a potentially useful approach to re-establish tolerance to desmogleins in these patients.

In the case of PF, fluorinated topical steroid creams may be used to treat moderate skin involvement. However the same systemic immunosuppressants used in PV are necessary to treat more extensive disease. Generally, less aggressive treatments are needed to treat PF than PV because morbidity and mortality are lower.

PNP is treated with the same range of systemic immunosuppressant agents as PV, but patients with PNP frequently do not respond well to treatment. Combined moderate dose corticosteroids with cyclosporin have proved beneficial in some cases.

5.3 Bullous pemphigoid

5.3.1 Clinical features

Bullous pemphigoid (BP) is the most common of the autoimmune bullous skin diseases and presents usually in old age (Table 5.4). It has a lower morbidity and mortality than pemphigus which may be partly due to the infrequent occurrence of mucosal lesions which, when they do appear, are mild and transient. Skin lesions may appear initially as itchy, red urticarial plaques on the trunk and extremities, and then develop into tense blisters and bullae (Fig. 5.6B, colour plate).

HLA-DR and HLA–DQ polymorphisms associated with BP vary in different ethnic groups with DQB1*0301 increased in Caucasian patients, whilst DRB1*0403, DRB1*0406, DRB1*1101 and DQB1*0302 are associated with BP in Japanese patients. In contrast, DRB1*08 and DQB1*06 alleles appear to be protective in Chinese BP patients.

Gestational pemphigoid (herpes gestationis) is a variant of pemphigoid, which occurs during the late second or third trimester of pregnancy and usually resolves after delivery. The autoimmune response in gestational pemphigoid cannot be distinguished from that of BP, unlike that of three other diseases (cicatricial pemphigoid, linear IgA disease and lichen planus pemphigoides), which are also associated with an autoimmune response to the same autoantigen BP180 (see below). These diseases can be differentiated on the basis of the isotype and subclass of the autoantibodies, as well by differences in their fine specificities and/or complement-fixing properties.

5.3.2 Autoantibodies to hemidesmosomal proteins

Histological analysis of BP skin lesions shows subepidermal blistering accompanied by a PMN and eosinophil infiltrate in the upper dermis and within the blister cavity. Direct immunofluorescent staining reveals an intense linear deposition of IgG and C3 along the basement membrane zone, which, in the areas of separation, localizes to the epidermal side of the blister (Fig. 5.7B, colour plate). Circulating IgG autoantibodies, which bind to the basement membrane of human skin or monkey oesophagus, are present in low concentrations in the sera of BP patients.

The main target antigens for the autoantibodies in BP patients are two hemidesmosomal proteins; a 230 kDa protein called bullous pemphigoid antigen 1 (BPAG1 or BP230), and a 180 kDa protein called bullous pemphigoid antigen 2 (BPAG2 or BP180). The latter is also referred to as type XVII collagen because it consists of collagen repeats in its extracellular domain. These proteins are important components of hemidesmosomes, adhesion structures that anchor the basal epidermal cells to the basement membrane underneath via linkages between intermediate filament proteins and basement membrane proteins, respectively. Other target antigens for autoantibodies in BP are laminin and β_4 integrin.

The BP230 antigen is an intracellular protein and a member of the plakin family. However, autoantibodies specific for this antigen have not been shown to induce subepidermal skin blisters in neonatal mice by passive transfer.

The BP180 antigen is a type II transmembrane protein with a short, non-collagenous ectodomain (NC16A) that lies adjacent to the plasma membrane, and a long carboxy-terminal collagenous ectodomain that projects into the extracellular region beneath the epidermal hemidesmosome (Fig. 5.8). In addition to its role in maintaining the integrity of the dermal-epidermal junction, there is evidence that BP180 is involved in transmembrane signal transduction and in the regulation of keratinocyte differentiation [36]. Autoantibodies specific for an immunodominant epitope in the short non-collagenous ectodomain of the BP180 protein have been shown to be pathogenic in passive transfer animal studies, accurately reproducing the human disease [37]. However, unlike the binding of pemphigus antibodies, which directly causes loss of cell-cell attachment, bullous pemphigoid antibody binding triggers a series of inflammatory events that are necessary for blister formation (Fig. 5.9). These include complement activation, which results in the formation of complement fragments such as C3a and C5a, and PMN recruitment attracted by the latter to the site. PMNs, in turn, release proteases such as gelatinase B and elastase, and reactive oxygen species that damage the basement membrane zone causing epidermal-dermal separation.

Anti-BP180 autoantibodies are of both the IgG$_1$ and IgG$_4$ subclasses, but there are conflicting reports as to which is the predominant subtype in the active stage of the disease. This is compatible with the secretion of both Th-1 and Th-2 cytokines by T cells reactive with BP180 (see below).

5.3.3 T cell autoreactivity to BP180 antigen

In BP patients expressing the DQB1*0301 allele, circulating T cells proliferate in response to the extracellular region of BP180 antigen. Furthermore normal individuals expressing the same HLA-DQ allele, but not other HLA-DQ alleles, also recognize the BP180 antigen. However, whilst BP180 specific CD4$^+$ T cell lines established from the blood of BP patients produced both Th-2 and Th-1 cytokines, those cultured from normal individuals produced IFN-γ only, suggesting that Th-2 cytokines are important for the disease process [38]. Since both autoreactive T cells and autoantibodies from BP (and linear IgA disease) patients recognize epitopes in the extracellular NC16A region of the BP180 protein, the autoreactive Th-2 cells may provide direct help to B cells to differentiate into plasma cells producing IgG$_4$ autoantibodies.

Peripheral blood T cells from BP patients also respond more frequently to synthetic peptides corresponding to the sequence of the BP230 antigen that is adjacent to regions containing epitopes recognized by circulating autoantibodies in the sera of patients with BP. These increased responses are more commonly observed in patients with generalized disease and those whose disease has lasted longer than 2 months, suggesting that responses to BP230 may be secondary to inflammation at the basement membrane.

A model for the immunopathogenesis of BP is presented in Fig. 5.12.

Figure 5.12 Model of the immunopathogenesis of BP

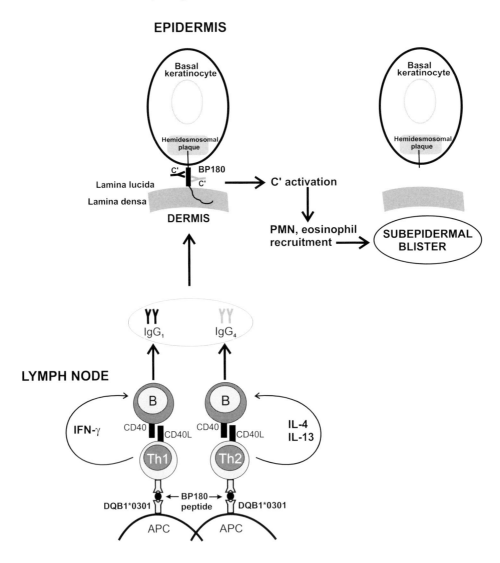

5.3.4 Treatment

Prednisone has been commonly used to treat BP as it has both anti-inflammatory and immunomodulatory effects which rapidly inhibit the formation of blisters. However, a topical steroid (clobetasol propionate) has been found to be more effective than oral prednisone and without the side-effects that accompany the use of systemic corticosteroids [39]. To avoid the use of steroids in mild disease, the anti-inflammatory drug, dapsone, or combined treatment with tetracycline and niacinamide may be used. Azathioprine or mycophenolate are other options for moderate disease, whilst in the relatively few cases when a more aggressive treatment is required, plasmapheresis and cyclosphamide can be very effective.

Summary

Urticaria

- Heterogenous group of skin diseases triggered by various stimuli with a common final pathway of antibody-induced mast cell degranulation and formation of short-lived erythematous and itchy weals.
- Majority of patients have chronic urticaria, which is mediated by pathogenic IgG autoantibodies in approximately one-third of cases.
- Acute urticaria is mainly IgE-mediated and more common in atopic individuals.
- Cell types present in urticarial skin lesions include degranulating mast cells, eosinophils, PMNs, monocytes, and $CD4^+$ and $CD8^+$ T cells with a Th-0 cytokine profile.
- Mediators involved in the disease process include histamine and leukotrienes released by mast cells, kinins, neuropeptides, and complement components produced as a result of complement activation.
- First-line treatments are H_1-antihistamines, which, if ineffective, are replaced by short-term corticosteroid therapy or leukotriene receptor antagonists.

Pemphigus

- Presents as three subtypes (PV, PF and PNP) with similar mechanisms
- Characterised by intraepidermal blistering in skin and/or mucosa
- Associated with specific HLA alleles, two of which are common to PV and PF.
- Mediated by pathogenic IgG autoantibodies to Dsg 3 and/or Dsg 1 without a requirement for complement activation
- Dsg-specific $CD4^+$ T cells provide help to autoreactive B cells:
  - o Response restricted by pemphigus-associated (or homologous) MHC Class II alleles
  - o Produce Th-2 type cytokines in pemphigus (also Th-1 in PV) but Th-1 cytokines in Dsg-responsive normal individuals.
  - o Clonally expanded
  - o Inhibited by antigen-specific Tr1 cells in Dsg-responsive normal individuals, but not in pemphigus

Bullous pemphigoid

- Characterised by subepidermal blisters in the skin
- Associated with specific HLA alleles which differ from those in pemphigus
- Mediated by pathogenic IgG autoantibodies to BP 180 which trigger a series of inflammatory events necessary for blister formation
- BP 180-specific $CD4^+$ T cells provide help to autoreactive B cells:
  - o Response restricted by bullous pemphigoid-associated MHC Class II allele
  - o Produce Th-1 and Th-2 cytokines (Th-1 only in BP 180-responsive normal individuals)

Treatment for pemphigus and bullous pemphigoid is targeted at preventing autoantibody production using systemic corticosteroids ± other immunosuppressive drugs. Plasmapheresis may also be used for immediate disease control.

References

1. Zuberbier T. Urticaria. Allergy 2003; **58:** 1224-34.

2. Gerard N.P & Gerard C. Complement in allergy and asthma. Curr.Opin.Immunol. 2002; **14:** 705-8.

3. Wallengren J., Moller H., Ekman R. Occurrence of substance P, vasoactive intestinal peptide, and calcitonin gene-related peptide in dermographism and cold urticaria. Arch.Dermatol. Res. 1987; **279:** 512-5.

4. Toth-Kasa I., Jancso G., Obal F. Jr., Husz S., Simon N. Involvement of sensory nerve endings in cold and heat urticaria. J.Invest.Dermatol. 1983; **80:** 34-6.

5. Doeglas H.M. & Bleumink E. Protease inhibitors in plasma of patients with chronic urticaria. Arch.Dermatol. 1975; **111:** 979-85.

6. Imai S. Serum alpha 1-protease inhibitor levels in patients with chronic idiopathic urticaria. Acta Dermatol.Venereol. 1993; **73:** 10-1.

7. Wong E., Eftekhari N., Greaves M.W., Ward A.M. Beneficial effects of danazol on symptoms and laboratory changes in cholinergic urticaria. Br.J.Dermatol. 1987; **116:** 553-6.

8. Cousin F., Philips K., Favier B., Bienvenu J., Nicolas J.F. Drug-induced urticaria. Eur. J.Dermatol. 2001; **11:** 181-7.

9. Dice J.P. Physical urticaria. Immunol. Allergy Clin.North Am. 2004; **24:** 225-46.

10. Greaves M.W. Chronic idiopathic urticaria. Curr.Opin.Allergy Clin.Immunol. 2003; **3:** 363-8.

11. Verneuil L., Leconte C., Ballet J.J. *et al.* Association between chronic urticaria and thyroid autoimmunity: a prospective study involving 99 patients. Dermatol. 2004; **208:** 98-103.

12. Greaves M. Autoimmune urticaria. Clin.Rev.Allergy Immunol. 2002; **23:** 171-83.

13. Ying S., Kikuchi Y., Meng Q., Kay A.B., Kaplan A.P. TH1/TH2 cytokines and inflammatory cells in skin biopsy specimens from patients with chronic idiopathic urticaria: comparison with the allergen-induced late-phase cutaneous reaction. Allergy Clin.Immunol. 2002; **109:** 694-700.

14. Kaplan A.P. C1 inhibitor deficiency: hereditary and acquired forms. J.Invest.Allergol.Clin. Immunol. 2001; **11:** 211-9.

15. Venzor J., Lee W.L., Huston D.P. Urticarial vasculitis. Clin.Rev.Allergy Immunol. 2002; **23:** 201-16.

16. Tedeschi A., Airaghi L., Lorini M., Asero R. Chronic urticaria: a role for newer immunomodulatory drugs? Am.J.Clin.Dermatol. 2003; **4:** 297-305.

17. Nousari H.C. & Anhalt G.J. Pemphigus and bullous pemphigoid. Lancet 1999; **354:** 667-72.

18. Lombardi M.L., Mercuro O., Ruocco V. *et al.* Common human leukocyte antigen alleles in pemphigus vulgaris and pemphigus foliaceus Italian patients. J.Invest.Dermatol. 1999; **113:** 107-10.

19. Takahashi Y., Patel H.P., Labib R.S., Diaz L.A., Anhalt G.J. Experimentally induced pemphigus vulgaris in neonatal BALB/c mice: a time-course study of clinical, immunologic,

ultrastructural, and cytochemical changes. J.Invest.Dermatol. 1985; **84:** 41-6.

20. Anhalt G.J., Patel H.P., Labib R.S., Diaz L.A., Proud D. Dexamethasone inhibits plasminogen activator activity in experimental pemphigus in vivo but does not block acantholysis. J.Immunol. 1986; **136:** 113-7.

21. Bhol K., Natarajan K., Nagarwalla N., Mohimen A., Aoki V., Ahmed R. Correlation of peptide specificity and IgG subclass with pathogenic and non-pathogenic autoantibodies in pemphigus vulgaris: A model for autoimmunity. Proc.Natl.Acad.Sci. USA 1995; **92:** 5239-43.

22. Vu T.N., Lee T.X., Ndoye A. *et al.* The pathophysiological significance of nondesmoglein targets of pemphigus autoimmunity. Development of antibodies against keratinocyte cholinergic receptors in patients with pemphigus vulgaris and pemphigus foliaceus. Arch. Dermatol. 1998; **134:** 971-80.

23. Veldman C., Stauber A., Wassmuth R., Uter W., Schuler G., Hertl M. Dichotomy of autoreactive Th1 and Th2 cell responses to desmoglein 3 in patients with pemphigus vulgaris (PV) and healthy carriers of PV-associated HLA Class II alleles. J.Immunol. 2003; **170:** 635–42.

24. Caproni M., Giomi B., Cardinali C. *et al.* Further support for a role for Th2-like cytokines in blister formation of pemphigus. Clin.Immunol. 2001; **98:** 264-71.

25. Hertl M., Karr K.W., Amagi M., Katz S.I. Heterogenous MHC II restriction pattern of autoreactive desmoglein 3 specific T cell responses in pemphigus vulgaris patients and normals. J.Invest.Dermatol. 1998; **110:** 388-92.

26. Hertl M., Amagi M., Sundaram H., Stanley J., Ishii K., Katz S.I. Recognition of desmoglein 3 by autoreactive T cells in pemphigus vulgaris patients and controls. J.Invest.Dermatol. 1998; **110:** 62-6.

27. Hacker-Foegen M.K., Fairley J.A., Lin M.-S. T cell receptor gene usage in desmoglein-3-specific T lymphocytes from patients with pemphigus vulgaris. J.Invest.Dermatol. 2003; **121:**1365-72.

28. Veldman C., Hohne A., Dieckmann D., Schuler G., Hertl M. Type I regulatory T cells specific for desmoglein 3 are more frequently detected in healthy individuals than in patients with pemphigus vulgaris. J.Immunol. 2004; **172:** 6468-75.

29. Moraes M.E., Fernandez-Vina M., Lazaro A. *et al.* An epitope in the third hypervariable region of the DRB1 gene is involved in the susceptibility to endemic pemphigus foliaceus (fogo selvagem) in three different Brazilian populations. Tissue Antigens 1997; **49:** 35-40.

30. Amagai M., Yamaguchi T., Hanakawa Y., Nishifuji K., Sugai M., Stanley J.R. Staphylococcal exfoliative toxin B specifically cleaves desmoglein 1. J.Invest.Dermatol. 2002; **118:** 845-50.

31. Hacker M.K., Janson M., Fairley J.A., Lin M.S. Isotypes and antigenic profiles of pemphigus foliaceus and pemphigus vulgaris autoantibodies. Clin.Immunol. 2002; **105:** 64-74.

32. Calvanico N.J., Swartz S.J., Diaz L.A. Affinity immunoblotting studies on the restriction of autoantibodies from endemic pemphigus foliaceus patients. J.Autoimmun. 1993; **6:** 145-57.

33. Moesta A.K., Lin M.S., Diaz L.A., Sinha A.A. T cell receptor beta chain gene usage in

endemic pemphigus foliaceus (fogo selvagem). J.Invest.Dermatol. 2002; **119:** 377-83.

34. Martel P., Loiseau P., Joly P. *et al*. Paraneoplastic pemphigus is associated with the DRB1*03 allele. Autoimmun. 2003; **20:** 91-5.

35. Aho S., Mahoney M.G., Uitto J. Plectin serves as an autoantigen in paraneoplastic pemphigus. J.Invest.Dermatol. 1999; **113:** 422-3.

36. Van den Bergh F. & Guidice G.J. BP180 (type XVII collagen) and its role in cutaneous biology and disease. Adv. Dermatol. 2003; **19:** 37-71.

37. Liu Z., Diaz L.A., Troy J.L. *et al*. A passive transfer model of the organ-specific autoimmune disease, bullous pemphigoid, using antibodies generated against the hemidesmosomal antigen, BP180. J.Clin. Invest. 1993; **92:** 2480-8.

38. Budinger L., Borradori L., Yee C. *et al*. Identification and characterization of autoreactive T cell responses to bullous pemphigoid antigen 2 in patients and healthy controls. J.Clin. Invest. 1998; **102:** 2082-9.

39. Fontaine J., Joly P., Roujeau J.C. Treatment of bullous pemphigoid. J.Dermatol. 2003; **30:** 83-90.

PART III: Immunological Mechanisms of Skin Disease

6

Systemic Lupus Erythematosus

Systemic lupus erythematosus (SLE) is an autoimmune disease characterised by the production of autoantibodies that form immune complexes (type III hypersensitivity), the deposition of which can affect the function of various organs including the kidneys, skin, joints, lungs and nervous system.

6.1 Clinical features

SLE is a chronic autoimmune disease which has a prevalence of 40-50 per 100,000 of the population, with some variability between ethnic groups, and occurs most frequently in young women in their 20s and 30s. Indeed, the ratio of female to males affected by SLE can be as high as between 8:1 to 13:1 in adults. The disease can vary from mild to life threatening, and is characterised by periods of remissions and acute or chronic relapses. SLE commonly presents at onset with fatigue, arthritis or arthralgia and skin involvement. In addition to fatigue, SLE patients frequently experience fever and weight loss. The fever may result from infectious complications that particularly affect the respiratory and urinary systems of approximately half the patients. The joints, skin, kidney, lungs, heart and central nervous system are often affected in different combinations in individual patients, but virtually every organ in the body can potentially be affected (Table 6.1). Classification of SLE is commonly made using the American Rheumatology Association revised criteria, four out of 11 of which are required to be met for a positive diagnosis to be made [1,2].

6.1.1 Joints and skin

Arthritis is experienced by the majority of patients at some time and is asymmetrical, particularly affecting the hands and knees. The arthritis is moderately painful and rarely deforming with infrequent, mildly inflammatory synovial effusions.

Skin involvement in SLE patients is also very common and can present in different forms after sun (UV) exposure. The most common skin manifestation is the butterfly rash, which is characterised by erythema over the cheeks and nose and, histologically, shows vacuolar degeneration of the basal cell layer and perivascular cellular infiltration (Fig. 6.1 and Fig. 6.2, colour plates). Patients may also develop discoid skin lesions, discrete scaly plaques with moderate cellular infiltration, in sun-exposed areas. On resolution, these plaques leave behind atrophic scars, telangiectasia (dilatation of capillary vessels) and patches of skin where pigment is either increased or decreased. Another photosensitive skin disorder that may present in SLE patients is subacute cutaneous lupus in which lesions begin as scaly, erythematous papules and develop into psoriasiform or large annular (ring-

Table 6.1 Organ involvement in SLE

Organ	Clinical presentation
Joints	Arthralgia Arthritis - asymmetric, hands, knees
Skin	Butterfly rash Discoid lesions Subacute cutaneous lupus Hair loss Raynaud's phenomenon
Kidney	Type II Mesangial nephritis Type III Focal proliferative nephritis Type IV Diffuse proliferative nephritis Type V Membranous nephritis
Lung	Chest pain: Chest wall muscle Pleuritis Pneumonitis
Heart	Pericarditis
CNS	Headaches Memory problems Anxiety and/or depression Generalised or partial complex seizures Strokes Peripheral neuropathy
Blood	Leukopenia Thrombocytopenia Mild anaemia Hypocomplementaemia Increased ESR, γ-globulin, ANA titres

like) lesions.

Hair loss is common in SLE patients and Raynaud's phenomenon (ischaemia of the fingers and toes) is a frequent complication. Many patients have erythema around the nails and develop oral, usually painless, ulcers.

6.1.2 Kidneys

Renal involvement develops during the first few years after diagnosis and presents clinically in about 50% of SLE patients. Furthermore, most of the remaining patients probably have subclinical renal disease. There are several types of glomerulonephritis that can be differentiated by histological examination of a renal biopsy. The most common form is diffuse proliferative (type IV) nephritis, which shows considerable inflammation and scarring of glomeruli, accompanied by marked urinary and serological abnormalities and hypertension. If left untreated, this type of glomerulonephritis can lead to renal failure.

Three other types (II, III and V) of glomerulonephritis each occur in approximately 10-20% of patients. In mesangial (type II) nephritis, immune deposits are detectable in the mesangium, and in focal proliferative (type III) nephritis, focal areas of glomerular proliferation and significant urinary and serological abnormalities are present. However, in both cases there is no, or rarely, progression to renal failure. In membranous (type V) nephritis, there is peripheral oedema and significant proteinuria, and the basement membrane is thickened, but there are no other urinary or serological disturbances and the prognosis is good with suitable therapy.

6.1.3 Lungs/Heart

Approximately half of SLE patients experience chest pain on breathing which is due to (uninflamed) chest wall muscle pain. Alternatively, pain on breathing may be due to inflammation of the pleura (pleuritis), which may be present in some patients accompanied by a small pleural effusion. A small proportion of patients develop pneumonitis characterised by fever, pleurisy, dyspnoea and pulmonary infiltrate. Histological analysis shows a severe alveolitis with PMN and mononuclear cell infiltration. Acute pneumonitis (which can be fatal without appropriate treatment) often becomes chronic causing decreased pulmonary function.

Pericarditis is relatively common in SLE patients and there may be evidence of a pericardial effusion. This does not usually, however, cause a significant clinical problem.

6.1.4 Central nervous system

Neurological and psychiatric problems are present in most SLE patients, either resulting directly from the disease itself, or from associated complications or treatments. The most common neurological complications are headaches, cognitive defects (usually memory problems) and anxiety and/or depression. In some patients, generalised or partial complex seizures, strokes or peripheral neuropathy may be experienced.

6.1.5 Haematological changes

Patients with SLE frequently develop haematological abnormalities such as leukopenia (not symptomatic), thrombocytopenia and mild anaemia. In addition, complement levels may be low, whilst the erythrocyte sedimentation rate, γ-globulin and anti-nuclear antigen (ANA) antibody titres (see below) may be increased.

6.2 Aetiology

The aetiology of SLE is unknown but susceptibility to the disease is undoubtedly multifactorial involving a combination of genetic, environmental, and hormonal factors.

6.2.1 Genetic factors

A genetic predisposition for SLE is strongly supported by the high concordance rate of 24-58% for monozygotic, compared to 2-5% for dizygotic twins. Furthermore, 5-12% of relatives of SLE patients also have the disease. However, the pattern of inheritance is not that of a single Mendelian gene; linkage and association studies of families containing SLE patients have indicated that several genes predispose individuals to the disease. In addition, the fact that the concordance rate for dizygotic twins is substantially less than 100% indicates that non-genetic factors also contribute to the immunopathogenesis (see below).

The threshold liability model, which states that individuals will develop disease when the disease liability exceeds a particular hypothetical threshold, has been used to explain the inheritance of multifactorial traits in SLE (and other multifactorial autoimmune diseases). The disease liability of an individual depends upon the number of susceptibility genes present and modification by environmental factors. Furthermore, complex interactions are likely to occur between disease susceptibility genes that promote disease onset, and suppressive genes that modify the effects of the disease susceptibility genes. Epistatic interactions between genes may also increase disease susceptibility.

6.2.1.1 Chromosomal linkage sites

Linkage analysis is used to measure the cosegregation of closely linked genomic sequences among several affected members in families in order to identify shared sequences associated with disease. The markers generally used for these studies are di-, tri- or tetra-nucleotide repeats or microsatellites that vary in numbers of repeats between individuals. During the last ten years, this approach has been widely used to map susceptibility loci in whole genome scans of SLE families. To avoid the inclusion of false positive results, likely to occur where large numbers of genetic markers are being used, thresholds for significant linkage have been proposed; a logarithm of odds (lod) score of 3.3 or 3.6, depending upon the linkage method used. A lod score of 1.9 or 2.2 is taken as suggestive of linkage, and confirmed linkage is defined as significant linkage from one or a combination of initial studies that has been confirmed with a p value of 0.01 in an independent sample [3].

Several genome-wide linkage analyses and targeted genome scans have been performed, using multiple cohorts of patients, in order to map various chromosomal regions for SLE susceptibility genes [4]. The findings of these studies show differences in the loci mapped, probably as a result of various factors including genetic and disease heterogeneity between the different ethnic groups studied, variation in sample sizes and differences in methods of linkage analysis. However, eight loci have reached the threshold for significant linkage to SLE and have been confirmed in at least one independent cohort for linkage to SLE (Table 6.2). Putative candidate genes have been identified

Table 6.2 Chromosomal loci with confirmed significant linkage to SLE

Chromosome	Locus	Locus name	Candidate genes within locus
1	1q23		FCGR2A (FcγR2A) FCGR3A (FcγR3A) FCGR2B (FcγR2B) FCGR3B (FcγR3B)
	1q25-31		Unknown
	1q41-42	SLEB1	PARP (Poly (ADP-ribose) polymerase)
2	2q35-37	SLEB2	PDCD1 (Programmed cell death 1)
4	4p16-15.2	SLEB3	Unknown
6	6p11-21		MHC antigens
12	12q24	SLEB4	Several
16	16q12		Unknown

within some of these loci and are the subject of fine mapping studies (Table 6.2). In addition, approximately 20 loci showed suggestive linkage; further studies using larger cohorts of patients are required to determine whether they contain any susceptibility genes for SLE.

To reduce the complicating effects of disease heterogeneity, linkage analysis of patients with SLE stratified according to the presence of a specific clinical manifestation (such as haemolytic anaemia, renal disease or thrombocytopenia) has been performed in several studies, but has the disadvantage of reducing the sample size. Alternatively, the principle component approach has been successfully used as a means of decreasing disease heterogeneity. Seven major SLE-related phenotypes, age at onset and ethnic group are used as principal components to perform multivariate analysis of the genome scan data. This method has revealed loci on chromosomes 2, 4 and 7 with evidence for linkage to SLE-related traits.

6.2.1.2 Candidate genes

The chromosomal regions identified by genome scans to have linkage to disease are large, being 10-30 centiMorgans (cM) intervals containing approximately 10-30 million base pairs of DNA and 100-300 candidate genes. To narrow down this interval so that candidate genes can be identified, linkage disequilibrium mapping is used. Linkage disequilibrium occurs when two alleles, which are situated close to each other on the chromosome, are inherited together more frequently than would be expected from their individual frequencies. Two main approaches are employed to investigate possible associations between candidate gene polymorphisms (especially coding for proteins with roles in the immune system) and susceptibility to SLE; population-based case-control studies and family-based transmission disequilibrium tests.

Population-based case-control studies compare the allele frequency of a candidate gene in SLE patients with that of normal controls. However, if the cases and controls are not matched adequately, false positive results may be obtained. Other potential problems associated with this approach are small sample size, moderate genetic effects and locus heterogeneity, which make confirmation of candidate genes difficult. Population-based association analysis has, however, provided supportive evidence for association between SLE and genes coding for MHC, classical complement components and low affinity receptors for IgG.

The family-based transmission disequilibrium test (TDT) avoids the potential problems associated with case-control studies. Using this method, preferential transmission of the test allele (or a specific haplotype) from heterozygous parents to affected children provides evidence for association of the test allele (or haplotype) with susceptibility to disease. TDT analysis has enabled the large linked genomic interval 6p11-21 to be narrowed down to a segment containing the MHC Class II genes (see below). Positional candidate genes (genes within the intervals linked to SLE) recently identified include Fcγ receptor (FCGR) 2A, FCGR2B and FCGR3A located at 1q23, Poly (ADP-ribose) polymerase (PARP) at 1q41-42, programmed cell death 1 (PDCD1) at 2q37 and the MHC gene complex at 6p21 (Tables 6.2 and 6.3).

MHC alleles

The HLA-DR2 and HLA-DR3 genes have been found to be consistently associated with SLE in Caucasian populations. However, strong linkage disequilibrium between genes within the MHC

Table 6.3 Polymorphisms of SLE susceptibility genes and their functional consequences

Candidate gene	Polymorphism	Relative risk for SLE/LN*	Functional consequences
MHC	DRB1*1501(DR2)/DQB1*0602 DRB1*0801(DR8)/DQB1*0402 DRB1*0301(DR3)/DQB1*0201	1.9 - 2.6	Presentation of autoantigenic peptides to T cells
Classical complement components	C1q C4AQ*0	2.3 - 4.87	Impaired clearance of immune complexes and apoptotic cells
FcγR	FCGR2A 131 H→R	1.3	Binds IgG$_2$ less well. Impaired immune complex clearance
	FCGR3A 158 V→F	1.2	Binds IgG$_1$ and IgG$_3$ less well. Impaired immune complex clearance
	FCGR2B 232 I→T	Unknown	Unknown
PDCD1	Intronic	2.6 European 3.5 Mexican	Alters binding site for transcription factor, RUNX1. Contributes to defective peripheral tolerance?
PARP	CA dinucleotide in promotor region: 85bp allele	2.3	Decreased PARP activity leading to impaired apoptosis and DNA repair
	97bp allele		Protective
ACE	Alu insertion-deletion - intron 16	Significant transmission (TDT) Non-Caucasians	Angiotensin II levels altered. May influence development of renal disease
	2 versus 3 copies of CT in 3' untranslated region		
	3 versus 4 G - intron 13	Unknown	Unknown
PTPN22	R620W 1858 C→T	1.37- 4.37	Impairs binding to Src tyrosine kinase, preventing downregulation of T cell signalling

* LN, lupus nephritis

region on chromosome 6p21.31 results in extended haplotypes of MHC Class I, II and III (complement and TNF-α) gene alleles, which are inherited together, and whose individual contribution to disease susceptibility is therefore difficult to determine.

Using TDT analysis of hundreds of families containing SLE patients, three MHC Class II-containing SLE risk haplotypes have been identified: DRB1*1501(DR2)/DQB1*0602; DRB1*0801(DR8)/DQB1*0402; DRB1*0301(DR3)/DQB1*0201 [5]. The DRB1*1501 haplotype was within a 500 kb genomic region which excluded the MHC Class I and III regions, whilst the risk region for the DRB1*0301 haplotype was larger (approximately 1 Mb) and contained the MHC Class I and III genes. The estimated relative risk for each of the three haplotypes is between 1.9 and 2.6-fold, which is increased in a dose-dependent manner when two copies of risk haplotypes are expressed.

Complement genes

SLE susceptibility is strongly associated with homozygous inherited deficiencies in components C1q, C1r, C1s, C2 and C4 of the classical complement pathway [6]. The severity of the disease and strength of the association is in the order C1q>C4>C2.

Homozygous C1q deficiency is rare, but is almost always associated with the development of SLE. C1r and C1s deficiencies, which are even more uncommon than that of C1q, usually occur together and, similarly, SLE occurs in the majority of these individuals. Homozygous C2 deficiency is the commonest inherited classical pathway complement deficiency, but only about a third of patients develop SLE. In contrast to the classical pathway components, homozygous C3 deficiency is rarely associated with SLE but predisposes to recurrent pyogenic infections and membranoproliferative glomerulonephritis.

In view of the above observations, it might be expected that partial deficiencies of C4 or C2 may also increase disease susceptibility. Two highly polymorphic genes in the class III MHC region code for the C4A and C4B proteins, which have slightly different functional activities. C4A preferentially binds to amino groups in proteins (e.g. in immune complexes), whilst C4B binds to carbohydrates on red cells. There are numerous allelic variants of the C4A and C4B genes, including non-expressed or null alleles, which have no identifiable protein product (expressed as C4AQ*0 and C4BQ*0 i.e. quantity zero). C4AQ*0 and C4BQ*0 are strongly associated with SLE, conferring risk in different ethnic populations in the context of several different MHC extended haplotypes [7].

In contrast, C2 deficiency is not associated with the development of SLE. The C2 null allele is associated with a DR2 haplotype whose frequency is not increased in SLE patients. Thus it appears unlikely that partial C2 deficiency is a susceptibility factor for SLE.

Overall, these findings suggest that classical complement activation, particularly at the early stages of the pathway, is protective for the development of SLE. The most likely mechanism for this protective effect is in the role that complement plays in clearance and processing of immune complexes and cellular debris (see Section 6.5).

Fcγ receptor genes

Genes that code for the low affinity Fcγ receptor for IgG (FCGR) are members of the immunoglobulin gene superfamily which are found clustered in a 100kb region at chromosome 1q23. Genetic polymorphisms of four of these receptor genes (FCGR2A, FCGR2B, FCGR3A and FCGR3B) have been associated with SLE, but FCGR2A and FCGR3A appear to be the most important. The molecules coded for by the latter (FcγRIIa (CD32) and FcγRIIIa (CD16)) bind IgG_2, or both IgG_1 and IgG_3, respectively, and trigger cellular activation via immunoreceptor tyrosine-based activation motifs (ITAMs) located in their cytoplasmic tails.

An inherited bi-allelic single base pair difference (single nucleotide polymorphism or SNP) in FCGR2A results in a change from histidine (H) to arginine (R) at amino acid 131, giving a FcγRIIa molecule that binds less well to IgG_2 which may affect clearance of IgG_2-containing immune complexes. This is supported by a recent study of the relationship between the FCGR2A alleles at position 131 and the composition of immune deposits in renal biopsies of lupus nephritis [8]. IgG_2 and IgG_3 are the major IgG subclasses found in renal immune deposits, which also contain C-reactive protein, a ligand for the R131 (but not H131) allele. The frequency of genotypes containing the low IgG_2-binding R131 allele was significantly greater than expected in patients with the proliferative class III or class IV nephritis and in patients with marked IgG_2 deposits. These findings suggest that the R131 allele of FcγRIIa may contribute to the risk of proliferative lupus nephritis by triggering phagocyte activation and the release of inflammatory mediators within glomeruli.

A consistent association between R/H 131 and susceptibility to SLE or the development of lupus nephritis has not, however, been found in more than 20 studies in several different ethnic populations. Furthermore, a meta-analysis (statistical analysis of pooled data) of 17 studies involving thousands of SLE patients was able to show that the low-binding R131 allele conferred a modest 1.3-fold risk for developing SLE, but no increased risk for renal disease in SLE patients [9].

A T-G polymorphism of the FCGR3A gene results in phenylalanine (F) replacing valine (V) at amino acid 158 of the mature FcγRIIIa sequence, which results in differences in IgG_1 and IgG_3 binding. Thus individuals homozygous for F-F bind the IgG subclasses less efficiently than those with V-V genotypes, and this may lead to defective clearance of IgG_1- or IgG_3-containing immune complexes. Numerous studies have addressed the possibility that there is an association between the FcγRIIIa polymorphism and susceptibility to SLE and/or to lupus nephritis. A meta-analysis of more than one thousand patients, comparing lupus nephritis with non-nephritis SLE patients, revealed a significant overrepresentation of the low-binding F158 allele among patients who developed renal disease (1.2-fold increased risk), without significant between-study heterogeneity [10].

A SNP (T-C) has also been identified in the FCGR2B gene coding for isoleucine (I)-threonine (T) at amino acid 232 in the transmembrane domain of the FcγRIIb protein. The frequency of the TT genotype is significantly increased in Japanese SLE patients compared to healthy controls [11]. FcγRIIB differs from the other Fc receptor subsets in its ability to transmit inhibitory signals via an immunoreceptor tyrosine-based inhibitory motif (ITIM). Possible functional consequences of this polymorphism remain to be investigated.

PDCD1

Programmed cell death 1 (PDCD1) is located in the chromosome 2q36 linkage region for SLE, and codes for an inhibitory immunoreceptor that is involved in maintenance of peripheral tolerance. An intronic SNP in PDCD1 has been shown to be associated with SLE susceptibility in a study of approximately 2,500 patients conferring a 2.6-fold or 3.5-fold increased risk in European and Mexican patients, respectively [12]. The associated allele of this SNP alters a binding site for a transcription factor, RUNX1 (runt-related transcription factor 1) located in an intronic enhancer, suggesting a mechanism for its role in the development of SLE. SNPs of positional candidate genes that influence RUNX1 binding sites have also been identified in association with other autoimmune diseases such as rheumatoid arthritis and psoriasis (see Chapter 9), suggesting a common basis for susceptibility.

PARP

The ADP-ribosyltransferase or poly (ADP-ribose) polymerase (PARP) gene is located in the chromosome 1q41-42 linkage region for SLE, and codes for an enzyme present in the nucleus that mediates post-translational modification (ADP-ribosylation) of proteins. The enzyme plays a role in the cellular response to DNA damage, apoptosis, stress and malignancy. In SLE patients, and to a lesser extent in unaffected relatives of SLE patients, PARP levels are decreased suggesting that it may play a role in the disease. Several alleles of a CA dinucleotide repeat of the promoter region of PARP, located close to a transcription factor binding site, have been investigated in a family study of SLE patients. The 85bp PARP allele was significantly associated with SLE, being transmitted from heterozygous parents to offspring affected with SLE in two-thirds of cases, whilst the 97bp PARP allele was protective [13]. However, these findings were not confirmed in further family-based and case-control studies. Four additional PARP promoter polymorphisms in linkage disequilibrium with the CA repeats have been shown to form haplotypes, one of which is associated with rheumatoid arthritis in the Spanish population. These haplotypes have yet to be investigated in SLE; PARP remains, therefore, a possible candidate gene for SLE.

ACE

Angiotensin-converting enzyme (ACE) is located at 17q23 and codes for an enzyme that is involved in the regulation of blood pressure and electrolyte balance via the conversion of angiotensin I into angiotensin II. An Alu insertion-deletion intronic polymorphism of ACE has been tested for association with SLE and/or lupus nephritis on the basis that angiotensin II may play a role in the development of renal disease in SLE, but with conflicting results. However, using TDT analysis of 644 families, a significant association between three ACE polymorphisms (including the Alu insertion-deletion polymorphism) and SLE or lupus nephritis in non-Caucasians was demonstrated [14]. Furthermore, two of the polymorphisms correlated with serum levels of ACE.

PTPN22

Protein tyrosine phosphatase N22 (PTPN22) is located on chromosome 1p13.2 and codes for a protein, LYP, that is involved in downregulation of T cell signalling via interaction with C-terminal Src tyrosine kinase. A missense polymorphism in the proximal proline-rich SH3-binding domain of PTPN22, which results in substitution of a highly conserved arginine with tryptophan (C1858T, R620W), affects its ability to both bind Src tyrosine kinase and inhibit T cell activation. An association was found between the R620W polymorphism and SLE with estimated minor (T) allele frequencies of 12-67% in SLE patients compared to 8.64% in controls [15]. This polymorphism has also been reported to be associated with both type 1 diabetes and rheumatoid arthritis, suggesting that PTPN22 may play an important role in immune cell regulation and the development of autoimmunity.

6.2.1.3 Mouse genetic models

SLE genetics has been extensively studied in mouse models in which either a single gene has been deleted (gene knockout) or spontaneous mutations have occurred [16]. The findings have proved to be highly complex involving clusters of candidate genes present at single loci, different phenotypes associated with single loci, epistatic interactions between loci, and sex-dependent or protective loci. Susceptibility to SLE in mouse models is associated with the elimination of genes associated with the apoptosis pathway (e.g. PDCD1, and Fas (MRL-lpr/lpr)), the regulation of T and B cell function and activation (e.g. CTLA-4), and the clearance of immune complexes and apoptotic debris (e.g. early classical complement components, C1q, C4 and C2, and DNase-1). These findings have aided the search for SLE susceptibility genes in humans by prioritising candidate genes in chromosomal regions linked to SLE, as in the case of PDCD1 (see above).

6.2.2 Environmental

Various factors such as viral infections, UV light, pregnancy or stress may precipitate SLE and/ or exacerbate disease, probably by their effects on the immune system. Patients with SLE have increased titres of antibodies to Epstein-Barr virus; antibodies to retroviruses, including to regions homologous to HLA antigens, are also present. The role of viral infections in the precipitation of SLE may, at least partially, be explained by the observation that autoantigens co-localise with viral proteins in apoptotic surface blebs of infected keratinocytes, which could facilitate the spreading of the immune response from viral to autoantigens. This is of relevance in view of the defective clearance of apoptotic cells in SLE (see Section 6.5). Exposure to the sun or UVB can exacerbate SLE, usually in the form of a skin rash. Various mechanisms may be involved, such as the increased accumulation of late apoptotic cells and nuclear autoantigens in the skin of individuals who have defective clearance of cellular debris, the stimulation of expression of small ribonucleoproteins on keratinocyte cell surfaces and the induction of keratinocyte cytokine production which could stimulate autoantibody production by B cells. In addition to local effects in the skin, UV light may interfere with antigen processing and activation of macrophages leading to increased systemic autoimmunity.

Pregnancy may also modulate disease activity, with a relapse being more likely to develop in the postpartum period; stress has also been implicated in disease exacerbation.

6.2.3 Hormonal factors

SLE occurs more frequently in women, which is thought to be due to an oestrogen hormonal effect. This is supported by the variation in female to male ratios in different age groups. Thus in children in whom sex hormones are unlikely to have any effects, the ratio ranges from 1.4:1 to 5.8:1, in adults from 8:1 to 13:1, and in older individuals, the ratio is 2:1. The aetiological effects of hormones in SLE are probably related to their stimulatory effects on various cells of the immune system, including thymocytes, CD4$^+$ and CD8$^+$ T cells, B cells and macrophages. Hormones also stimulate the release of IL-1, HLA expression, and endothelial expression of the adhesion molecules VCAM and ICAM. In contrast, androgens tend to be immunosuppressive. Dehydroepiandrosterone, an intermediate in the testosterone synthesis pathway, is present in decreased levels in the serum of SLE patients; this may be mediated by impaired IL-2 production in these patients. An increased level of prolactin, another hormone that affects the immune system, is also associated with lupus flares.

6.3 Immune Dysregulation

The recognition of antigen by the immune system involves specialized receptors on the surface of T and B cells which, when engaged by antigen, and in the presence of accessory signals, trigger a signaling cascade which results in the activation of specific genes in the nucleus. This process can have a variety of different outcomes such as cell activation, proliferation, cytokine or antibody production, development of effector functions, anergy and programmed cell death. Numerous alterations in these functions have been identified in patients with SLE. Some of these are unrelated to disease activity and/or treatment and thus may represent intrinsic abnormalities causative of disease, whilst others may be secondary to the disease process. In particular, the aberrant signalling of SLE lymphocytes may result from a genetic defect(s) that predisposes to the disease.

6.3.1 Defective T cell signalling

6.3.1.1 Increased protein tyrosine phosphorylation and Ca^{2+} influx

The binding of specific antigen or anti-receptor antibody to the TCR (or B cell receptor) triggers a sequence of intracellular events including activation of protein tyrosine phosphorylation and Ca^{2+} mobilization, culminating in the transcription of early immune response genes (Fig. 6.3).

In SLE T cells, early TCR signalling events are abnormal [17] (Fig. 6.4). When SLE T cells are activated with anti-CD3 monoclonal antibodies, there is a significantly increased production of tyrosine phosphorylated cellular proteins with abnormal time kinetics. Thus whilst in normal T cells there is a gradual increase in phosphotyrosine production over a 3 min period, in SLE T cells there is an initial 1 min burst of elevated activity, followed by a steep decline to baseline levels.

Furthermore, the production of the principal mediator of intracellular Ca^{2+} release, 1,4,5-inositol triphosphate ($InsP_3$) is slightly increased, whilst Ca^{2+} responses are significantly increased compared to responses of normal T cells or those from other systemic autoimmune diseases. These abnormally high Ca^{2+} responses result from the release of intracellular stored Ca^{2+}, rather than the influx of extracellular Ca^{2+}, and may result from a deficiency in the Ca^{2+} response regulator, c-AMP-dependent protein kinase A type I (PKA-1). Activation of PKA-1 in lymphocytes negatively regulates the $InsP_3$ receptor causing a decrease in the release of stored Ca^{2+}. Thus a lack of regulation in SLE T cells may be responsible for the abnormally high release of intracellular Ca^{2+} in response to TCR/CD3 activation. This "signalling phenotype" was found not only in various T cell subsets, including $CD3^+$ $CD4^-$ $CD8^-$ T cells, short-term and antigen-specific T cell lines, but also in B cells.

Cross-linking of the CD2 molecule on the surface of T cells (and NK cells) can also initiate an intracellular pathway which is dependent upon CD3/TCR subunits and which is similarly defective. Bypassing the early TCR/CD3 signalling events by stimulation with phorbol esters restores the deficient CD2 response in SLE T cells to normal levels.

Figure 6.3   TCR-mediated signalling pathway in normal T lymphocytes. PTK = protein tyrosine kinase; P = phosphate group; PLCγ1 = phospholipase Cγ isozyme 1; InsP$_3$ = 1,4,5-inositol triphosphate; ER = endoplasmic reticulum; PKA-1 = protein kinase A-1; NF-AT = nuclear factor of activated T cells; AP-1 = activating protein 1.

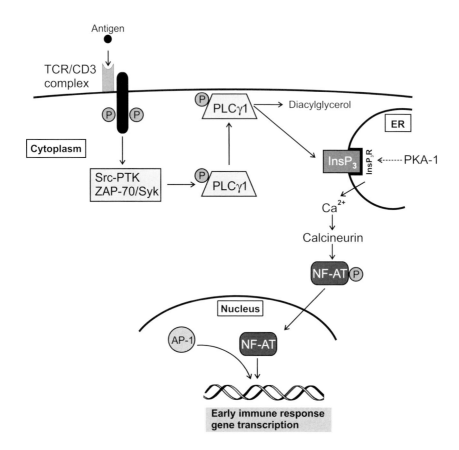

6.3.1.2 TCR/CD3ζ chain deficiency

Analysis of immunoblots of lysates of SLE T cells activated via the TCR/CD3 receptor revealed the loss or deficiency of a 16 kDa protein band in three quarters of the patients studied. This band was identified as the CD3ζ chain, a part of the hetero-oligomeric TCR/CD3 complex [18]. The absence of the CD3ζ protein was accompanied by a lack of mRNA specific for CD3ζ, both of which were present in normal individuals or patients with a systemic autoimmune disease other than SLE. In common with the invariant CD3 γ, δ and ε chains, the CD3ζ homodimer is involved in signal transduction rather than antigen recognition. The CD3ζ chain is also a signal-transducing subunit of the NK cell marker CD16 (FcγRIII).

The CD3ζ chain can also be absent in tumour-infiltrating lymphocytes, activated T cells or in T cells cultured with activated macrophages, but the defect in these cases differs from that of SLE

Figure 6.4 Abnormal early signalling events in SLE versus normal T cells. InsP$_3$ = 1,4,5-inositol triphosphate

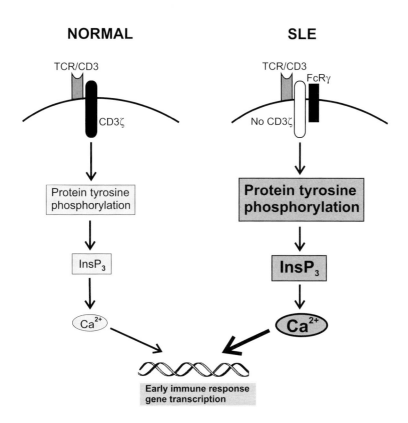

T cells in that it is reversible. The lack of CD3ζ chain in activated T cells is due to degradation of the polypeptide. Although circulating activated T cells are increased in active SLE, there is no correlation between disease activity, clinical manifestations or treatment and the level of CD3ζ chain expression.

6.3.1.3 Mechanisms involved in decreased transcription of CD3ζ chain

The absence of both mRNA specific for CD3ζ and the CD3ζ protein suggests a genetic defect rather than a post-translational modification or degradation. Extensive sequencing of the CD3ζ chain promotor failed to find any mutations. However, evidence for decreased production of the transcription factor Elf-1 that binds to the ζ chain promotor has been found in patients with SLE [19]. Elf-1 mRNA codes for a 619 amino acid protein which is subsequently phosphorylated and O-N-acetylglucosamine (O-GlcNAc) glycosylated to give a 80 kDa protein present in the cytoplasm (Fig. 6.5). The 80 kDa form of Elf-1 undergoes further phosphorylation and O-GlcNAc glycosylation to become a 98 kDa protein, which is the dominant nuclear form that can bind DNA.

Although the 80 kDa form of Elf-1 is produced by SLE T cells in sufficient amounts, two defects of

Figure 6.5 Post-translational modification of Elf-1 protein; possible sites of defects in SLE T cells. O-GlcNAc = O-N-acetylglucosamine

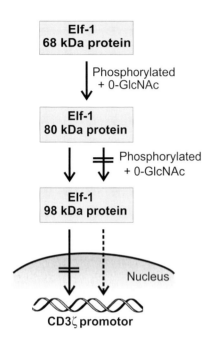

the nuclear form have been found [19] (Fig. 6.5). Firstly, the 98 kDa form is absent suggesting a defect in phosphorylation and/or O-GlcNAc glycosylation of the 80 kDa form. The absence of the 98 kDa form is associated with a lack of binding of Elf-1 to the CD3ζ chain promotor. Secondly, the 98 kDa form is produced but does not bind DNA due to insufficient phosphorylation. These findings may have implications for the expression of other genes such as CD4 or IL-2. Thus decreased Elf-1 activity could contribute to the leukopenia and decreased IL-2 production (see below) observed in patients with SLE.

Other mechanisms such as increased degradation and decreased stability may also contribute to the reduced expression of the CD3ζ chain. Ubiquitination is a process involved in the degradation of several CD3 chains; ubiquitinated forms of the ζ chain are present in increased amounts in SLE T cells. In addition, CD3ζ mRNA has a shorter half-life in T cells from SLE patients than from normal individuals, although the reasons for this decreased stability have yet to be elucidated.

6.3.1.4 Overexpression of FcRγ

The FcRγ chain, originally identified as part of the FcεRI, could potentially become part of the TCR and replace the function of the CD3ζ chain. Although it is absent from normal T cells, T cells from SLE patients show increased expression of the FcRγ molecule which becomes tyrosine phosphorylated following cross-linking of the CD3ε chain with which it is associated [20](Fig. 6.4). In addition, the FcRγ chain associates with the Syk kinase in SLE T cells forming a complex which signals 100 times more effectively than the CD3ζ-ZAP-70 (ζ associated protein-70) complex which it partly replaces [21]. This may explain the increased and accelerated response of SLE T cells. As would be expected, normal T cells transfected with the FcRγ chain also showed increased tyrosine phosphorylation and Ca²⁺ responses to CD3 stimulation, resulting from incorporation of the chain into the TCR/CD3 complex. In addition, it was observed that CD3ζ mRNA and protein was decreased, and phosphorylated Syk increased in stimulated FcRγ transfected cells. These findings suggested that, in SLE T cells, overexpression of the FcRγ chain might precede the decrease in CD3ζ chain, and be followed by Syk kinase phosphorylation.

An additional factor called linker for activation of T cells (LAT) is also implicated in the decreased excitation threshold of SLE T cells [21]. LAT is present together with CD3ζ and CD3ε in patches on the surface membrane of SLE T cells, analogous to patches observed on normal cells stimulated for 2 minutes with anti-CD3 antibody. During capping experiments in which surface molecules are mobilized to the poles of the cell at 37°C, patches on SLE T cells formed complete caps within only two minutes in contrast to the 10 minutes required by normal T cells. Thus the presence of preformed patches of signalling molecules on the surface of SLE T cells may contribute to their rapid signalling response.

6.3.2 Altered T cell function

6.3.2.1 Decreased proliferative/cytotoxic response

In SLE, patients have impaired *in vivo* cellular responses to new and recall antigens. Furthermore their *in vitro* proliferative responses to recall antigens such as tetanus toxoid, and to mitogens are decreased. T cell responses to such antigens require a costimulatory signal produced by interaction between CD28 on T cells and B7 molecules expressed by APC. The lack of this second signal leads to defective T cell IL-2 production and a long-lasting state of unresponsiveness called anergy. In SLE, up-regulation of the B7 (CD80) molecule on APC in response to IFN-γ has been found to be significantly reduced compared to that of normal controls [22]. Abnormalities in the expression/ function of other surface membrane molecules, such as FcγR, may also be involved.

The defective function of SLE APC also appears to contribute to the impaired generation of non-MHC-restricted cytotoxic T lymphocyte activity in mononuclear cells isolated from the peripheral blood (PBMC) of SLE patients. This was shown in reconstitution experiments in which T and non-T fractions from pairs of monozygotic twins discordant for SLE were cocultured in a criss-cross pattern [23].

6.3.2.2 Decreased IL-2 production

In both mice and humans with SLE, T cell production of IL-2 is decreased. IL-2 induces proliferation of T cells, generation of effector cytotoxic T cells and increased survival of activated T cells, all of which are affected in SLE.

Both the mRNA specific for IL-2, as well as the ability of the IL-2 promotor to drive the expression of a reporter gene, are decreased in SLE T cells indicating that decreased transcription is responsible for the reduction in IL-2 levels (Fig. 6.6). The co-operative binding of transcription factors to the IL-2 promotor regulates IL-2 gene expression. Decreased transcription of the IL-2 gene in SLE has been shown to be the result of both decreased enhancer and increased repressor transcriptional activity [reviewed in Ref 24].

Activity of the gene transcription enhancer, NF-κB, is decreased in SLE T cells due to a lack of p65 chain (possibly due to degradation) and therefore of activating p50-p65 complexes. NF-κB p50-p50 homodimers are present but are associated with inhibition rather than activation, and are most likely responsible for the repression of IL-2 transcription. In addition, SLE T cells differ from normal T cells in the binding of the gene transcription repressor CREM (cAMP response element modulator) rather than CREB (cAMP response element binding protein) to the same site on the IL-2 promotor region. Activation of normal T cells results in a delayed increase in expression of CREM, which contributes to termination of the immune response by limiting IL-2 production. CREM represses the transcriptional activity of the IL-2 promotor by increasing the density of non-acetylated histones

Figure 6.6   Inhibition of IL-2 promotor transcription in SLE T cells. NF-κB = Nuclear Factor kappa B; CREM = cAMP response element modulator; CREB = cAMP response element binding protein.

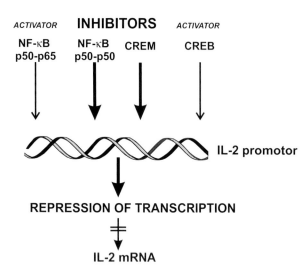

that are associated with the IL-2 promotor, and by making the promotor inaccessible to endonucleases.

6.3.2.3 Th-1 and Th-2 cytokines

Both Th-1 and Th-2 derived cytokines appear to play a role in SLE. Elevated serum levels of IL-4, IL-10, IL-6, IL-12 and IL-18 (IFN-γ-inducer) have been reported; in addition, disease activity has been correlated with either IL-10 or IL-18 in different studies [25]. The major source of IL-10 and IL-6 in the serum of SLE patients has, however, been shown to be monocytes and B cells, which are induced by immune complexes via a FcγRII-dependent mechanism. These two Th-2 type cytokines have been demonstrated to be important for the production of disease-associated autoantibodies specific for double-stranded DNA (dsDNA) (see below). Circulating Th-1 and Th-2 cells have been identified in SLE patients by cytokine-specific intracellular staining of polyclonally stimulated PBMC. However, reported Th-1/Th-2 ratios are variable in different studies probably as a result of differences in disease activity and/or the presence/absence of renal disease.

6.3.2.4 Autoreactive helper T cells

Antibody production by B cells requires T cell help that is mediated by interaction between surface molecules CD40 and CD40 ligand (CD40L), respectively on the two cell types, and by T cell-derived cytokines. In SLE, B cells produce autoantibodies directed against various components of the nucleus (see below). Autoreactive CD4+ T cells that can drive the production of anti-dsDNA antibodies by autologous B cells have been isolated from both SLE patients and normal individuals. The TCR αβ-positive CD4+ T cell lines from SLE patients are oligoclonal, respond to various DNA-binding nucleoproteins, and produce IL-2 and IFN-γ either with (Th-0) or without (Th-1) IL-4 [26,27]. In addition, SLE T cells expressing TCRγδ and lacking CD4 and CD8 can also act as helper T cells for B cell autoantibody production. Thus DNA-protein complexes appear to act as autoantigens in SLE, with B cell-specific epitopes located on the DNA, and T cell epitopes on the DNA-binding protein.

6.3.2.5 Apoptosis

Apoptosis or programmed cell death is an important mechanism used by the immune system for deleting lymphocytes and other cell types. It is employed in the thymus to delete self-reactive lymphocytes, is the mechanism used by cytotoxic lymphocytes and NK cells to kill infected cells, and is necessary for the termination of an antigen-induced T cell response. Autoreactive T cells in SLE use at least two mechanisms to resist being eliminated by apoptosis. In contrast, there is increased spontaneous apoptosis of SLE T cells *in vitro*, probably induced by activation *in vivo*.

Increased spontaneous apoptosis *in vitro*

Lymphocytes from patients with active SLE show an increase in spontaneous apoptosis compared to normal and disease (rheumatoid arthritis) controls during 5 days in culture. This is not due to a lack of growth-enhancing cytokines in the culture system, but appears to be an activation-induced cell death (AICD) resulting from lymphocyte activation *in vivo*, and correlates with disease activity [28]. Circulating T cells of SLE patients exhibit increased expression of activation markers such as Fas, FasL, CD45RO, CD40L and adhesion molecules indicating chronic activation *in vivo*. Apoptosis of SLE lymphocytes *in vitro* is inhibited by specific antibody to FasL, but not to TNF-α, showing that FasL is the dominant death effector. In addition the process is promoted by IL-10, the serum levels of which are elevated in SLE patients. IL-10 may exert this effect by inhibiting both T cell production of IL-2, a cytokine that can partially overcome T cell anergy or apoptosis, and the synthesis of APC-derived IL-12, a cytokine that protects T cells from AICD. Thus the enhanced cell death exhibited by SLE T cells *in vitro* appears to reflect AICD initiated *in vivo*.

Resistance to apoptosis i*n vivo*

In apparent conflict with these findings is the increased level of Bcl-2 (an inhibitor of apoptosis) in a proportion of circulating T cells of SLE patients. These enhanced levels correlate with disease activity and may allow inappropriate survival of autoreactive T cells. Furthermore, recently it has been shown that activated T cells of SLE patients resist anergy and apoptosis by markedly up-regulating and maintaining cyclooxygenase-2 (COX-2) expression [29]. Inhibition of COX-2 causes apoptosis of the anergy-resistant SLE T cells (and in some cases, suppresses the production of anti-DNA autoantibodies) by augmenting Fas signalling and markedly decreasing the survival molecule c-FLIP (cellular homologue of viral FLICE inhibitory protein). Moreover, COX-2-mediated regulation of apoptosis is selective for anergy-resistant SLE T cells, and does not occur in cancer cells or other autoimmune T cells.

These apparently opposite findings of increased spontaneous apoptosis *in vitro*, and resistance to apoptosis *in vivo* may be explained by the existence of different T cell subsets with varying sensitivity to apoptosis.

Apoptotic cells as a source of autoantigens

The clearance of apoptotic cells by phagocytes is necessary not only for their removal from the tissues but also to prevent the cells proceeding to secondary necrosis and releasing their inflammatory and toxic contents. Furthermore, the uptake of apoptotic cells can also actively suppress inflammation via the production of anti-inflammatory factors such as TGF-β, PGE$_2$ and PAF. Apoptotic cells can potentially act as a source of autoantigens with nuclear antigen such as DNA, RNA and chromatin present in apoptotic blebs. However, under these conditions, the presentation of peptides derived from apoptotic cell antigens by macrophages or dendritic cells leads to immunological tolerance.

In contrast in SLE there is inefficient removal of apoptotic cells, due at least in part to complement deficiencies (see Section 6.3.5.2), resulting in release of cellular contents. In this inflammatory environment, macrophages and dendritic cells can undergo maturation, and their ability to present processed autoantigens derived from internalised apoptotic cells to antigen-specific T cells is enhanced. Thus in SLE there is a loss of tolerance to autoantigens, which is facilitated by a failure to efficiently remove apoptotic cells.

6.3.3 Defective B cell signalling

Engagement of the B cell receptor (BCR) by specific antigen or an anti-receptor antibody triggers the same signalling events as that of T cells (Fig. 6.3). In SLE, B cells display signalling defects which are very similar to those described in anti-CD3 antibody-stimulated SLE T cells, and result in their characteristic hyperactivity. Engagement of BCR (surface IgM or IgD) with either anti-human IgM or anti-IgD antibodies, respectively, results in significantly increased release of intracellular Ca^{2+}, a slight but consistently increased production of $InsP_3$ and increased production of tyrosine phosphorylated cellular proteins. The enhanced Ca^{2+} pathway results in the increased transcription of genes, such as those coding for CD40L and FasL, by NF-AT. Although CD40L is usually a T cell marker, SLE B cells express increased CD40L levels that increase further upon activation. This may promote CD40-CD40L interactions with T cells, resulting in increased B cell activation and autoantibody production.

6.3.4 Autoantibodies

The presence of circulating IgM and IgG autoantibodies to host tissue components is characteristic of SLE. In the majority of patients, antibodies against various components of the nucleus are found. In addition, intracellular proteins such as Ro, La and calreticulin, and non-proteins such as phospholipids are targeted (Table 6.4).

6.3.4.1 Nuclear antigens

Anti-nuclear antigen (ANA) antibodies are present in virtually all patients with SLE at a titre of 1:160 or higher and are therefore the best screening test for diagnosis of the disease. The probability of having SLE is less than 0.14% if the ANA test is negative. However ANA antibodies are also present, although usually at lower titres, in other diseases such as Sjögren syndrome (68%), scleroderma (40-75%), juvenile rheumatoid arthritis (16%) and rheumatoid arthritis (25-50%).

Anti-dsDNA antibodies

Antibodies to dsDNA are the most common of the antibodies to nuclear antigens produced by SLE patients and are more specific for SLE than ANA antibodies. In healthy individuals, anti-dsDNA antibodies are low affinity, usually of the IgM isotype, are encoded by unmutated germ line sequences and are extensively cross-reactive. In contrast the anti-dsDNA antibodies in SLE patients are high affinity, often of the IgG isotype and contain somatic mutations with a frequent

Table 6.4 Autoantibodies in SLE

Specificity	Specific clinical association	Other diseases with autoantibodies
Nuclear antigen	None	Sjögren syndrome Scleroderma Juvenile rheumatoid arthritis Rheumatoid arthritis
Double- stranded DNA	Lupus nephritis	None
Sm (RNA-protein complex)	Lupus CNS system disease Lupus nephritis	None
Single-stranded DNA	None	Rheumatoid arthritis
Nucleoprotein	None	Rheumatoid arthritis
Ribonucleoprotein	Raynaud's phenomenon Less severe lupus	Scleroderma
Ro (SS-A)	Lymphopenia Photosensitivity Neonatal lupus C2 deficiency Subacute cutaneous lupus	Sjögren syndrome
La (SS-B)	Neonatal lupus	Sjögren syndrome
Ribosomal P	Lupus psychosis	None
Phospholipid	Strokes Miscarriages	None

bias towards arginine and asparagine in their antigen-binding sites. The latter enhances the binding of the antibodies to DNA and suggests selection by DNA itself. The characteristics of the anti-dsDNA antibodies in SLE implicate the involvement of an antigen-driven T cell-dependent immune response.

Antibodies to other nuclear antigens

Other nuclear antigens against which antibodies are produced in SLE patients include single-stranded DNA (ssDNA), nucleoprotein, chromatin, nucleosome, histones and the U1 and Sm small nuclear ribonucleoprotein particles. Antibodies to ribonucleoproteins are associated in SLE patients with the presence of myositis, Raynaud's phenomenon and less severe lupus, and are also present in scleroderma. Anti-ribosomal P antibodies are associated with lupus psychosis, and anti-Sm with lupus central nervous system disease and nephritis in SLE patients.

6.3.4.2 Intracellular proteins

Ro (SSA) is a conserved 60 kDa protein which can exist in the nucleus alone or complexed with the short uridine-rich, structural human cytoplasmic (hY) RNAs. Ro binds 5S ribosome RNA variants that are misfolded and probably targets them for degradation. Antibodies to Ro are present in approximately 40% of SLE patient sera and are associated with several features of SLE, including characteristic skin disease, photosensitivity, a lack of renal disease (when present with antibodies to La) and neonatal lupus. Infusion of purified anti-Ro antibodies into human skin-grafted mice produces a pattern of deposition that is identical to that of SLE skin lesions. Furthermore, anti-Ro antibodies specifically bind to UV-exposed keratinocytes, suggesting a mechanism for the association between these antibodies and UV-induced skin disease in SLE.

The La protein can be physically associated with the Ro particle. Autoantibodies to La are found in a subset of patients with anti-Ro, as are antibodies to 52 kDa Ro, a fraction of the Ro molecule.

Calreticulin is detected in the serum of some patients with SLE, and approximately 40% of patients have autoantibodies directed against calreticulin. Calreticulin is one of various host proteins that are released or secreted from cells during inflammatory episodes and bind to C1q. Calreticulin inhibits the binding of immune complexes by competing for immunoglobulin binding sites on the globular head of C1q, resulting in reduced complement activation. This lack of complement activation causes defective processing of immune complexes, a characteristic feature of SLE.

6.3.4.3 Phospholipids

Antibodies to phospholipids complexed to β_2-glycoprotein I are relatively frequent in patients with SLE. β_2-glycoprotein I acts as an anticoagulant and its effects are inhibited by antibodies to the complex. This may explain the association between anti-phospholipid antibodies and thrombotic complications, a major clinical problem in some patients.

6.3.5 Immune complexes

Immune complexes are formed when soluble antibodies bind to circulating antigens, microorganisms, chemicals and infected or transformed cells, facilitating their removal and regulating subsequent inflammatory events. The formation and clearance of immune complexes is a normal consequence of antibody-soluble antigen interactions.

6.3.5.1 Normal clearance of immune complexes

Large antigens with multiple binding sites form large antibody complex lattices, which are easily cleared from the circulation but deposit in tissues more readily, whereas small antigens are difficult to clear effectively. Latticed immune complexes are cleared rapidly from the circulation by cells of the reticuloendothelial system, which express receptors for immunoglobulin Fc (FcR) and complement (CR).

FcR on phagocytes

When antibodies bind to antigen, they undergo conformational changes that enable their Fc regions to bind with high affinity to FcR present on a number of cell types. There are three families of FcR that bind exclusively to IgG (FcγR) but differ in their affinity for certain immune complexes, and in their cellular distribution. They are expressed in high density on phagocytic cells such as macrophages, dendritic cells, LCs and Kupffer cells (liver), but can also be found on PMNs, B cells, NK cells, eosinophils and mast cells. Furthermore, cross-linking of FcR on the surface of some inflammatory cells can also send intracellular signals resulting in changes in gene expression, cytokine or chemokine production, expression of adhesion molecules, and other cellular functions.

CR on phagocytes

In addition to antigens, complement binds antibodies associated with antigen in immune complexes. This can be either a specific interaction as between C1q and the complement-binding domains of immunoglobulins (see Chapter 4), or non-specific, as in the opsonisation of antibodies by complement degradation products, particularly C3b (see Chapter 3). The binding of complement to immune complexes modifies their structure facilitating immune complex lattice formation and enhancing their delivery to cells for phagocytosis via interaction with complement receptors, particularly CR1, on the cell surface. CR1, which binds to immune complexes containing C3b, iC3b (cleavage product of C3b) or C4b, is highly expressed on erythrocytes, and is also present on phagocytic cells and lymphocytes. When erythrocytes circulate through the liver, the Kupffer cells effectively remove the large complement-containing immune complexes, solubilise them into smaller pieces and facilitate their uptake by phagocytes. This process is dependent upon the greater affinity for the immune complexes of the FcγR on Kupffer cells, compared to that of the erythrocyte-expressed CR1.

6.3.5.2 Defective clearance of immune complexes in SLE

When FcR and CR fail to function normally, or are present in insufficient numbers to handle the number of immune complexes generated, and/or complement is decreased, immune complexes are inappropriately deposited in tissues, initiating inflammatory pathways and resulting in diseases such as SLE.

In SLE, there is evidence that defective clearance of immune complexes is a causative factor in the development of the disease. Thus a SNP in the FCGR2A gene, and another in the FCGR3A gene are significant risk factors for the development of SLE or lupus nephritis (see Section 6.2.1.2). These polymorphisms are functionally relevant as they result in FcγRIIa and FcγRIIIa molecules that bind less well to IgG, resulting in inefficient immune complex clearance. In addition, inherited deficiencies of complement components, C1q, C4 and, to a lesser extent, C2 also predispose to SLE. Furthermore, the null allele of C4, C4AQ*0, is strongly associated with SLE and these patients have fewer CR1 and C3bR expressed on their erythrocytes.

6.4 Model of Pathogenesis

SLE is an immune complex-mediated disease caused by a loss of self-tolerance to nuclear antigens that results from ineffective clearing of apoptotic cells and immune complexes (Fig. 6.7).

In the early stages of cell death, apoptotic cells are recognized by innate molecules such as complement components, and are subsequently engulfed by macrophages without the induction of inflammation or an immune response. In SLE, defective clearance of apoptotic cells caused by early complement component deficiencies allows apoptotic cells to undergo secondary necrosis and release their toxic and inflammatory intracellular contents.

Under these inflammatory conditions dendritic cells mature and express high levels of MHC and costimulatory molecules. Furthermore, they gain access to nuclear antigens released from the dying cells, which they process and present to T cells specific for DNA-binding proteins, inducing activation, proliferation and the release of cytokines.

In turn, these autoantigen-specific T cells provide help to DNA-specific B cells via CD40L-CD40 interactions and cytokine release, resulting in their activation, proliferation and differentiation. In addition, cytokines such as IL-10 and IL-6 produced by monocytes also contribute to B cell activation. These activated B cells produce copious amounts of autoantibodies specific for DNA, which form immune complexes with the released nuclear antigens.

Defective clearance of immune complexes due to functional polymorphisms of the genes coding for FcγRIIa and FcγRIIIa and decreased early complement components leads to deposition in various organs including the skin, joints, lungs and kidneys. Persistence of immune complexes at these sites leads to complement activation and the release of chemotactic factors that attract phagocytes to the site. Phagocytosis of immune complexes induces the release of mediators, resulting in an inflammatory response and eventually tissue damage.

6.5 Pathogenesis of skin lesions

In SLE, skin lesions induced by sun exposure are characterized by the deposition of autoantibodies at the dermal/epidermal junction, basal KC damage and a moderate inflammatory infiltrate. One hypothesis for the mechanism of UV-induced autoimmunity in the skin is that the binding of anti-nuclear antibodies to KCs induces cellular cytotoxicity (ADCC) [30]. Of the anti-nuclear antibodies, antibodies against Ro antigen are the most closely associated with photosensitivity. Exposure to UVB light can damage KCs and result in the translocation of Ro antigen from the nucleus and cytoplasm to apoptotic blebs on the cell surface. This would make the antigen accessible to binding by autoantibodies.

UV light also induces the expression of adhesion molecules on vascular endothelium and KCs facilitating the recruitment of immune cells such as T cells and plasmacytoid dendritic cells (also called natural IFN-α-producing cells) to the skin.

The infiltrating CD3+ T cells in chronic cutaneous LE show elevated frequencies of certain Vβ families (Vβ3.1, Vβ8.1, Vβ13.3) suggesting that these may be oligoclonal populations induced by specific antigen(s) [31]. The phenotype, function and antigen specificity of these T cells has yet to be determined, but could potentially include autoantigen-specific helper and cytotoxic CD4+ and/or CD8+ T cell subsets that contribute to the pathogenesis.

Plasmacytoid dendritic cells are also recruited to the dermis of SLE skin lesions [32], possibly via activation of their CXCR3 receptor by the chemokine IP-10 (IFN-α or -γ-inducible protein). Immune complexes consisting of DNA/anti-DNA or RNA-protein/anti-ribonucleoprotein induce the production of IFN-α by these dendritic cells, either via internalization through the receptor FcγRII or possibly via stimulation of TLR9 and TLR7, respectively. Plasmacytoid dendritic cells

Figure 6.7   Model of immunopathogenesis of SLE. See text for further details.

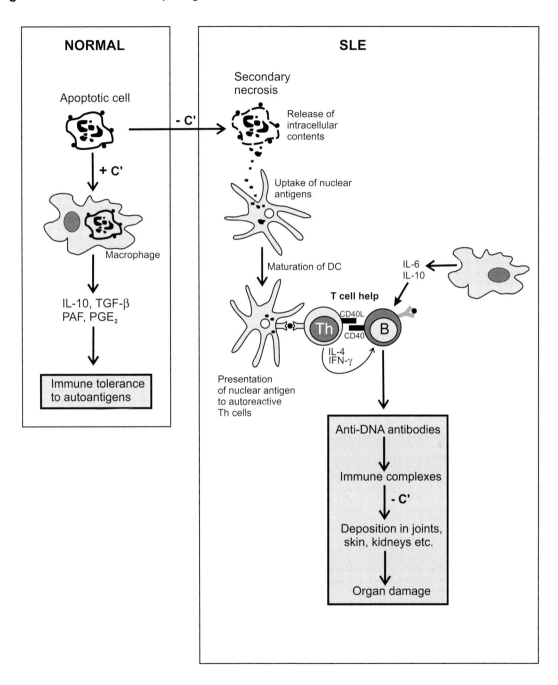

could potentially present peptides derived from internalized nuclear antigens to antigen-specific T cells, their activation being promoted by the concomitant production of costimulatory IFN-α.

6.6 Treatment

Treatment of SLE involves predominately the use of non-specific anti-inflammatory and immunosuppressive drugs to control symptoms. Novel therapies are being investigated which are more selective in their approach in order to avoid the toxic side-effects of these drugs, and to provide more effective ways of inducing resolution of disease. Interestingly, long-lasting clinical remission occurs in 6% of patients, whilst the proportion of patients that experience treatment-free remission for at least one year increases with the duration of disease.

6.6.1 Anti-inflammatory and immunosuppressive drugs

Treatment of SLE primarily involves anti-inflammatory and immunosuppressive drugs, the combination and dose of which varies with clinical expression. Anti-inflammatory treatments suitable for treatment of moderate disease include non-steroidal anti-inflammatory drugs (NSAIDs), which are employed to treat arthritis, anti-malarial agents (usually hydroxychloroquine) for skin involvement (and arthritis if NSAIDs are ineffective), low dose corticosteroids and methotrexate. Retinoids may also be used to treat skin lesions, or thalidomide if skin involvement is refractory. However, severe disease involving organs such as the CNS, lungs or kidneys requires aggressive treatment, and high dose systemic corticosteroids (methylprednisolone) with or without immunosuppressive, cytotoxic agents such as cyclophosphamide, cyclosporin, methotrexate and azathioprine are commonly employed.

Anticoagulants (for example, warfarin) may also be used to treat thrombotic disease in SLE patients, especially those with anti-phospholipid syndrome. Furthermore, intravenous gamma globulin has been successfully used in the treatment of lupus nephritis, vasculitis, and acute thrombocytopenia. In patients with severe disease refractory to existing treatments, plasmapheresis and immunoadsorption may be used to remove autoantibodies and immune complexes from the circulation. Immunoadsorption appears to be more effective than plasmapheresis but randomized controlled trials have yet to be carried out to evaluate the value of this therapeutic approach.

6.6.2 New approaches to treatment

The use of immunosuppressive drugs to treat SLE have been accompanied by several problems partly caused by their non-specificity, including a lack of efficacy in some patients, toxic side effects, premature coronary artery disease and susceptibility to serious infections. Thus new approaches to treatment that target specific immune mechanisms, and are consequently more effective and less likely to incur harmful side effects, have been actively investigated. Novel therapies that are currently being tested or developed for use in SLE include an immunosuppressant, immunoablation and stem cell transplantation, a B cell toleragen and depleting antibody, blocking of costimulatory pathways, anti-cytokine, hormonal and gene therapy [33,34] (Table 6.5).

Table 6.5 Novel treatments for SLE

Treatment	Target	Mechanism
Immunosuppressant		
Mycophenolate mofetil	T and B cells	Inhibits T cell proliferation Induces apoptosis of activated T cells Inhibits antibody production Inhibits lymphocyte expression of adhesion molecules
Immunoablation		
Immunoablation ± stem cell transplantation	T and B cells	Removes pathogenic T and B cells and replaces with stem cells
Tolerance		
LIP 394 (abetimus)	B cells	Inactivation
Anti-CD20	B cells	Depletion
Blocking of costimulatory pathways		
Anti-CD40L	Activated T cells	Blocks costimulation of B cells
CTLA4-Ig	T cells	Binds to B7 on APC Blocks costimulation by CD28-B7
Anti-cytokine		
Anti-IL-10	Circulating monocyte-derived IL-10	Decreased activation of immune and endothelial cells
Infliximab	TNF-α	Blocks effects of TNF-α
Hormones		
Dehydroepiandrosterone	Immune system	Immunosuppressive
Oestrogen receptor modulators	Oestrogen receptors	Immunosuppressive
Bromocriptine	Prolactin	Immunosuppressive
Gene Therapy		
Gene therapy	Signalling defects etc.	Restores normal function

6.6.2.1 Immunosuppressant

Patients whose disease responds poorly to existing treatments and who have a poor prognosis are a particular focus for new therapies. Mycophenolate mofetil, a drug originally developed for organ transplantation, is a potent immunosuppressive with a low incidence of serious adverse effects. It inhibits lymphocyte proliferation, T cell-dependent antibody responses and the expression of adhesion molecules involved in cell trafficking, and induces apoptosis of activated T cells. Mycophenolate mofetil is now being used in SLE as an alternative treatment option for patients with lupus nephritis who do not respond to high dose cyclosphamide or azathioprine.

6.6.2.2 Immunoablation

Another approach being used in various autoimmune diseases, including SLE, to treat refractive disease is immunoablation with or without autologous haemopoietic stem cell transplantation. The elimination of T and B lymphocytes using chemotherapy and monoclonal antibodies followed by stem cell transplantation has produced encouraging preliminary results, but will require follow-up to determine the longevity of the induced disease remission.

6.6.2.3 B cells as targets

B lymphocytes are an obvious target for new treatments in SLE. Inactivation of autoreactive B cells producing anti-dsDNA antibodies has been demonstrated in mouse models using a B cell toleragen called LJP 394 (abetimus). LJP 394 is a construct, which consists of four double-stranded oligonucleotides attached to a non-immunogenic polyethylene glycol framework. It induces tolerance in B cells by cross-linking surface antibodies in the absence of T cell epitopes. This drug is now being tested in SLE patients, particularly those with kidney involvement.

Selective depletion of B cells using a chimeric mouse-human monoclonal antibody against the B cell-specific antigen CD20 (rituximab), which is involved in B cell activation, proliferation and differentiation, has been widely used to treat B cell lymphomas, and is now being tested in SLE. Recent open-label studies indicate that rituximab is safe and may be efficacious in the treatment of SLE.

6.6.2.4 Blocking of costimulatory molecules

Costimulatory molecules expressed by T lymphocytes are also the focus for new treatments for nephritis in SLE. A monoclonal antibody to CD40L (IDEC-131), a molecule expressed on activated T cells that binds to CD40 on B cells inducing antibody production, has been tested in SLE patients. However, although well tolerated, the antibody was ineffective; furthermore, thromboembolic complications have been reported in association with anti-CD40L monoclonal therapies.

The interaction of B7 on APCs and CD28 on T cells provides an important second signal for T cell activation. T cell-APC interactions can be blocked with CTLA4-Ig, a soluble fusion protein of the extracellular domain of CTLA-4 with the constant region of human immunoglobulin-γ, which binds to B7 with higher affinity than CD28. This fusion protein blocks autoantibody production and retards autoimmune nephritis in a mouse model of SLE, and is being considered for use in SLE patients.

6.6.2.5 Anti-IL-10/TNF-α therapy

IL-10, whose levels are increased in the serum of patients with active SLE and correlate with disease activity, is another target for treatment. Preliminary studies with a murine anti-IL-10 antibody have been encouraging, with improvement in skin and joint symptoms, decreased activity of immune and endothelial cells and decreased dependency on prednisone. Further studies will require the development of a suitable human monoclonal antibody, to avoid the induction of neutralizing antibodies and corresponding reduction in efficacy.

Although TNF-α has also been reported to be increased in serum, and, in addition, has been detected in renal biopsies of SLE patients, experiments in animal models did not show a consistent role for the cytokine in the disease process. Furthermore, a preliminary study involving treatment of SLE patients with moderate disease activity with infliximab (a chimeric monoclonal antibody against TNF-α) showed beneficial effects in only a proportion of patients. The usefulness of this approach in SLE remains, therefore, to be established.

6.6.2.6 Modulation of hormone system

Sex hormones are known to play a role in SLE. Novel therapies that target the hormone system are the mild androgen dehydroepiandrosterone, selective oestrogen receptor modulators and the prolactin inhibitor, bromocriptine. Dehydroepiandrosterone (prasterone) has been tested in multiple clinical trials, but controversy still exists over its efficacy.

6.6.2.7 Gene therapy

Gene therapy, involving the delivery of genes that code for immunomodulatory molecules such as cytokines or soluble receptors have been used extensively in animal models of SLE. However, to obtain a more effective therapeutic outcome in patients with SLE, a more specific approach, such as the correction of defined immunological abnormalities, is needed. *In vitro*, SLE T cells transfected with genes coding for the missing CD3ζ chain or NF-κB p65 protein showed restored IL-2 production and normal signalling [20]. Similarly, elimination of CREM by introduction of an antisense CREM plasmid into SLE T cells *in vitro* also up-regulated IL-2 production by decreasing the amount of CREM bound to the IL-2 promotor [20]. These findings suggest that specific gene therapy may be a feasible option for treatment of SLE in the future.

Summary

- SLE is an autoimmune disease characterised by the formation of immune complexes, which deposit in various organs including skin causing tissue damage.

- Inheritance of the disease involves multiple susceptibility genes; eight chromosomal loci show significant linkage to disease, approximately 20 show suggestive linkage.

- Candidate genes include those coding for MHC Class II antigens, C1q, C4, FcγR, PDC1, PARP, ACE and PTPN22.

- Disease is modified by environmental factors such as viral infections, UV light, pregnancy or stress, and by hormonal factors.

- T cells show defective signalling, decreased proliferation and cytotoxic responses and decreased IL-2 production.

- B cells, which also show defective signalling, produce autoantibodies to various nuclear components (especially dsDNA), intracellular proteins such as Ro, La and calreticulin, and phospholipids.

- Oligoclonal Th-1 and Th-0 cells with specificity for various DNA-binding nucleoproteins drive autoantibody production by B cells.

- Enhanced spontaneous apoptosis of lymphocytes *in vitro* probably reflects activation-induced cell death initiated *in vivo*. In contrast, activated SLE T lymphocytes show resistance to apoptosis *in vivo*.

- Inefficient removal of apoptotic cells and immune complexes by phagocytes leads to a loss of tolerance to autoantigens, and the formation and persistence of immune complexes.

- Conventional treatments include anti-inflammatory and immunosuppressive drugs. Novel, more selective, therapies being used or tested include mycophenolate mofetil, immunoablation, blocking or depleting B cells, blocking costimulatory pathways, anti-cytokine, hormonal or gene therapy.

References

1. Tan E.M., Cohen A.S., Fries J.F. *et al*. Special article: The 1982 revised criteria for the classification of SLE. Arthr.Rheum. 1982; **25:** 1271-7.
2. Hochberg M.C. Updating the American College of Rheumatology revised criteria for the classification of systemic lupus erythematosus. Arthr.Rheum. 1997; **40:** 1725-34.
3. Lander E.S. & Kruglyak L. Genetic dissection of complex traits: guidelines for interpreting and reporting linkage results. Nat.Genet. 1995; **11:** 241-7.
4. Shen N. & Tsao B. Current advances in the human lupus genetics. Curr.Rheumatol.Rep. 2004; **6:** 391-8.
5. Graham R.R., Ortmann W.A., Langefeld C.D. *et al*. Visualizing human leukocyte antigen class II risk haplotypes in human systemic lupus erythematosus. Am.J.Hum.Genet. 2002; **71:** 543-53.
6. Pickering M.C. & Walport M.J. Links between complement abnormalities and systemic lupus erythematosus. Rheumatol. (Oxford) 2000; **39:** 133-41.
7. Yang Y., Chung E.K., Zhou B. *et al*. The intricate role of complement component C4 in human systemic lupus erythematosus. Curr.Dir.Autoimmun. 2004; **7:** 98-132.
8. Zuniga R., Markowitz G.S., Arkachaisri T., Imperatore E.A., D'Agati V.D., Salmon J.E. Identification of IgG subclasses and C-reactive protein in lupus nephritis: the relationship between the composition of immune deposits and FCgamma receptor type IIA alleles. Arthr. Rheum. 2003; **48:** 460-70.
9. Karassa F.B., Trikalinos T.A., Ioannidis J.P.; Fc gamma RIIa-SLE Meta-Analysis Investigators. Role of the Fcγ receptor IIa polymorphism in susceptibility to systemic lupus erythematosus and lupus nephritis: a meta-analysis. Arthr.Rheum. 2002; **46:** 1563-71.
10. Karassa F.B., Trikalinos T.A., Ioannidis J.P.; Fc gamma RIIIA-SLE Meta-Analysis Investigators. The Fc gamma RIIIA-F158 allele is a risk factor for the development of lupus nephritis: a meta-analysis. Kidney Int. 2003; **63:** 1475-82.
11. Kyogoku C., Dijstelbloem H.M., Tsuchiya N. *et al*. Fcgamma receptor gene polymorphisms in Japanese patients with systemic lupus erythematosus: contribution of FCGR2B to genetic susceptibility. Arthr.Rheum. 2002; **46:** 1242-54.
12. Prokunina L., Castillejo-Lopez C., Oberg F. *et al*. A regulatory polymorphism in PDCD1 is associated with susceptibility to systemic lupus erythematosus in humans. Nat.Genet. 2002; **32:** 666-9.
13. Tsao B.P., Cantor R.M., Grossman J.M. *et al*. PARP alleles within the linked chromosomal region are associated with systemic lupus erythematosus. J.Clin.Invest. 1999; **103:** 1135-40.
14. Parsa A., Peden E., Lum R.F. *et al*. Association of angiotensin-converting enzyme polymorphisms with systemic lupus erythematosus and nephritis: analysis of 644 SLE families. Genes Immun. 2002; **3 Suppl 1:** S42-6.
15. Kyogoky C., Langefeld C.D., Ortmann W.A. *et al*. Genetic association of the R620W polymorphism of protein tyrosine phosphatase PTPN22 with human SLE. Am.J.Hum. Genet. 2004; **75:** 504-7.

16. Cunninghame Graham D.S. & Vyse T.J. The candidate gene approach: have murine models informed the study of human SLE? Clin.Exp.Immunol. 2004; **137:** 1-7.

17. Tsokos G. & Liossis S.-N. C. Immune cell signalling defects in lupus: activation, anergy and death. Immunol. Today 1999; **120:** 119-24.

18. Liossis S.N., Ding X.Z., Dennis J.G., Tsokos G.C. Altered pattern of TCR/CD3-mediated protein-tyrosyl phosphorylation in T cells from patients with systemic lupus erythematosus. Deficient expression of the T-cell receptor ζ chain. J.Clin.Invest. 1998; **101:** 1448-57.

19. Juang Y.T., Tenbrock K., Nambiar M.P., Gourley M.F., Tsokos G.C. Defective production of the 98 kDa form of Elf-1 is responsible for the decreased expression of TCR ζ chain in patients with systemic lupus erythematosus. J.Immunol. 2002; **169:** 6048-55.

20. Enyedy E.J., Nambiar M.P., Liossis S.N., Dennis G., Kammer G.M., Tsokos G.C. Fc epsilon receptor type I γ chain replaces the deficient T cell receptor ζ chain in T cells of patients with systemic lupus erythematosus. Arthr.Rheum. 2001; 44: 1114-21.

21. Tsokos G.C., Nambiar M.P., Tenbrock K., Juang Y.-T. Rewiring the T-cell: signalling defects and novel prospects for the treatment of SLE. Trends Immunol. 2003; **24:** 259-63.

22. Tsokos G.C., Kovacs B., Sfikakis P.P., Theocharis S., Vogelgesang S., Via C.S. Defective antigen-presenting cell function in patients with systemic lupus erythematosus. Arthr. Rheum. 1996; **39:** 600-9.

23. Stohl W., Hamilton A.S., Deapen D.M., Mack T.M., Horwitz D.A. Impaired cytotoxic T lymphocyte activity in systemic lupus erythematosus following *in vitro* polyclonal T cell stimulation: a contributory role for non-T cells. Lupus 1999; **8:** 293-9.

24. Tenbrock K. & Tsokos G.C. Transcriptional regulation of interleukin 2 in SLE T cells. Int. Rev.Immunol. 2004; **23:** 333-45.

25. Amerio P., Frezzolini A., Abeni D. *et al*. Increased IL-18 in patients with systemic lupus erythematosus: relations with Th-1, Th-2, pro-inflammatory cytokines and disease activity. IL-18 is a marker of disease activity but does not correlate with pro-inflammatory cytokines. Clin.Exp. Rheumatol. 2002; **20:** 535-8.

26. Desai-Mehta A., Mao C., Rajagopalan S., Robinson T., Datta S.K. Structure and specificity of T cell receptors expressed by potentially pathogenic anti-DNA autoantibody-inducing T cells in human lupus. J.Clin.Invest. 1995; **95:** 531-41.

27. Voll R.E., Roth E.A., Girkontaite I. *et al*. Histone-specific Th0 and Th1 clones derived from systemic lupus erythematosus patients induce double-stranded DNA antibody production. Arthr.Rheum. 1997; **40:** 2162-71.

28. Georgescu L., Vakkalanka R.K., Elkon K.B., Crow M.K. Interleukin-10 promotes activation-induced cell death of SLE lymphocytes mediated by Fas ligand. J.Clin.Invest. 1997; **100:** 2622-33.

29. Xu L., Zhang L., Yi Y., Kang H.K., Datta S.K. Human lupus T cells resist inactivation and escape death by upregulating COX-2. Nat.Med. 2004; **10:** 411-5.

30. Furukawa F. Antinuclear antibody-keratinocyte interactions in photosensitive cutaneous lupus erythematosus. Histol.Histopathol. 1999; **14:** 627-33.

31. Furukawa F., Tokura Y., Matsushita K. *et al*. Selective expansions of T cells expressing V beta 8 and V beta 13 in skin lesions of patients with chronic cutaneous lupus erythematosus.

J. Dermatol. 1996; **23:** 670-6.

32. Blomberg S., Eloranta M.L., Cederblad B., Nordlin K., Alm G.V., Ronnblom L. Presence of cutaneous interferon-alpha producing cells in patients with systemic lupus erythematosus. Lupus 2001; **10:** 484-90.

33. Zandman-Goddard G. & Shoenfeld Y. Novel Approaches to Therapy for SLE. Clin.Rev. Allergy Immunol. 2003; **25:** 105-12.

34. Goldblatt F. & Isenberg D.A. New therapies for systemic lupus erythematosus. Clin.Exp. Immunol. 2005; **140:** 205-12.

PART III: Immunological Mechanisms of Skin Disease

7

Allergic Contact Dermatitis

Allergic contact dermatitis (ACD), also known as allergic contact eczema, is a common condition that results from contact with chemical compounds that sensitise through the skin inducing a delayed-type hypersensitivity (type IV) reaction on subsequent exposure.

7.1 Clinical features

ACD is more common in females than males and incidence increases with age. The lesions are localised to the area of skin in contact with the allergen, but clinical features may vary depending upon the type of allergen responsible. To identify the allergen involved it is necessary to consider the different sources of allergens that a patient may be exposed to, in the home, at work and during recreational activities. Table 7.1 shows the common allergens that cause ACD, and their sources. A more comprehensive list of allergens can be found in Chapter 4 (Table 4.2) which gives the standard panel for contact dermatitis patch testing.

In dermatitis induced by contact with nickel present in jewellery, watch straps, metal clips in bra straps or studs in jeans, there is pruritus, erythema, scaling and induration of the skin at the site of contact on the neck, wrist, back or lower abdomen (Fig. 7.1, colour plate). Occasionally the eyelids or the nape of the neck may be affected. ACD commonly manifests itself after ear-piercing which may explain its increasing frequency in the male population. Other nickel-containing items associated with ACD are spectacle frames, coins and household utensils. A spot test using diamethylglyoxime, which gives a pink colour with nickel, can be used to determine whether nickel is present in a metal-containing item suspected of causing skin lesions.

Chromate is a common cause of contact dermatitis of the hands and forearms, which presents as a dry, lichenified form of dermatitis. Hexavalent metal salts of chromate found in cement, bleaches and match heads, and used in tanning leather are responsible for the contact reaction.

Formaldehyde is present in preservatives, cosmetics, cigarettes, newspapers, fabric softeners, and coating for drip-dry shirts. Ethylenediamine is used as a preservative in topical medications, and is also found complexed to theophylline or as a catalyst in rapid-drying polymer paints. Sensitivity to ethylenediamine may also result in cross-reactivity to some anti-histamines, such as hydroxyzine and promethazine.

Mercaptobenzothiazole and thiurams are accelerators used in the manufacture of rubber found in kitchen gloves and Wellington boots; the former may also cause contact dermatitis to catheters. Thiurams are also found as fungicides in paints and soap.

Paraphenylenediamine is a major component of permanent hair dyes and is also used in dyeing

Table 7.1 Common ACD-inducing allergens and their sources

Allergen	Source
Nickel	Metal-containing items such as jewellery, coins, clasps, studs and zippers in clothing, glasses frames, watch straps
Chromate	Leather (shoes, gloves), bleaches, matches, cement
Formaldehyde	Preservatives, cosmetics, cigarettes, newspapers, fabric softeners, coating for drip-dry shirts
Ethylenediamine	Preservatives in creams, aminophylline, paints
Mercaptobenzothiazole	Rubber products (boots, gloves), catheters
Thiurams	Rubber products, fungicide in paint and soap
Paraphenylenediamine	Permanent hair dye, clothing dye in stockings and tights
Plants	*Primula obconica* (Europe), *Rhus*-poison ivy (USA)

stockings and tights, and can cause ACD of the scalp or legs, respectively.

Plants can cause ACD via the release of airborne allergenic particles, which induce marked facial oedema and erythema. In the UK, primin released by *Primula obconica* is a common cause of contact dermatitis, whilst in the USA, *Rhus* (poison oak or poison ivy) causes a severe form of ACD, often presenting with linear vesicles. Other plants associated with ACD include dahlias and chrysanthemums, and tulip bulbs that cause a dry cracked dermatitis on the fingertips of bulb growers.

ACD can be difficult to distinguish clinically from irritant contact dermatitis but the mechanisms involved are different. Irritant contact dermatitis usually occurs on the hands and is caused by contact with substances such as detergents and oils, which are toxic to epidermal cells. Sensitisation is not required, and there is no hypersensitivity reaction. Patch testing will result in only a non-eczematous irritant reaction in almost all cases. This type of response tends to be more common in patients with atopic dermatitis (see Chapter 8).

7.2 Genetics

Since exposure to allergens only manifests itself as an inflammatory skin response in certain individuals, genetic factors are implicated in susceptibility to the disease. In support of this, a study of female Danish twins with a history of nickel sensitivity showed a significant increase in the concordance rate of monozygotic compared with dizygotic twins [1]. Studies to date have shown that genetic polymorphisms associated with ACD triggered by nickel or paraphenylenediamine involve genes located on chromosomes 6p21 and 8p22 (Table 7.2).

Table 7.2 Genetic polymorphisms asociated with ACD

Contact Allergen	Chromosome	Gene	Alleles with positive association	Alleles with negative association	Functional consequences
Nickel	6p21	DQA (MHC Class II)	Taq 1 DQA allelic restriction fragment		No correlation with T cell responses to nickel
Nickel	6p21	Bf (MHC Class III)	Bf-F Bf-FB		Not known
Nickel	6p21	TAP	TAP2B	TAP2C	Effect on antigen transfer?
PPD	8p22	NAT2	NAT2*4 (wild type)		Rapid acetylator
			NAT2*4/ NAT1*10		Rapid acetylator
				NAT2*5b/ NAT2*6a	Slow acetylator
PPD + others	6p21	TNFA	TNFA-308*1/2 TNFA-308*2/2		?Altered TNF-α production

7.2.1 Nickel-induced ACD

Although inflammatory diseases are commonly associated with particular HLA genes, several investigations of MHC Class I and II antigens in nickel-allergic patients failed to show any associations, with one exception. Restriction fragment length polymorphism analysis of DNA digested with Taq I revealed a 4.5-kb DQA fragment whose expression was significantly associated with ACD to nickel [2]. However, there was no correlation between expression of the DQA fragment and the T cell response to nickel *in vitro*.

Associations with the HLA class III polymorphisms, complement B factor (Bf), C4A, and C4B have also been studied in ACD. Although no associations were detected when ACD patients with different allergen sensitivities were considered as a whole, the ACD patients with nickel sensitivity alone showed a significant association with two Bf alleles, Bf-F and Bf-FB [3].

A more recent study has investigated the possibility that TAP1 and TAP2 (transporter associated with antigen processing) genes are involved in susceptibility to nickel allergy [4]. These genes have a role in antigen transport and processing making them relevant candidates. PCR typing of nickel-sensitive individuals revealed an increase in TAP2B and a decrease in the frequency of TAP2C alleles compared to nickel non-sensitive individuals, suggesting that TAP2B allele increases the risk for nickel allergy.

Thus patients with nickel-induced ACD show positive associations with a DQA fragment, two alleles of the BF protein and a TAP2 allele implicating these proteins in the response to nickel.

7.2.2 Paraphenylenediamine-induced ACD

In patients with ACD to paraphenylenediamine, functional genetic polymorphisms of N-acetyltransferases 1 and 2 (NAT1 and NAT2), enzymes, which catalyse the O-acetylation of N-hydroxylamines, have been studied for possible association with disease [5]. Carriers of the NAT2*4 wild type allele, which are rapid acetylators, were more common in the contact allergy group than in that of the healthy controls, whilst slow acetylators carrying the NAT2*5b/2*6a genotype were significantly less frequent among patients. There was no difference between the frequency of patients and controls expressing the NAT1*10 allele, but an increased frequency of the NAT2*4/NAT1*10 haplotype was present in the patient group. The latter is at least partly due to disequilibrium between the alleles on chromosome 8p22. Thus acetylation may enhance contact sensitivity to paraphenylendiamine, or, alternatively, the NAT2*4 and NAT1*10 alleles may be linked to an unknown susceptibility factor.

A further study of patients with both sensitivity to para substituted aryl compounds (e.g. paraphenylenediamine) and to at least one other structurally unrelated allergen, investigated functional polymorphisms in genes encoding for several proinflammatory cytokines (TNF-α, IL-1β, IL-1ra, IL-6) associated with ACD [6]. Only the distribution of TNFA-308 genotypes was significantly different in the patient versus control group. Carriers of the TNFA-308*1/2 (*G/A) and TNFA 308*2/2 (*A/A) genotypes, rather than the wild type genotype TNFA-308*1/1 (*G/G), tended to be more common in the patient group. The functional consequences of these findings in ACD patients have yet to be determined.

These relatively limited studies suggest that there may be several different susceptibility genes for ACD, which may vary in different groups of patients depending upon the initiating contact allergen.

7.3 Immunopathology of skin lesions

The immunopathology of ACD is of a non-specific dermatitis, which can be acute, subacute or chronic. In acute dermatitis, oedema and spongiosis are present in the epidermis, and a mainly T lymphocytic perivascular infiltrate with oedema in the papillary dermis (Fig. 7.2, colour plate). Spongiosis is characterised by diminution and rounding of KCs, widening of intercellular spaces and stretching of remaining intercellular contacts, which result in a sponge-like appearance. This may develop to form small intraepidermal vesicles. Varying numbers of mononuclear cells are also present in the epidermis.

In subacute dermatitis lesions, the epidermal oedema is less prominent, there is some epidermal thickening (acanthosis), and the dermal perivascular infiltrate is more pronounced. After several months of allergen exposure, chronic dermatitis develops with a significant thickening of the epidermis and a moderate dermal infiltrate.

The erythema and oedema observed in these skin lesions are caused by increased blood flow in the vessels and increased vascular permeability, respectively. Itching (pruritus) which commonly accompanies the dermatitis is induced by the release of mediators.

7.4 Sensitisation to allergens

Contact allergens are small antigenic determinants (haptens) that need to be coupled to larger molecules (carriers) before they can become antigenic. Haptens can readily penetrate the skin barrier and, once in the extravascular spaces, bind covalently to a carrier protein, either serum proteins or the cell membranes of KCs or LCs. Although some agents such as 2,4-dintro-1-chlorobenzene (DNCB) can sensitise more than 90% of normal individuals after only one exposure, most contact allergens require repeated skin contact to induce a subsequent reaction.

Sensitisation takes 10-14 days to develop after epicutaneous application of the allergen and is initiated by bone marrow-derived LCs (see Chapter 1). LCs form a network of cells along the epidermis whose function is to trap and process antigens that cross the skin barrier. The allergen attaches to the LC membrane and is then internalised and processed. The resulting allergen fragments are then expressed in association with MHC Class II molecules on the surface of the cell.

7.4.1 Langerhans cell migration to lymph nodes

The next stage in the sensitisation process is the migration of the allergen peptide-carrying LCs from the epidermis to the dermis and into the draining lymphatics, and then on to the regional lymph nodes. Three cytokines have been identified as being necessary for the mobilisation, maturation and migration of LCs in response to skin sensitisation by an allergen; IL-1β, TNF-α and IL-18 (Table 7.3). These cytokines are synthesized by epidermal cells and are present at increased levels in sensitised skin. The sequence of events has not been fully established, but the following hypothesis

Table 7.3 Epidermal regulators of Langerhans cell migration

Stimulators		Inhibitors	
IL-18	Maintains enhanced levels of IL-1β and TNF-α	IL-10	Down-regulates IL-1 and TNF-α production
LC-derived IL-1β	Stimulates LC mobilisation Stimulates KC production of TNF-α	TGF-β	Inhibits up-regulation of CCR7 by TNF-α Increases LC E-cadherin expression
KC-derived TNF-α	Stimulates LC mobilisation Up-regulates CCR7 expression by LCs	Lactoferrin	Suppresses *de novo* TNF-α synthesis
		β_2 adrenoreceptors	Activated by catecholamines Up-regulate IL-10
		Adenosine receptors	Activated by adenosine Down-regulate migration-associated molecules

Figure 7.3   Mobilisation and maturation of Langerhans cells by cytokines in response to skin sensitisation.

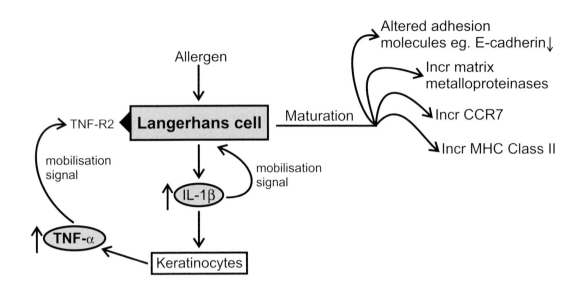

has been proposed based upon experimental findings [7].

IL-18 does not appear to act directly on LCs, but there is an early requirement for the cytokine, which may be necessary for maintenance of the increased levels of IL-1β and TNF-α. In contrast, it is likely that both IL-1β and TNF-α act directly on LCs, delivering mobilisation and maturation signals that facilitate their migration to the lymph nodes (Fig. 7.3). In mice it has been shown that LCs produce enhanced levels of IL-1β almost immediately in response to epicutaneous allergen application, and that the cytokine acts in an autocrine manner to stimulate mobilisation [8]. In contrast, in irritant contact dermatitis induced by sodium lauryl sulphate, IL-1α instead of IL-1β is involved in LC migration. Moreover, LC-derived IL-1β stimulates KCs to produce increased levels of TNF-α, which in turn signals via TNF-R2 (p75) on the LC surface. These interactions result in various changes in the phenotype of the LC. These include the altered expression of adhesion molecules to enable detachment from neighbouring KCs (down-regulation of E-cadherin) and interaction with the extracellular matrix during migration through the dermis, and increased matrix metalloproteinase (MMP-2 and MMP-9) production to facilitate the migration of LCs across the dermal-epidermal junction and through the collagen meshwork. CCR7 expression is also increased to allow homing and entry into the T cell-dependent area of the lymph node, whilst MHC Class I and II and costimulatory molecules are up-regulated resulting in enhanced antigen-presenting capacity.

Various other factors are also implicated from animal studies in the trafficking of LCs (and DDCs) from the skin to the draining lymph nodes. These include interferon consensus sequence-binding protein (ICSBP), PGE$_2$ and CD40 [9-11]. ICSBP is a transcription factor belonging to the interferon regulatory factor (IRF) family whose members are involved in modulation of cellular responses to interferons and viral infections, and in the regulation of cell growth and transformation. Dendritic cells from mice deficient in ICSBP exhibit an immature phenotype and reduced migration resulting in failure to induce a contact hypersensitivity response. PGE_2 signalling through one of its receptors, EP4 on LCs, also facilitates the initiation of skin immune responses by promoting migration and maturation of LCs, whilst CD40 stimulation is an effective signal for migration but not maturation of LCs.

7.4.2 Regulation of Langerhans cell migration to lymph nodes

In healthy skin, cytokines and other molecules regulate the migration of LCs from the epidermis to the regional lymph node (Table 7.3). The cytokine IL-10, which is up-regulated in epidermal cells following skin sensitisation, plays an important role via its ability to down-regulate IL-1β and TNF-α and inhibit contact sensitisation. Deletion of the IL-10 gene in mice results in increased numbers of antigen-bearing dendritic cells in the draining lymph nodes after skin sensitisation, which can be reversed by treatment with anti-TNF-α antibody or IL-1ra [12]. $TGF-β_1$ is also likely to contribute to regulation of LC migration. This pleiotropic cytokine inhibits up-regulation of CCR7 by TNF-α, and increases E-cadherin expression on dendritic cells, thus contributing to their retention in the epidermis [13,14]. Lactoferrin, an iron-binding protein found in extracellular secretions and expressed in normal skin, may also play a role. Exogenous topical lactoferrin inhibits allergen-induced migration of LCs and cutaneous inflammation via suppression of *de novo* TNF-α synthesis [15].

Two types of receptors, β2 adrenoceptors and adenosine receptors, expressed by LCs may also exert regulatory effects on LC migration (and other functions). Activation of β2 adrenoceptors by catecholamines has been shown to inhibit LC migration; this may involve up-regulation of IL-10 production [16]. Selective inhibition of dendritic cell migration by activation of adenosine receptors with adenosine, an immunomodulatory molecule, has also been reported [17]. In this case, inhibition is accompanied by down-regulation of a number of molecules involved in dendritic cell migration, such as CCR5 and MIP-3β (CCL19).

7.4.3 Antigen presentation within lymph nodes

The antigen-bearing LCs undergo a change in form on their way to the lymph node appearing as veiled cells in the afferent lymphatics. They then congregate in the paracortical (T cell dependent) areas of the regional lymph nodes, taking the form of interdigitating cells. Here these mature immunostimulatory dendritic cells present the allergen peptides carried from the skin to naïve T cells (Fig. 7.4). Sensitisation results in the generation of subpopulations of antigen-specific sensitised CD4[+] and CD8[+] T cells, which express CLA and recirculate through the skin. This can be demonstrated in an individual who has been sensitised with DNCB. About 10 days after epicutaneous application of the allergen, an eczematous flare reaction characterised by an influx of CD8[+] T cells and KC expression of MHC Class II antigens, is present at the application site. However, sensitisation is generally asymptomatic, and it is the elicitation of contact sensitivity that manifests as ACD.

Figure 7.4   Sensitisation of allergen-specific T cells in regional lymph nodes by allergen-carrying Langerhans cells from the skin.

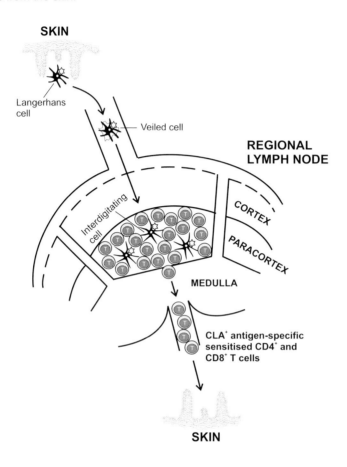

7.5 Elicitation of ACD

The elicitation of ACD is composed of two parts, both of which are necessary for full expression of the T cell response to contact allergens. The first involves non-specific, proinflammatory effects by haptens on skin cells. This conditions the skin for the second stage in which antigen-specific T cells are activated and generate an inflammatory response leading to further recruitment of leukocytes and the manifestation of clinical contact dermatitis.

7.5.1 Non-specific proinflammatory effects of haptens

Prior to their uptake by LCs, haptens can exert non-specific proinflammatory effects on skin cells, particularly KCs (Fig. 7.5). This has the effect of preparing the skin for hapten-induced elicitation (see below), and also to a lesser extent sensitisation (see above). Various *in vitro* (cell lines) and *in vivo* studies in mice and humans have demonstrated that direct contact of haptens with KCs, in the

Figure 7.5 Proinflammatory effects of haptens on KCs. Direct interaction of haptens with KCs results in the up-regulation of MHC Class II, adhesion and costimulatory molecules on the cell surface and the production of cytokines and chemokines. This facilitates both the presentation of allergen to specific T cells, and the recruitment of leukocytes to the skin.

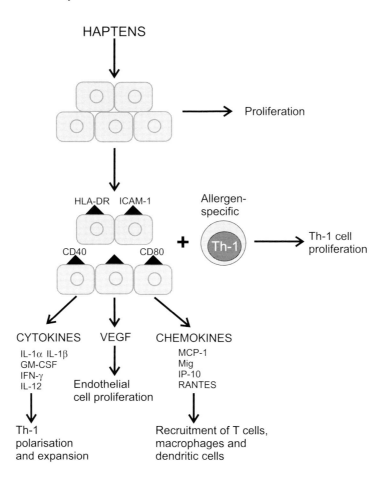

absence of antigen-specific recognition, induces proliferation, up-regulation of various cell surface molecules (HLA-DR, ICAM-1, CD80 (B7) and CD40) and increased production of cytokines (IL-1α, IL-1β, GM-CSF, IFN-γ, IL-12), chemokines (MCP-1, Mig, IP-10, RANTES) and the growth factor VEGF [18,19]. These changes facilitate leukocyte recruitment, adhesion and activation. Furthermore, KCs activated by allergens *in vitro* can induce allergen-specific T cell proliferation, and polarization of activated T lymphocytes to the Th-1 phenotype [18].

Overall the effects exerted by haptens on KC phenotype and function serve to promote the subsequent elicitation of the allergen-specific response by sensitised T cells. Contact irritants will also induce many of these same proinflammatory responses in KCs. Thus, simultaneous application of a contact irritant will increase the magnitude of an allergen-induced contact sensitivity response.

7.5.2 Activation and recruitment of T cells to the skin

When a sensitised individual is re-exposed through the skin to the sensitising allergen, LCs take it up, process it and express it on their cell surface in association with MHC Class II molecules. As in the sensitisation phase, the LCs migrate rapidly (within 24 hours) from the epidermis via the dermal lymphatics to the paracortical region of the draining lymph nodes. In the lymph nodes, the interdigitating cells present the allergen peptides to sensitised memory CD4+ and CD8+ T cells resulting in their activation, expression of CLA, and expansion. These antigen-specific T cells return to the site of allergen exposure in the skin, where they are reactivated and exert their effector functions.

In the skin, cytokines (IL-1 and TNF-α) released by activated KCs induce the up-regulation of adhesion molecules on endothelial cells facilitating the entry of sensitised memory T cells to the site of allergen exposure. Activated KCs also produce various chemokines, which contribute to leukocyte recruitment in a complex spatial and temporal pattern [20] (Fig. 7.6, colour plate). Thus only 6 hours after epicutaneous application of allergen, MCP-1 (CCL2) is expressed by basal KCs, clearly preceding the infiltration of monocytes and T cells. Increasing basal expression of MCP-1, and, in addition, the synthesis of another monocyte/macrophage/T lymphocyte chemoattractant, RANTES (CCL5) after 12 hr is paralleled by infiltration of mononuclear cells into the dermis and epidermis. Both basal and suprabasal KCs subsequently produce two other T lymphocyte-specific chemokines, Mig (CXCL9) and IP-10 (CXCL10), in response to IFN-γ released by recruited Th-1 and Tc-1 cells. Expression of these chemokines results in the preferential recruitment of hapten-specific CD8+ T cells into the epidermis as a result of their high expression of the CXCR3 receptor.

These chemokines are also expressed to a lesser extent in perivascular mononuclear cells in the dermis, together with three further chemokines MDC (macrophage-derived chemoattractant; CCL22), TARC (CCL17) and PARC (pulmonary and activation-regulated chemokine; CCL18), which are found exclusively in the dermis. In addition, dermal dendritic cells release TARC and MDC and predominately promote the recruitment of hapten-specific CCR4+ CD4+ T cells.

7.5.3 Amplification of T cell response

Allergen peptides are presented by LCs (or other APC such as DDCs, macrophages or activated KCs) to the recruited sensitised CLA+ T cells which become activated, proliferate and produce a variety of cytokines including the Th-1 cytokines, IL-2 and IFN-γ (Fig. 7.7). (It should be noted that certain chemical allergens that cause respiratory sensitisation, such as trimellitic anhydride, stimulate Th-2 type responses and the production of IgE antibodies).

Cytokines released by activated T cells, particularly IFN-γ and TNF-α, activate KCs (and other skin cells) in various ways such as by induction of surface molecules, and up-regulation of cytokine and chemokine production. These effects contribute to the amplification of the inflammatory response by attracting more leukocytes to the site, and promoting their interaction with skin cells.

Furthermore, T cell-derived cytokines/chemokines amplify the response by attracting in both antigen-specific (representing <10% of T cells) and antigen non-specific T cells, and macrophages to the epidermis and dermis. These mononuclear cells in turn also release cytokines that contribute to further inflammation and persistence of the allergic contact hypersensitivity response.

Figure 7.7   Model for the elicitation phase of ACD. Ts = sensitised T cell.

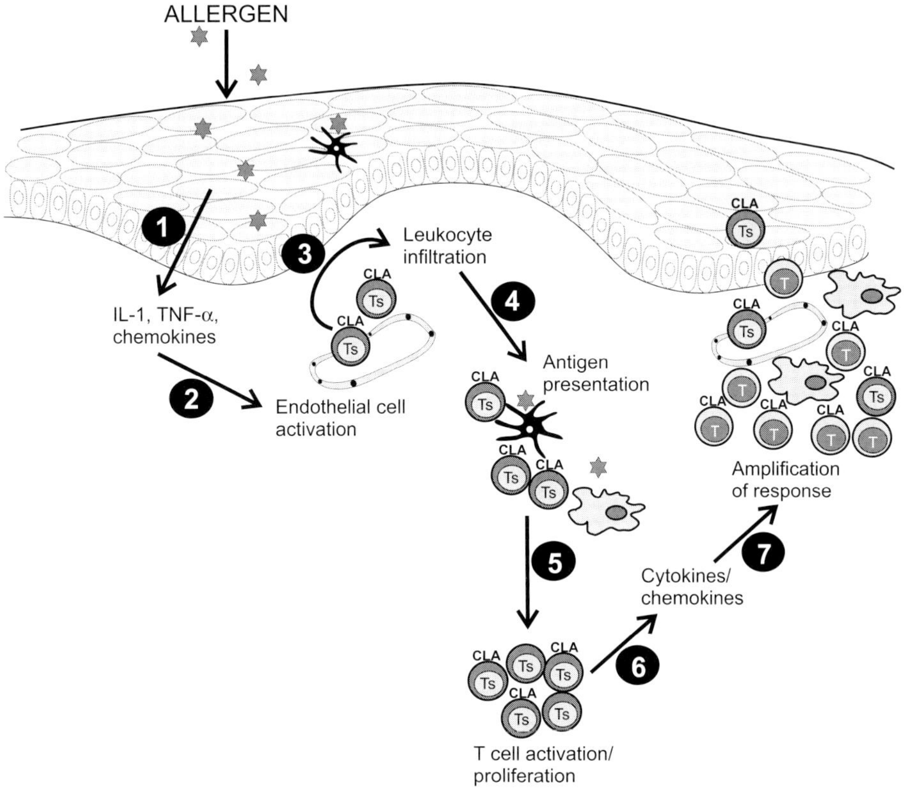

7.5.4 T cell-mediated keratinocyte damage

It has previously been suggested that cytotoxic CD8$^+$ T cells are the main effector cells in contact sensitivity, but more recent evidence from gene knockout mice support a role for both CD4$^+$ and CD8$^+$ T cell subsets in the elicitation of the cutaneous response to allergens [21]. These include CD4$^+$ and CD8$^+$ cytotoxic T lymphocytes (CTL) with a Th-1/Tc-1 (IFN-γ-producers) pattern of cytokine production, which are implicated in the KC damage characteristic of ACD skin lesions. At least two mechanisms appear to be involved; cytotoxicity mediated by perforin and granzyme B, and the Fas/FasL pathway.

In skin lesions of ACD, < 20-30% of T cells (CD4$^+$ and CD8$^+$) scattered in the dermis, at the dermo-epidermal junction and infiltrating the epidermis, are positive for perforin and granzyme B [22]. These cytotoxic granule proteins, stored in secretory lysosomes of NK cells and CTLs, are important mediators of cell-mediated cytotoxic reactions that are released upon cell activation. Perforin kills target cells by forming pores in the cell membrane and inducing cell lysis, whilst granzymes enter via these pores and trigger cell death by inducing degradation of DNA (Fig. 7.8). The cytotoxic protein-containing T cells are situated at sites of marked epidermal spongiosis in

Figure 7.8 Mechanisms of T cell-induced KC damage in the elicitation phase of ACD. Mechanism 1: CTL-derived perforin forms pores in the KC membrane allowing entry of granzymes, which trigger cell death by inducing degradation of DNA. Mechanism 2: IFN-γ produced by activated T cells induces the up-regulation of Fas on KCs facilitating Fas/FasL interaction between the two cell types. Caspases cleave E-cadherin on the KC surface, followed by DNA fragmentation and KC apoptosis.

Mechanism 1: Perforin/granzyme B-mediated

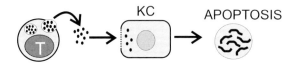

Mechanism 2: Fas-mediated

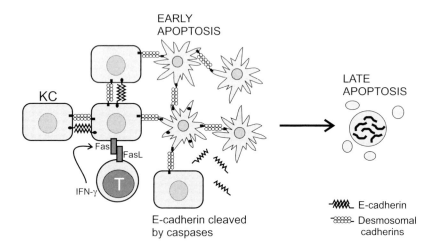

close proximity to KCs, some of which show signs of cell damage. In addition, expression of KC membrane E-cadherin is down-regulated at these sites, a mechanism associated with KC apoptosis. Therefore, the location and cytotoxic potential of the CD4$^+$ and CD8$^+$ T cells suggest that they are responsible for the injury to the epidermis.

It is well established that CTLs can also mediate cytotoxicity via the Fas/FasL pathway. KCs normally express low levels of Fas protein, but the molecule is up-regulated by IFN-γ stimulation. Apoptosis of IFN-γ-activated KCs can be induced *in vitro* by addition of anti-Fas antibody, soluble FasL, supernatant from activated T cells or direct contact between KCs and activated T cells expressing FasL (Fig. 7.8). In ACD skin lesions, KCs express increased levels of Fas protein and are in close proximity to activated FasL-positive T cells. Furthermore, there is DNA fragmentation and membrane phosphatidylserine expression by some KCs in lesional skin indicating on-going apoptosis. In the early stages of apoptosis, E-cadherin on the KC surface is cleaved by caspases that remove the β-catenin-binding domain (which links to actin microfilaments) from its cytoplasmic tail [23]. However, desmosomal cadherins such as desmogleins and desmocollins, which bind to the cytoplasmic proteins plakoglobin and desmoplakin and are linked to keratin filaments (see Chapter 5), are unaffected.

Further studies using skin and blood-derived nickel-specific CD4$^+$ and CD8$^+$ T cell subsets revealed that there were differences in the mechanisms used to kill autologous KCs in each case [24]. Thus Tc-1 and Tc-2 cells showed significant cytotoxic activity against resting nickel-modified KCs mediated by perforin, whilst Th-2 cells, which lacked perforin, used a FasL-mediated mechanism. In contrast, Th-1 cell clones were only able to target KCs preactivated with IFN-γ, and utilised both mechanisms to induce apoptosis.

7.5.5 Immunoregulation of the contact sensitivity response

In preventing autoimmunity, autoreactive T cells that escape central tolerance are suppressed by regulatory T cells (Trs), originally termed suppressor cells. In allergic contact sensitivity, a similar mechanism of immunoregulation exists (Fig. 7.9).

Several classes of specialized Tr subsets, with specific surface phenotypes and cytokine profiles after activation, have now been identified. Most of these Tr subsets are CD4$^+$ and suppress immune responses either by the release of anti-inflammatory cytokines or by a cell-cell contact-dependent mechanism. These include cross-regulatory Th-1 and Th-2 cells, TGF-β-secreting Th-3 cells, IL-10-producing type 1 Tr cells (Tr1) and naturally occurring CD4$^+$CD25$^+$ T cells.

Although most CD4$^+$ T cells in contact sensitivity responses belong to the Th-1 subset, there is a small subpopulation of Th-2 cells induced after hapten challenge that produce IL-4 and IL-10, but little IFN-γ [25]. These cells appear to have a regulatory role, including the suppression of inflammatory genes such as that specific for the chemokine IP-10 whose expression is up-regulated by CD8$^+$ T cells during elicitation of contact sensitivity.

Th-3 cells suppress immune responses via production of TGF-β and are probably involved in the induction of oral tolerance to foreign and self antigens. However, these regulatory cells do not appear to play a significant role in hapten-induced skin hypersensitivity responses.

The two classes of regulatory T cells that are of significance in ACD are Tr1 and naturally occurring CD4$^+$CD25$^+$ T cells.

7.5.5.1 IL-10-producing Tr1 cells

Characteristics of Tr1 cells

IL-10-producing Tr1 cells derived from culture of peripheral blood T cells have been recently characterised [26]. Upon activation, Tr1 cells produce predominately IL-10 and TGF-β, with some IFN-γ and no IL-2 or IL-4, and have a low proliferative capacity, which can be overcome by the addition of IL-15. In contrast, skin-derived Tr1 cells produce low and inconsistent levels of TGF-β. Tr1 cells express CD4, CD25 (IL-2 receptor α chain), the β$_2$ chain of the IL-12 receptor and other surface markers expressed by Th-1 cells.

Figure 7.9   Modulation of contact sensitivity to allergens by Tr1 regulatory cells in ACD.

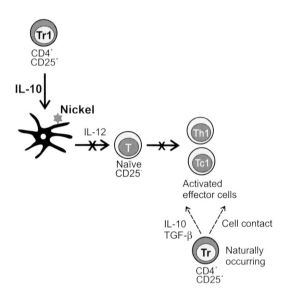

Tr1 cells specific for a variety of antigens also develop *in vivo*, but can be cultured from naïve CD4+ T cells *in vitro*, in the presence of IL-10 and IFN-α. Tr1 cells suppress naïve and memory Th-1 or Th-2 antigen-specific responses via production of IL-10 (and TGF-β).

Immature dendritic cells can also induce an IL-10-producing regulatory T cell subpopulation, which proliferates poorly after stimulation. However, these CD4+ T cells inhibit antigen-specific proliferation and cytokine production of Th-1 cells in a cell contact-dependent manner. In addition, Th-1 cells which have been activated in an incomplete or defective manner causing them to become anergic to antigen, also produce high levels of IL-10 and can suppress immune responses via effects on dendritic cells.

Tr1 cells and ACD

The isolation of nickel-specific CD4+ IL-10-producing Tr1 cells from skin challenged with nickel, and from the peripheral blood of nickel-allergic and healthy individuals provided evidence for a role for Tr1 cells in the regulation of the T cell response to epicutaneous allergens [27]. These Tr1 cells inhibited nickel-specific Th-1 and Tc-1 cell responses via IL-10-mediated effects on dendritic cell function (Fig. 7.9). Both the differentiation and maturation of monocyte-derived dendritic cells, including production of IL-12, was impaired by IL-10 released by the Tr1 cells in response to nickel.

7.5.5.2 CD4+CD25+ regulatory T cells

Characteristics of CD4+CD25+Tr cells

A subpopulation of CD4+ T cells which express CD25 and have potent immunoregulatory properties (CD25+ Tr) has been identified as the major subset of T cells mediating peripheral self-tolerance in experimental animals and humans [28]. These regulatory T cells differentiate in the thymus, constituting 5-10% of the circulating naïve CD4+ T cell repertoire of normal mice and humans, and have therefore been termed naturally occurring. Freshly isolated CD25+ Tr cells must be stimulated via the TCR to induce suppressive function, and, once activated, can inhibit both CD4+ and CD8+ T cell responses in an antigen non-specific (bystander) fashion. Most studies show that this suppression is not mediated by cytokines but by a mechanism involving cell-cell contact.

However, *in vivo*, the mechanism by which CD25$^+$ Tr cells regulate immune responses is unknown and cytokines (IL-10, TGF-β) may be involved in some circumstances depending upon factors such as the nature of the target organ and the extent of the inflammatory response. In either case, the underlying mechanism of suppression remains to be elucidated.

Identification of CD25$^+$ Tr cells on the basis of surface marker expression is, however, problematic since many of the molecules including CD25, CTLA-4, PDCD1 (programmed cell death 1), TNFR2 and GITR (glucocorticoid-induced TNF receptor) are also found on activated CD4$^+$ T cells. Thus the functional significance, if any, of the expression of these surface molecules is unclear. However, a transcription factor Foxp3 (scurfin) has recently been shown to be a functional marker of CD25$^+$ Tr cells in mice and humans and plays an important role in their generation [29]. Thus mice whose Foxp3 gene has been deleted develop an autoimmune pathology secondary to loss of CD25$^+$ Tr cell function, whereas mice over-expressing the transcription factor have increased CD25$^+$ Tr cells and can potently suppress the development of autoimmune disease. In addition, it has also been demonstrated that an intact IL-2/IL-2R pathway is a prerequisite for thymic generation and peripheral homeostasis of CD25$^+$ Tr cells.

The antigen specificity of CD25$^+$ Tr cells remains unknown. The polyclonal TCR repertoire of these cells suggests, however, that they may recognise a variety of different antigens including self and pathogen-derived antigens.

CD4+CD25+ Tr cells and ACD

CD25$^+$ Tr cells have been isolated from several peripheral tissues including skin. Indeed, approximately 30% of circulating CD25$^+$ Tr cells coexpress CLA, which is up-regulated during T cell activation in skin-draining lymph nodes. In non-allergic healthy individuals, circulating CD25$^+$ Tr cells, which were themselves anergic to nickel, strongly inhibited nickel-specific activation of T cells in a cytokine-independent, but cell contact-dependent manner [30]. Furthermore, regulatory T cells coexpressing CLA were more efficient at suppressing nickel responsiveness of CD25$^-$ T cells than those that lacked CLA. About two-thirds of the circulating CD25$^+$ Tr cells expressed the CCR7 chemokine receptor and markedly inhibited naïve T cell activation to nickel.

The site of a negative patch test in response to nickel showed a T cell infiltrate consisting of approximately 20% CLA$^+$CD4$^+$ and CD25$^+$ T cells [29]. These skin-derived T cells also suppressed nickel-specific responses of circulating CD25$^-$ T cells. These findings suggest that CD25$^+$ Tr cells migrate from the blood to the lymph node and then into the skin, possibly suppressing T cell responses to hapten at both sites.

In contrast, CD25$^+$ Tr cells isolated from the peripheral blood of nickel-allergic patients were poor or non suppressors of nickel-specific T cell responses suggesting that defective immunoregulation may contribute to the development of ACD [30]. Relevant to these findings is the observation that CD25$^+$ Tr cells can induce CD25$^-$ T cells in co-culture to become IL-10-producing Tr1-like cells with a suppressive phenotype [31]. Functional circulating and skin nickel-specific Tr1 cells have been isolated from nickel-allergic individuals (see above). However, it is possible that CD25$^+$ Tr cells play a more important role than Tr1 cells and that the latter may not be able to compensate fully for their lack of function. In addition, CD25$^+$ Tr cells have been shown to control the expansion of memory CD8$^+$ T cells [32]. A lack of CD8$^+$ T cell regulation may be of relevance to the major role of this T cell subset in ACD.

7.6 Treatment

When a patient presents with ACD, the likely cause of the inflammatory skin response is determined using patch testing (see Chapter 4). Avoidance of the offending material is the best prevention, but this may not remove the problem entirely as complete avoidance of some allergens may not be possible. Protective barrier creams may be used as an additional preventative measure for ACD. For example a barrier cream containing a chelating agent (10% diethylenetriaminepenta-acetic acid) has proved effective for preventing positive patch test responses in nickel, cobalt and copper-sensitive individuals [33].

Treatments given to patients with ACD are predominately aimed at reducing inflammation, and have usually involved the use of topical corticosteroids, with the adjunct of antihistamines, wet dressings, and emollients for alleviation of symptoms. Corticosteroids have inhibitory effects on inflammatory and immune responses, primarily through the modulation of expression of transcription factors, such as AP-1 and NF-κB. Two new topical non-steroidal anti-inflammatory agents, pimecrolimus and tacrolimus, are now being tested as alternatives to steroids in the treatment of inflammatory skin diseases.

Pimecrolimus (SDZ ASM 981), an ascomycin derivative, is one of the new classes of immunomodulating macrolactams and has significant anti-inflammatory activity and immunomodulatory capabilities [34]. It is a calcineurin inhibitor which blocks the T cell signal transduction pathway and inhibits the synthesis of both Th-1 and Th-2 type cytokines. The drug has also been shown to prevent the release of cytokines and proinflammatory mediators from mast cells. Pimecrolimus has proved to be as effective as topical steroids in ACD (atopic dermatitis and psoriasis) but without the side effects, such as skin atrophy, associated with steroid use. Furthermore, it has little effect on the systemic immune response as blood levels are very low after topical application and there is no accumulation after repeated applications. However, in one recent study in the US, the application of topical pimecrolimus was found to be ineffective in the treatment of ongoing Toxicodendron (poison ivy)-induced ACD.

Tacrolimus (FK506) is an immunosuppressive macrolide that is currently used to prevent organ rejection in transplantation. In common with pimecrolimus, it is a calcineurin inhibitor, preventing the transcription of messenger RNA for various inflammatory cytokines in both Th-1 and Th-2 cells, and acts by binding to an intracellular binding protein (FKBP). In addition, tacrolimus modulates the expression of various surface molecules (IL-2R, B7-1, CD40, MHC Class I and II antigens) on LCs, which probably contributes to its therapeutic effects. Topical tacrolimus been shown to be significantly more effective than placebo in the resolution of nickel-induced ACD (and atopic dermatitis) [35].

Summary

- ACD results from a dysregulated T cell response to haptens in contact with the skin.
- Tc-1 cells are principally responsible for expression of ACD via cytotoxic damage to KCs.
- Th-1 cells augment disease expression by secreting proinflammatory cytokines and contributing to KC damage.
- Th-2 cells suppress contact sensitivity in mice, but their role in human ACD is controversial.
- Circulating nickel-specific T cells are present in non-allergic individuals suggesting that they have been sensitised to the hapten. However, IL-10-producing Tr1 cells and CD4$^+$ CD25$^+$ regulatory T cells prevent elicitation by inhibiting dendritic cell function and allergen-specific T cell responses, respectively.
- In ACD, CD4$^+$ CD25$^+$ regulatory T cells are poor suppressors of T cell response to allergens leading to persistence of the skin inflammatory response.
- Other possible causes of the dysregulated skin inflammatory response include
  - o   Lack of suppressive cytokine production (IL-10, TGF-β), which could lead to increased LC numbers in the draining lymph nodes and unregulated T cell responses.
  - o   Altered levels/function of lactoferrin leading to unregulated TNF-α production, and increased LCs in the draining lymph nodes.
  - o   Increased susceptibility of KCs to proinflammatory effects of haptens and/or to apoptosis.

References

1. Menné T. & Holm N.V. Nickel allergy in a female twin population. Int.J.Dermatol. 1983; **22:** 22-8.

2. Olerup O. & Emtestam L. Allergic contact dermatitis to nickel is associated with a Taq I HLA-DQA allelic restriction fragment. Immunogenet. 1988; **28:** 310-3.

3. Orecchia G., Perfetti L., Finco O., Dondi E., Cuccia M. Polymorphisms of HLA Class III genes in allergic contact dermatitis. Dermatol. 1992; **184:** 254-9.

4. Silvennoinen-Kassinen S., Ikaheimo I., Tiilikainen A. TAP1 and TAP2 genes in nickel allergy. Int.Arch.Allergy Immunol. 1997; **114:** 94-6.

5. Westphal G.A., Reich K., Schulz T.G., Neumann C., Hallier E., Schnuch A. N-acetyl transferase 1 and 2 polymorphisms in para-substituted arylamine-induced contact allergy. Br.J.Dermatol. 2000; **142:** 1121-7.

6. Westphal G.A., Schnuch A., Moessner R. *et al.* Cytokine gene polymorphisms in allergic contact dermatitis. Contact Dermatitis 2003; **48:** 93-8.

7. Cumberbatch M., Dearman R.J., Griffiths C.E.M., Kimber I. Epidermal Langerhans cell migration and sensitisation to chemical allergens. A.P.M.I.S. 2003; **111:** 797-804.

8. Enk A.H. & Katz S.I. Early molecular events in the induction phase of contact sensitivity. Proc.Natl.Acad.Sci. USA 1992; **89:** 1398–402.

9. Schiavoni G., Mattei F., Borghi P. *et al.* ICSBP is critically involved in the normal development and trafficking of Langerhans cells and dermal dendritic cells. Blood 2004; **103:** 2221-8.

10. Kabashima K., Sakata D., Nagamachi M., Miyachi Y., Inaba K., Narumiya S. Prostaglandin E_2-EP4 signaling initiates skin immune responses by promoting migration and maturation of Langerhans cells. Nat.Med. 2003; **9:** 744-9.

11. Jolles S., Christensen J., Holman M., Klaus G.B., Ager A. Systemic treatment with anti-CD40 antibody stimulates Langerhans cell migration from the skin. Clin.Exp. Immunol. 2002; **129:** 519-26.

12. Wang B., Zhuang L., Fujisawa H. *et al.* Enhanced epidermal Langerhans cell migration in IL-10 knockout mice. J.Immunol. 1999; **162:** 277–83.

13. Sato K., Kawasaki H., Nagayama H. *et al.* TGF-beta 1 reciprocally controls chemotaxis of human peripheral blood monocyte-derived dendritic cells via chemokine receptors. J.Immunol. 2000; **164:** 2285–95.

14. Riedl E., Stockl J., Majdic O., Scheinecker C., Knapp W., Strobl H. Functional involvement of E-cadherin in TGF-beta 1-induced cluster formation of *in vitro* developing Langerhans cell type dendritic cells. J.Immunol. 2000; **165:** 1381–6.

15. Griffiths C.E.M., Cumberbatch M., Tucker S.C. *et al.* Exogenous topical lactoferrin inhibits allergen-induced Langerhans cell migration and cutaneous inflammation in humans. Br.J.Dermatol. 2001; **144:** 715–25.

16. Maestroni G.J. & Mazzola P. Langerhans cell beta 2-adrenoceptors: role in migration, cytokine production, Th priming and contact hypersensitivity. J. Neuroimmunol. 2003; **144:** 91-9.

17. Hofer S., Ivarsson L., Stoitzner P. *et al*. Adenosine slows migration of dendritic cells but does not affect other aspects of dendritic cell maturation. J.Invest.Dermatol. 2003; **121:** 300-7.

18. Banerjee G., Damodaran A., Devi N., Dharmalingam K., Raman G. Role of keratinocytes in antigen presentation and polarization of human T lymphocytes. Scand.J.Immunol. 2004; **59:** 385-94.

19. Palacio S., Schmitt D., Viac J. Contact allergens and sodium lauryl sulphate upregulate vascular endothelial growth factor in normal keratinocytes. Br.J. Dermatol. 1997; **137:** 540-4.

20. Goebeler M., Trautmann A., Voss A., Bröcker E.-B., Toksoy A., Gillitzer R. Differential and sequential expression of multiple cytokines during elicitation of allergic contact hypersensitivity. Am.J.Pathol. 2001; **158:** 431-40.

21. Wang B., Fujisawa H., Zhuang L. *et al*. CD4[+] Th1 and CD8[+] type 1 cytotoxic T cells both play a crucial role in the full development of contact hypersensitivity. J.Immunol. 2000; **165:** 6783-90.

22. Yawalkar N., Hunger R.E., Buri C. *et al*. A comparative study of the expression of cytotoxic proteins in allergic contact dermatitis and psoriasis. Spongiotic skin lesions in allergic contact dermatitis are highly infiltrated by T cells expressing perforin and granzyme B. Am. J.Pathol. 2001; **158:** 803-8.

23. Trautmann A., Akdis M., Bröcker E.-B., Blaser K., Akdis C.A. New insights into the role of T cells in atopic dermatitis and allergic contact dermatitis. Trends Immunol. 2001; **22:** 530-2.

24. Traidl C., Sebastiani. S, Albanesi C. *et al*. Disparate cytotoxic activity of nickel-specific CD8[+] and CD4[+] T cell subsets against keratinocytes. J.Immunol. 2000; **165:** 3058-64.

25. Xu H., DiIulio N.A., Fairchild R.L. T cell populations primed by hapten sensitization in contact sensitivity are distinguished by polarized patterns of cytokine production: interferon gamma-producing (Tc1) effector CD8[+] T cells and interleukin (Il) 4/Il-10-producing (Th2) negative regulatory CD4[+] T cells. J.Exp.Med. 1996; **183:** 1001-12.

26. Roncarolo M.G., Bacchetta R., Bordignon C., Narula S., Levings M.K. Type 1 T regulatory cells. Immunol.Rev. 2001; **182:** 68-79.

27. Cavani A., Nasorri F., Prezzi C., Sebastiani S., Albanesi C., Girolomoni G. Human CD4[+] T lymphocytes with remarkable regulatory functions on dendritic cells and nickel-specific Th1 immune responses. J.Invest.Dermatol. 2000; **114:** 295-302.

28. Piccirillo C.A. & Thornton A.M. Cornerstone of peripheral tolerance: naturally occurring CD4[+]CD25[+] regulatory T cells. Trends Immunol. 2004; **25:** 374-80.

29. Khattri R., Cox T., Yasayko S.A., Ramsdell F. An essential role for Scurfin in CD4[+]CD25[+] T regulatory cells. Nat.Immunol. 2003; **4:** 337-42.

30. Cavani A., Nasorri F., Ottaviani C., Sebastiani S., De Pita O., Girolomoni G. Human CD25[+] regulatory T cells maintain immune tolerance to nickel in healthy, nonallergic individuals. J.Immunol. 2003; **171:** 5760-8.

31. Dieckmann D., Bruett C.H., Ploettner H., Lutz M.B., Schuler G. Human CD4[+]CD25[+] regulatory, contact-dependent T cells induce interleukin 10-producing, contact-independent

type 1-like regulatory T cells. J.Exp.Med. 2002; **196:** 247–53.

32. Kursar M., Bonhagen K., Fensterle J. *et al.* Regulatory CD4$^+$CD25$^+$ T cells restrict memory CD8$^+$ T cell responses. J.Exp.Med. 2002; **196:**1585–92.

33. Wohrl S., Kriechbaumer N., Hemmer W. *et al.* A cream containing the chelator DTPA (diethylenetriaminepenta-acetic acid) can prevent contact allergic reactions to metals. Contact Dermatitis. 2001; **44:** 224-8.

34. Gupta A.K. & Chow M. Pimecrolimus: a review. J.Eur.Acad.Dermatol.Venereol. 2003; **17:** 493-503.

35. Saripalli Y.V., Gadzia J.E., Belsito D.V. Tacrolimus ointment 0.1% in the treatment of nickel-induced allergic contact dermatitis. J.Am.Acad.Dermatol. 2003; **49:** 477-82.

PART III: Immunological Mechanisms of Skin Disease

$$\boxed{8}$$

Atopic Dermatitis

Atopic dermatitis (AD), also known as atopic eczema, is a common, chronic fluctuating skin disease which is often associated with type I hypersensitivity-mediated conditions such as allergic rhinitis, allergic conjunctivitis, asthma and IgE-mediated food allergy. In contrast, AD skin lesions are characterised by a T cell-mediated type IV hypersensitivity response to environmental antigens.

8.1 Clinical features

AD is a common disease that affects people of all ages, all over the world, with a prevalence in children of between 7 and 17%. In 60% or more of these affected children, the disease can persist into adulthood. Frequently, AD is associated with development of allergic rhinitis and/or asthma later in childhood.

Presentation of the disease commonly occurs within the first 2 years of life. A high proportion of infants with AD have a positive family history of AD, asthma or allergic rhinitis in one or both parents. In the young infant, the cheeks and trunk are commonly involved and the lesions are erythematous and oozing (Fig. 8.1, colour plate). As the child grows, the hands, neck area and feet become affected, whilst in the older child the lesions are predominantly behind the knees, in the elbow folds and frequently on the face. Adults with AD show a more generalised distribution, commonly with diffuse involvement of the trunk and upper thigh area. The lesions are erythematous and often exudative, with a varying degree of secondary bacterial infection. Intense itching causes constant rubbing and excoriation (stripping) of the skin, which becomes lichenified with a thickened coarse appearance. A high proportion of patients with chronic AD have an associated dry skin, which is frequently hypersensitive and mildly pruritic.

8.2 Aetiology

Atopy is defined as an increased propensity to produce IgE antibodies to common allergens. AD is one of the clinical manifestations of atopy and is strongly associated with other atopic conditions such as asthma, allergic rhinitis, conjunctivitis and food allergies. AD is a multifactorial disease in which both hereditary and environmental factors play a role.

8.2.1 Genetics

The significantly increased concordance rates for AD in monozygotic (77%) compared to dizygotic (15%) twins supports the involvement of genetic factors in susceptibility to the disease. Furthermore, a genetic contribution to atopy/IgE responsiveness has also been confirmed by twin studies using a variety of atopic-associated parameters.

The genetics of AD has been investigated using two approaches; by determining chromosomal regions of genetic linkage in families, and by testing the frequency of polymorphisms in candidate genes in patients and controls.

8.2.1.1 Genetic linkage

In children with AD, two genome scans have been performed. The first identified linkage to a region on chromosome 3q21 in German and Scandinavian children [1], whilst the second found three regions of linkage to AD, or to AD plus asthma, on chromosomes 1q21, 17q25 and 20p [2] (Table 8.1). Evidence for linkage of total serum IgE levels to 3q21, and to two other regions, 5q31 and 16qtel, have been reported, but is weaker than the evidence for linkage to AD. A third genome scan has been carried out on adult patients with AD in Sweden [3] which identified several possible regions of linkage including 3p24-22, and, for AD with raised allergen-specific IgE, 18q21. In addition, using a severity score, suggestive linkage to chromosomes 3q14, 13q14, 15q14-15 and 17q21 was found. In common with the chromosome 13q14 linkage site, an association with which was reported in an earlier study, the linkage sites on chromosomes 3q and 17q in adults may correspond to those reported in children with AD.

Several regions of linkage to atopy have been identified and confirmed on chromosomes 5q35, 6p21 (MHC complex), 11q13, 12q, 13q14, 14q and 16q in patients with asthma and allergy. These loci mostly differ from those with strongest linkage to AD suggesting that many of the AD susceptibility genes code for proteins with atopic-unrelated functions.

8.2.1.2 Linkage sites shared by AD and psoriasis

The four linkage sites found in the two genome scans of children with AD (3q21, 1q21, 17q25, 20p) closely correspond to four of the loci reported to contain susceptibility genes for psoriasis (see Chapter 9) [2]. These shared regions of linkage could, therefore, contain genes that control skin inflammation and immunity in both AD and psoriasis.

Chromosome 1q21 (Epidermal differentiation cluster)

The shared linkage site for AD and psoriasis on chromosome 1q21 contains the epidermal differentiation complex (EDC), which consists of three gene families coding for small proline-rich proteins (SPRRs), several S100A calcium-binding proteins, and late envelope proteins (LEPs). Several of the proteins coded for by the EDC are involved in the formation of the cornified cell envelope, and expression is linked to KC terminal differentiation. Furthermore, the S100A calcium-binding proteins are often secreted and have various immunological functions including chemotactic activity (S100A2, S100A7 (psoriasin) and S100A8), cytostatic and anti-microbial

Table 8.1 Chromosomal linkage sites in AD

Linkage sites	Candidate gene	Comment	Other diseases with same linkage
1q21	Epidermal differentiation complex	Formation of cornified cell envelope S100A proteins - various immunological functions	Psoriasis
3p24-22	Unknown	Adult AD	
3q21 (3q14)	Unknown	Scandinavian mutation? Candidate gene in psoriasis: SLC12A8	Asthma, Psoriasis
13q14	PHF11	Associated with high IgE	Asthma
15q14-15	Unknown	Adult AD	
17q25	Unknown	Candidate genes in psoriasis: SLC9A3R1/NAT9 RAPTOR	Psoriasis, multiple sclerosis, rheumatoid arthritis, epidermodysplasia verruciformis
18q21	Unknown	Associated with AD and raised allergen-specific IgE	
20p	Unknown	AD with asthma subset	Psoriasis, leprosy, SLE

activities (S100A8/S100A9 complex), inhibition of macrophage activation and immunoglobulin synthesis (S1008.S100A9), and proinflammatory effects on endothelial cells and inflammatory cells (S100A12).

Chromosome 3q21

Linkage to chromosome 3q21 has been found for AD, psoriasis and asthma. In psoriasis, a potassium/chloride transporter, SLC12A8, has been proposed as a candidate susceptibility gene for the disease. Interestingly, linkage to this site has been found in 3 genome scans of Scandinavian families and in one of mixed German and Swedish families raising the possibility that the gene mutation involved is more frequently expressed in individuals of Swedish origin.

Chromosome 17q25

The AD/psoriasis linkage site on chromosome 17q25, which is also shared by multiple sclerosis and rheumatoid arthritis, has been linked to a single gene disorder called epidermodysplasia verruciformis. Patients with this disorder suffer from chronic infections with the oncogenic human papillomavirus, type V and are susceptible to development of skin carcinomas. Family-based association tests in psoriasis have led to the identification of two peaks containing susceptibility loci; one peak contains SLC9A3R1 (PDZ domain-containing phosphoprotein) and NAT9, and the other RAPTOR (p150 target of rapamycin (TOR)-scaffold protein containing WD-repeats) (See Chapter 9). The possible role of these genes in AD susceptibility is currently being investigated.

Chromosome 20p

Linkage to chromosome 20p was found in a subset of children who had both AD and asthma and in whom IgE levels were higher than in children with either of the diseases alone [2]. Furthermore, leprosy and SLE have shown genetic linkage to this region. Although ADAM33, a susceptibility gene for asthma and bronchial hyperresponsiveness, is also located in this region it does not appear to be the gene responsible for linkage in AD patients.

8.2.1.3 Candidate genes

Investigation of the frequencies of polymorphisms in candidate genes can often be statistically more powerful than genetic linkage, so that a candidate gene may show association in a region that does not show linkage. Several candidate genes for AD have been implicated including FcεRI-β, SPINK5, Th-1/Th-2 cytokines, IL-4 receptor, RANTES, IRF2, CARD4/Nod1, CARD15/Nod2, TLR2/TLR4, Tim-1 and HSCCE (Table 8.2)

FcεRI-β gene

FcεRI, the high affinity IgE receptor on the surface of mast cells, plays a pivotal role in the allergic response. The β chain of the receptor stabilises its surface expression and acts as an amplifying element, but is not essential for its function. Refinement of the diagnostic criteria for AD enabled the association between AD and FcεRI-β polymorphisms to be investigated. Significant sharing of maternal alleles for AD and allele 2 of Rsal intron 2 (Rsalvin2*2) and allele 1 of Rsal exon 7 (Rsalvex7*1) FcεRI-β gene polymorphisms was found [4]. These polymorphisms also showed association with asthma.

SPINK5

SPINK5 has been identified as the gene underlying a rare and severe autosomal recessive skin disorder called Netherton disease that is characterised by congenital ichthyosis, a specific hair-shaft defect and atopic manifestations with high IgE levels. SPINK5, on chromosome 5q31, codes for a serine proteinase inhibitor (LEKT1, lympho-epithelial Kazal-type-related inhibitor), which is expressed in epithelial and mucosal tissues, and in the thymus. Six coding polymorphisms in SPINK5 have been identified; transmission disequilibrium tests have been used to study associations between AD and three of these polymorphisms (Asn368→Ser, Asp386→Asn and Glu420→Lys) that have a minor allele frequency of greater than 10% [5]. In the first group of families consisting of children with AD, asthma, or both, two alleles (Asn 368 and Lys420) were significantly associated with increased risk of atopy when maternally inherited. Similar associations were observed to AD and to total serum IgE concentrations, but only a weak association between Lys 420 and asthma was found. When a second panel of families were tested, significant associations between atopy, AD, asthma and total serum IgE levels and Lys420 were observed, but associations with Asn368 were

Table 8.2 Candidate genes in AD

Chromosomal location	Gene	Alleles/Haplotypes	Functional consequences
11q12-13	FcεR1β	Allele 2 of Rsal intron 2 Allele 1 of Rsal exon 7	Regulatory effect on IgE production
5q31-33	SPINK5 (LEKT1)	Glu420→Lys	Netherton disease Decreased serine proteinase activity?
5q31-33	IL-4	590T	Increased IL-4
5q31-33	IL-13	Arg130Gln 4257bp (G→A) Arg130Gln + -589C/T (IL-4)	Increased IL-13 and IgE
16p12-p11	IL-4Rα	Q551R	Increased function
5q31-33	IL-12p40	1188A decreased	Decreased IL-12p40
19p13.1	IL-12RB1	-111(A/T)	Decreased IL-12RB1 mRNA
11q22	IL-18	+113 (T/G) (exon 1) +127 (C/T) (exon 1) -137 (G/C) (promotor 1) -133 (C/G) (promotor 2)	Increased IL-18
5q31-33	GM-CSF	677*C/C	Protective
17q11-q21	RANTES	-401A (promotor)	New consensus binding site for GATA transcription factor family Increased RANTES
4q35	IRF2	-467G (promotor) -467G + 921A + 1739(ATCC)8	Transcriptional activity affected?
7p14-p15	CARD4/Nod1	rs 2907748 rs 2907749 rs 2075822	Impaired recognition of bacterial peptidoglycan
16q12	CARD15/Nod2	C2722 C3020	Impaired recognition of bacterial peptidoglycan
4q32	TLR2	R753Q	Increased susceptibility to infection and colonisation, especially with *S. aureus*
9q32-q33	TLR4	D299G T3991	Increased susceptibility to infection and colonisation
5q31-33	TIM-1	5383_5397 del	Th-2 cytokine bias
19q13.3	HSCCE (KLK7)	AACC insertion	Altered stratum corneum proteins

not found [5].

The Glu420→Lys polymorphism of the SPINK5 gene introduces an additional basic residue into the linker sequence between 2 of the 15 proteinase inhibitor domains of LEKT1. This may be relevant to the proteolysis of the protein by extraneous proteinases, which cleaves the linker sequences to release the inhibitory domains. The failure of LEKT1 to act as an efficient inhibitor of serine proteinases could potentially influence allergic disease in various ways. LEKT1 expressed in the upper layers of AD skin may be protective to the effects of allergens, which can also act as serine proteinases. This may also be relevant in the airways of the lung since allergens can cleave complement C5 into its active components. In addition proteinase-activated receptors on KCs, activated by tryptase and chymase released by mast cells, may also be regulated by LEKT1.

Th-1/Th-2 cytokines

Proximal to SPINK5 on chromosome 5q31-33 is a cluster of genes coding for cytokines. Gene polymorphisms of cytokines and their receptors are attractive candidates as genetic factors for immune-mediated diseases, and several have been investigated in AD, particularly those involved in regulation of IgE production.

The Th-2 cytokines, **IL-4** and **IL-13**, are increased in acute AD skin lesions and stimulate B cells to produce IgE antibodies. Thus functional polymorphisms of the genes coding for these cytokines may contribute to the genetic basis of AD. Transmission disequilibrium testing of Japanese families showed a significantly preferential transmission to AD offspring of the T allele of the -590C/T polymorphism of the IL-4 gene [6]. The T allele is associated with increased IL-4 gene promotor activity compared to that of the C allele, and could therefore contribute to the susceptibility of individuals to develop AD.

In a more recent study, the Arg130Gln allele of another Th-2 cytokine, **IL-13**, was found to be associated with atopy and with AD in Canadian children [7]. Furthermore, haplotypes consisting of IL-13 Arg130Gln and the T allele of the 589C/T polymorphism of the IL-4 gene were also associated with both AD and atopy. In another study, a novel IL-13 coding region variant at 4257 bp (G to A, fourth exon) was identified and shown to be significantly associated with both high IgE levels and AD [8].

In addition, polymorphisms of the gene coding for the α chain of the **IL-4 receptor**, present on chromosome 16p12-p11, have been investigated in relation to susceptibility to AD. A positive association between the gain of function mutation Q551- >R and AD has been found in at least two studies [9,10]. In one study, the presence of the polymorphism was positively associated with flexural eczema in children up to 6 months old who had not been given antibiotics (i.e. had not had an infection), but not in those who had [10]. There was, however, no association with positive skin prick tests or serum IgE levels.

In contrast to the Th-2 cytokines, **IL-12** suppresses IgE production, and induces IFN-γ and Th-1 cytokine profiles. To determine whether a functional polymorphism of IL-12 may be associated with AD, the PCR-fragment length polymorphism method was used to genotype patients with AD or psoriasis (Th-1 cytokine-mediated), and healthy controls for the presence of a SNP at position 1188 in the 3' untranslated region of the IL-12p40 gene (1188A/C) [11]. The 1188 alleles show different levels of IL-12p40 mRNA expression in cell lines, with expression significantly reduced in the C/C genotype relative to the A/A genotype cell line. In keeping with these differences in IL-

12p40 expression, the A allele was significantly decreased in AD patients, but increased in psoriasis patients compared with controls, suggesting that the IL-12p40 polymorphism is associated with susceptibility to both AD and psoriasis, presumably by affecting Th-1/Th-2 balance.

Furthermore, in a case-control association study, promotor polymorphisms -111A/T and -2C/T of the IL-12 receptor gene (IL-12RB1) were shown to be significantly associated with an increased risk of AD in a recessive model [12]. The -111T/T genotype was increased in AD patients in an IgE level-dependent manner, and cells from these individuals expressed lower levels of IL-12RB1 mRNA.

IL-18, a cytokine associated with induction of Th-1 and Th-2 cytokines, is increased in the serum of AD patients during exacerbation of disease. In addition, PBMC from AD patients produce more IL-18 than healthy controls after stimulation with SEB. Consistent with these observations, restriction fragment length polymorphism analysis revealed significant associations of SNPs +113(T/G) and +127(C/T) in exon 1, -137(G/C) in promotor region 1, and -133(C/G) in promotor region 2 in AD patients [13].

Proinflammatory cytokines

No association between AD and polymorphisms in genes coding for the proinflammatory cytokines, TNF-α, IL-1β, IL-6, IL-1ra or IL-10 have been found. However, investigation of polymorphisms of the GM-CSF gene in AD showed that inheritance of the homozygous 677*C/C genotype was associated with complete absence of severe AD [14]. Furthermore, in children without this genotype, the odds ratio of having AD was 7.5 (2.2-25.0). Thus this GM-CSF genotype appears to be protective for AD.

RANTES

The C-C chemokine RANTES, which is chemotactic for monocytes, memory CD4$^+$ T cells and eosinophils, causes the release of histamine from basophils, and activates eosinophils, is up-regulated in AD skin lesions. A functional mutation in the proximal promotor of the RANTES gene on chromosome 17q11-q21 (some distance from the region of linkage to AD and psoriasis) has been identified which results in a new consensus binding site for the GATA transcription factor family. This mutant allele, which has a significantly higher frequency in people of African descent compared to Caucasians, was found to be associated with AD, but not with asthma, in German children [15]. An up to 8-fold higher constitutive transcriptional activity of the mutant versus wild-type promoter was demonstrated in a human mast cell line and the Jurkat T cell line suggesting that its presence leads to higher RANTES levels, consistent with that found in AD skin lesions.

IRF2

Interferon regulatory factor 2 (IRF2) is a member of a family of transcriptional factors involved in the modulation of cellular responses to interferons and viral infection, and in the regulation of cell growth and transformation. IRF2 modulates the transcriptional regulation of IFN-inducible genes by IRF-1, another member of the same family. CD4$^+$ T cells from IRF1-deficient mice show altered cytokine patterns with increased production of Th-2 type cytokines, whilst mice that have had the IRF2 gene deleted show defective Th-1 cell development, impairment of NK cells and spontaneous development of an inflammatory skin disease characterised by the presence of CD8$^+$ T cells [16,17].

Patients with AD were screened for mutations in the 5' flanking and coding regions of the IRF2 gene by single-strand conformational polymorphism analysis [18]. Three mutations were found in the promotor region, one silent mutation in exon 9 and a 10-bp deletion in the 3' untranslated region. Of these, the –467G allele (promotor), and the haplotype of the –467G (promotor), 921A (silent mutation) and 1739(ATCCC)8 (deletion) alleles were transmitted preferentially to AD-affected children suggesting that alteration in IRF2 levels may contribute to susceptibility to AD.

Any association between AD and polymorphisms of the IRF1 gene, located on chromosome 5q31.1 in a region containing various polymorphisms associated with the disease, remains to be investigated.

CARD/Nod proteins

Caspase recruitment domain containing protein 15 (CARD15)/Nod2, and the closely related CARD4/Nod1, are intracellular peptidoglycan receptor proteins (see Chapter 3). Polymorphisms in the CARD15/Nod2 gene that result in changes in peptidoglycan recognition have been reported to be associated with susceptibility to Crohn's disease, an inflammatory disease of the bowel [19]. Three functional relevant CARD15 polymorphisms have been investigated in children with asthma and allergy by PCR-based restriction enzyme assays [20]. Children with the polymorphic allele C2722 had a more than 3-fold risk to develop allergic rhinitis and an almost 2-fold risk for AD. In addition, the T2104 allele was associated with an almost 2-fold risk for allergic rhinitis, whilst a C insertion at position 3020 increased the risk of atopy by 50% and serum IgE levels were increased. Recently, an association between AD and CARD4/Nod1 polymorphisms have been reported in a study that examined the effects on atopy phenotypes of 11 SNPs covering the complete gene [21]. One CARD4/Nod1 haplotype and three polymorphisms (rs 2907748, rs 2907749, rs 2075822) were significantly associated with AD in a population-based cohort, case-control population or a family-based association analysis. These polymorphisms were also associated with asthma and total serum IgE levels, but not with allergic rhinoconjunctivitis or specific sensitisation. These findings suggest that impaired recognition of microbial antigens may contribute to the development of AD.

TLR2 and TLR4

TLR2 and TLR4 are pattern recognition receptors that recognise various microbial components from Gram-positive bacteria and yeasts (peptidoglycan, lipotechoic acid, lipoproteins, zymosan) or Gram-negative bacteria (LPS), respectively (see Chapter 3). Two SNPs have been described for each of the receptors, which result in changes in amino acid sequences. One of the TLR2 polymorphisms (R753Q), which is located within the intracellular part of the receptor and has been particularly associated with *S. aureus* infections, was found to be present in a higher frequency in AD patients compared to controls [22]. The subgroup of AD patients carrying this polymorphism had increased disease severity characterised by markedly elevated IgE antibodies to *S. aureus* superantigens and house dust mite (HDM) allergens. In addition, a further subgroup of AD patients expressed a higher frequency of the two TLR4 polymorphisms (D299G and T399I) than controls [22]. These cosegregating polymorphisms, located in the extracellular domain of the receptor, have previously been reported in patients with septic shock, particularly that induced by Gram-negative bacteria, and are linked to LPS hyporesponsiveness. These recent findings provide further evidence for an impaired response to microorganisms in AD.

TIM-1

TIM-1 (T-cell immunoglobulin domain and mucin domain protein-1) is a membrane protein associated with the development of Th-2-biased immune responses, and which is selectively expressed on Th-2 cells. Analysis of the allele and genotype frequencies of the 5383_5397del variation of the Tim-1 gene revealed a significant association with AD [23]. The genotype, but not allele, frequency of another polymorphism of the Tim-1 gene, 5509_5511delCAA, was associated with asthma. These findings may have functional relevance in view of the Th-2 type biased response to allergens in atopic individuals.

HSCCE

Human stratum corneum chymotryptic enzyme (HSCCE) is thought to play a vital role in desquamation of the epidermis via its effects on proteins of the stratum corneum. A significant association was found between a 4 bp (AACC) insertion in the 3'UTR of the HSCCE gene (also know as KLK7, a member of the kallikrein gene family) and AD, suggesting that an alteration in HSCCE activity may contribute to the abnormal skin barrier in these patients [24].

These findings reveal the complex polygenic nature of the inheritance of AD [25], in common with other immune-mediated diseases such as MS, diabetes and psoriasis. A summary of the suggested genetic abnormalities and their functional consequences are shown in Fig. 8.2.

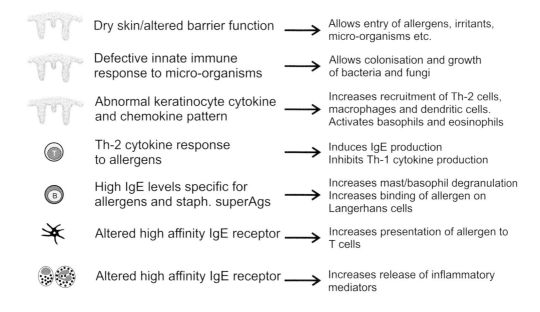

Figure 8.2   Suggested genetic abnormalities and their functional consequences in AD.

Table 8.3 Environmental factors implicated in AD

Foods
▶ Eggs, milk, nuts, fish, shellfish
Aeroallergens
▶ HDM, pollens, moulds, animal dander
Bacteria
▶ *S. aureus*
Fungi
▶ *Malassezia*
Contact irritants
Stress
Reduced microbial exposure in early life

8.2.2 Environmental factors

The involvement of environmental factors interacting with susceptibility genes is strongly suggested by the incomplete concordance rate for monozygotic twins with AD. Several environmental factors are involved in the precipitation and exacerbation of AD, including foods, HDM allergens, secondary microbial infections, stress and contact with skin irritants (Table 8.3). In addition, other risk factors include season of birth and low birth weight, higher gestational age at birth, animal exposure during first few months of life, maternal smoking, early infection with respiratory syncytial virus, and vaccination against *Bordetella pertussis*.

8.2.2.1 IgE-mediated allergy

IgE-mediated allergy appears to play a role in the majority of AD patients. In severe AD, high levels of IgE antibodies are produced against inhaled allergens such as grass pollen, HDM and animal dander, and sometimes also to various foods. These patients tend to have accompanying atopic conditions including allergic asthma, seasonal rhinitis, allergic conjunctivitis and sometimes IgE-mediated food or drug allergy (Table 8.4).

However, approximately 20% of AD patients have normal serum IgE levels and no allergen-specific IgE, and negative skin prick tests and RAST to common inhaled and food allergens. These patients tend to be at the mild end of the disease spectrum with moderate skin involvement, and without other atopic clinical manifestations (Table 8.4).

This suggests that IgE mechanisms are not fundamental to the aetiology of the disease; rather they act as exacerbating factors (see below). In support of this, AD patients with allergic rhinitis and asthma often experience a worsening of their skin lesions when in close contact to dogs or cats that trigger their respiratory symptoms.

The existence of different subsets of AD has led to the proposal that AD should be referred to as "atopic eczema/dermatitis syndrome" (AEDS) [26]. The IgE-associated "extrinsic" type would then be known as allergic AEDS, and the non-IgE-associated "intrinsic" type as non-allergic AEDS.

8.2.2.2 Food allergens

IgE-mediated food allergy to common foods such as eggs, milk, nuts, fish and shellfish occurs in approximately 25% of patients with severe AD, accompanied by high allergen-specific IgE levels. This results in various immediate hypersensitivity responses including angioedema, urticaria, contact urticaria, wheeze and, the most severe response, systemic anaphylaxis, within 15 minutes of ingestion. However, a late reaction consisting of pruritus and exacerbation of skin lesions may also

Table 8.4 Comparison of characteristics of allergic and non-allergic AEDS

Characteristic	Allergic AEDS	Non-allergic AEDS
Systemic		
Total IgE	Markedly increased	Normal
Allergen-specific IgE	Present	Absent
Activated B cells expressing FcεRII	Present	Absent
Skin prick tests to aeroallergens or foods	Positive	Negative
Associated allergic asthma, seasonal rhinitis, allergic conjunctivitis, food or drug allergy	Present	Absent
Lesional skin		
Epidermal dendritic cell phenotype	High FcεRI expression on LCs	Low FcεRI expresssion on LCs
Cytokine production	Higher IL-5 and IL-13 levels	Lower IL-5 and IL-13 levels
Cellular infiltrate	Higher numbers of eosinophils	Lower numbers of eosinophils

occur 8-24 hr later, consistent with a type IV hypersensitivity response.

IgE-mediated allergy is much more common in children, who develop it during the first year of life after weaning from breast milk. The elimination of cow's milk from the diet can result in a marked improvement in their skin lesions, but most children will outgrow this type of food intolerance by the age of 5 years. In contrast, AD is often not outgrown until the age of approximately 14 years.

In addition, certain foods such as food colourings (tartrazine), highly spiced foods and excess alcohol may also cause exacerbation of AD skin lesions, a day after ingestion. These responses appear to be mediated by non-IgE-mediated mechanisms.

8.2.2.3 Aeroallergens

Food allergy is often followed by sensitivity to aeroallergens such as HDM, pollens, moulds and animal dander. Widespread recognition of HDM allergens at both the humoral and T cell level in AD patients suggest that these inhaled antigens can act as a trigger or exacerbating factor for the disease. Thus 75% of patients with severe AD produce high levels of HDM-specific IgE, and high circulating T cell proliferative responses to HDM allergens have been reported in the majority of AD patients. Furthermore, a high frequency of HDM-specific CD4[+] T cells have been isolated from lesional AD skin suggesting that they play a role in the immunopathogenesis of the skin lesions (see Section 8.6.3).

In patients who are sensitised, aeroallergens, such as cat dander or HDM, can also elicit skin lesions when directly applied to the skin (atopy patch test). Under standardised conditions, 30-40% of AD patients have positive atopy patch tests, whilst the test is negative in non-atopic individuals. Patch test skin reactions are clinically and histologically similar to AD and contain allergen-specific T cells and are therefore used as an *in vivo* model for AD.

8.2.2.4 Secondary microbial infections

Patients with AD are highly susceptible to certain cutaneous bacterial and viral infections as a result of impaired innate and acquired immune responses (see Sections 8.3 and 8.4). Colonisation with *S. aureus* is the most common (over 90% of AD patients), resulting in weeping, crusting, folliculitis and pyoderma, although the bacteria may be present on AD skin in the absence of clinical infection. Colonisation is not specific for AD as these bacteria are also found on the lesional skin of psoriasis patients. However in AD patients, there appears to be a causative relationship between the numbers of bacteria present on the skin and the severity of disease . Furthermore, treatment-induced removal of the bacteria is associated with improvement in skin lesions. The mechanisms by which *S. aureus* cause exacerbation of AD skin lesions are discussed below.

AD patients also have an increased incidence of warts caused by the human papillomavirus, and of cutaneous fungal infections such as that caused by *Trichophyton rubrum.* In addition, they are particularly susceptible to severe infections caused by herpes simplex type 1 virus (leading to a condition called eczema herpeticum or Kaposi's varicelliform eruption), vaccinia virus (leading to eczema vaccinatum) coxsackieA virus and molluscum contagiosum virus. These viral infections can represent serious complications in AD, and if not treated promptly have the potential to be life threatening.

8.2.2.5 The Hygiene Hypothesis

Reduced microbial exposure and increased prevalence of allergy

Over the last 3 decades there has been a continuously increasing prevalence of allergic asthma, allergic rhinitis and AD, especially in industrial countries where it can be as high as 20-37% of the population [27]. Studies of children who move in early life from developing to Westernised countries, such as from China to Hong Kong, have shown that the prevalence of allergic disease increases suggesting that environmental factors are involved. Factors that have been implicated include increased air pollution, increased indoor exposure to HDM antigens in less ventilated modern homes, and dietary changes. However, there is little consistent evidence that these factors can account for the rise in atopic diseases. A more relevant factor, which is temporally associated with the rise of atopy, is a decrease in childhood infections. Furthermore, changes in the modern lifestyle such as the use of antibiotics, the reduction in family size (allergic sensitisation is higher in the first-born, but is less frequent in children from large families), and the increase in hygiene standards have also contributed to decreased exposure to microbial antigens. This relationship between reduced microbial exposure of children associated with Westernisation, and the increasing severity and prevalence of atopic disorders has been called the "hygiene hypothesis" [28].

Human foetal lymphocytes appear to be biased towards a Th-2 cytokine profile as a result of intrauterine priming by placental cytokines and hormones. During the postnatal period, the Th-2 cytokine profile switches to a Th-1 cytokine profile, probably due to immune stimulation by components derived from microorganisms, such as CpG-containing deoxyribonucleic acid sequences, peptidoglycan and endotoxin. However, the normal bacterial colonisation of the newborn has changed in modern times. The newborn no longer predominately inherits the mother's aerobic Gram-negative intestinal flora, for example *E. coli,* at delivery, but instead, is often initially colonised with Gram-positive bacteria, and does not encounter Gram-negative organisms until some weeks later. These changes may affect the development of immune tolerance in the gut, which requires Gram-negative bacteria, particularly endotoxin, and allows the development of allergic diseases in genetically predisposed individuals. In addition, the use of antibiotics before the age of 3 years markedly increases the risk of developing allergic diseases, possibly via effects on intestinal flora. In support of this view, systemic administration of the probiotic *Lactobacillus rhamnosus* before or after birth has been shown to lead to a 50% reduction in the development of AD in Finnish children at risk [29].

Mechanisms involved in hygiene hypothesis

Two mechanisms have been proposed to explain the development of enhanced Th-2 cell responses to allergens as a result of decreased exposure to pathogenic and non-pathogenic organisms; a lack of immune deviation from a Th-2 type to a Th-1 type profile, and/or a reduction in T cell regulatory activity [30] (Fig. 8.3).

In the first case, the reduced exposure to microbial antigens during childhood results in decreased stimulation of the innate immune response via dendritic and NK cells. The innate immune response is mediated via interaction between PAMPs synthesised by microorganisms, and pattern recognition receptors such as TLR expressed by innate immune cells (see Chapter 3). This interaction results in the production of various cytokines including TNF-α, type I IFNs and IL-12, the combination of which is dependent upon the nature of the ligand and the TLRs expressed by the cell. The production of IL-12 promotes the development of naïve Th cells into Th-1 type effector cells; IFN-α produced by dendritic cells, as well as IFN-γ produced by NK cells, also contributes to Th-1 polarisation.

In contrast, when IL-4 is produced early at the site of antigen presentation in the absence of IL-12 or IFN-γ, it binds to IL-4 receptors on naïve cells and induces their maturation into Th-2 type effector cells. Thus Th-2 priming can occur as a default pathway, which is converted into a Th-1 response by the activation of innate immune cells by microbial ligands. In the presence of fewer pathogens and PAMPs, less IL-12 is produced, Th-1 polarisation is reduced and the response to innocuous environmental antigens (allergens) becomes biased towards a Th-2 type response. In addition, Th-2 differentiation may also be directly induced by activation of TLRs on APCs. It has been shown that Pam3Cys, a synthetic ligand for TLR2, can induce suppression of IL-12 and bias the T cell response towards a Th-2 profile, thereby favouring the development of experimental asthma [31]. Furthermore, low (but not high) doses of LPS can induce Th-2 priming via the TLR4 receptor.

The second mechanism that has been proposed is that of a reduction in T cell regulatory activity. Reduced stimulation of Tr cells by decreased microbial exposure during childhood would result in increased Th-1 and Th-2 responses leading to an increased prevalence of both autoimmune and allergic disorders, consistent with what has been observed. Balance between Th-1 and Th-2

Figure 8.3   Possible mechanisms for increased prevalence of allergy by improved hygiene. (Source: Baker B.S. Review: *The Role of Microorganisms in Atopic Dermatitis*. Clin.Exp.Immunol. 2006, in press, with permission from Blackwell Publishing Ltd, Oxford, UK.)

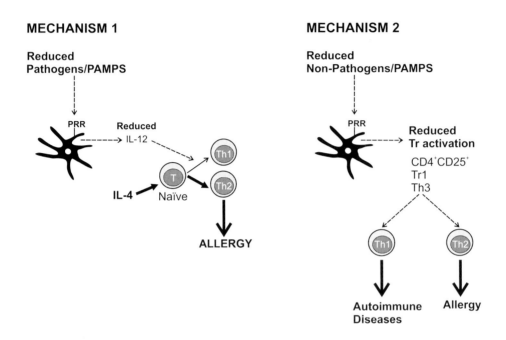

responses is partially regulated by mutual antagonism between the two subgroups; IL-4 inhibits the development of Th-1 cells, whilst IFN-γ inhibits the development of Th-2 cells. However, further regulation is provided by three types of Tr cells, natural CD4⁺CD25⁺ Tr, IL-10-producing Tr1 and TGF-β-secreting Th-3 cells (see Chapter 7). Natural CD4⁺CD25⁺ Tr cells, which do not produce cytokines and act by cell-to-cell contact, express the products of the Foxp3 and GITR genes, which are essential for their differentiation and counter-regulation, respectively. Foxp3 gene mutations in humans result in a disorder (immune dysregulation, polyendocrinopathy, enteropathy and X-linked inheritance syndrome, (IPEX)) characterised by Th-1-mediated rather than allergic pathologies, and by defective responses to pathogens [32]. This suggests that Foxp3-expressing Tr cells are more important for suppressing Th-1 rather than Th-2-mediated disorders. However, allergen-specific Tr cells producing IL-10 and/or TGF-β appear to regulate airway inflammation by inhibiting Th-2 responses in some animal studies. Furthermore, *L.reuteri* and *L.casei* prime monocyte-derived dendritic cells to drive the development of IL-10 producing regulatory T cells providing a possible mechanism for the beneficial effects of *Lactobacillus* administration in AD and circumstantial evidence of defective T cell regulation [33].

8.3 Innate immune system

The immune response to microbial pathogens is initiated by the innate immune system (see Chapter 3). Deficiencies in innate immune factors and altered microbial receptor function have been reported in AD patients, which may contribute to their susceptibility to bacterial and viral infections (Fig. 8.4).

8.3.1 Innate immune factors

8.3.1.1 Anti-microbial peptides

The innate immune system of the epidermis is the first line of defence against invasion by microorganisms, which gain entry after the skin is damaged. Anti-microbial peptides form part of this defence system, three of which are triggered by injury or inflammation of the skin: the β defensins HBD-2 and HBD-3, and a cathelicidin, LL-37. Immunostaining, measurement of specific mRNA by real-time reverse-transcriptase-PCR or GeneChip microarray analysis for these peptides in acute and chronic lesions from patients with AD showed a significant decrease in expression as compared to those from psoriasis patients, which in turn showed increased expression as compared to normal skin [34,35]. IL-4 and/or IL-13, has been shown to suppress the TNF-α or IFN-γ-induced up-regulation of HBD-2 and HBD-3 mRNA in KCs or normal skin explants. Thus, the reductions in anti-microbial peptides may be explained by the predominance of Th-2 type cytokines and low levels of proinflammatory cytokines IFN-γ and TNF-α in AD skin lesions (see below).

Clinical isolates of *S. aureus* from AD patients can be killed by a combination of HBD-2 and LL-37 at the concentrations found in psoriatic lesions, but the levels present in AD skin are too low to be effective. Thus the relative absence of HBD-2, HBD-3 and LL-37 in the epidermis of AD compared to psoriatic skin lesions is partially responsible for their susceptibility to bacterial colonisation and infection. In addition, since these antimicrobial peptides also have activity against viruses and fungi, their paucity may also explain the increased susceptibility of AD patients to infections caused by herpes simplex and *Trichophyton rubrum*.

The innate skin defense system of patients with AD is further compromised by a deficiency of dermcidin-derived antimicrobial peptides in sweat, which correlates with infectious complications [36]. Dermcidin is specifically and constitutively expressed in sweat glands in the dermis of skin, secreted into sweat and transported to the skin surface (see Chapter 3). In common with HBD-3 and LL-37, dermcidin has a broad spectrum of activity against a variety of pathogenic microorganisms. In healthy individuals, a significant reduction in viable bacterial cells on the skin surface occurs after sweating, but this is not the case in AD patients [36]. Furthermore the sweat rate of production, and the secretion of IgA in sweat are reduced in patients with AD, contributing to the impaired innate immune response [37,38].

8.3.1.2 IL-8 and induced nitric oxide synthetase

GeneChip microarray analysis of total RNA from lesional skin biopsies has been used to compare AD and psoriasis for the expression of more than 40 innate immune genes, including those coding

Figure 8.4   Defective innate immunity in AD skin. Altered intracellular and extracellular PRR expression, and decreased antimicrobial molecule production (due to inhibition by Th-2 cytokines) results in an impaired innate immune response to microorganisms, which gain entry to the epidermis as a result of an altered barrier function. HBD-2/HBD-3 = human β-defensin-2/3; LL-37 = a member of the cathelicidin family; iNos = induced nitric oxide synthetase. (Source: Baker B.S. Review: *The Role of Microorganisms in Atopic Dermatitis.* Clin.Exp.Immunol. 2006, in press, with permission from Blackwell Publishing Ltd, Oxford, UK.)

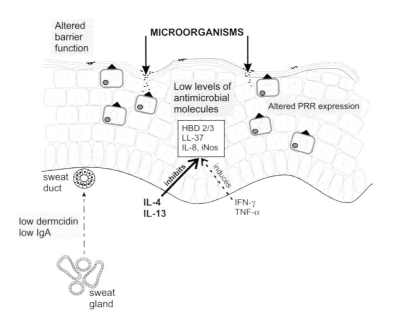

for cytokines, chemokines, TLRs, phagocytosis-promoting receptors, complement components, anti-microbial peptides and signal transduction molecules [35]. Most of the genes were expressed similarly in the two diseases except for HBD-2 (see above), IL-8 and induced nitric oxide synthetase (iNOS) which each showed a two-fold or greater reduction of expression in AD compared to psoriasis. Expression of HBD-1, TLR2, CD14, cathepsin D and H were also reduced in AD versus psoriatic skin, but the difference was less than two-fold. IL-8 is a chemokine that attracts PMNs into the skin where they phagocytose and kill bacteria, whilst iNos can kill viruses, bacteria and fungi through production of nitric oxide. In common with the anti-microbial peptides, production of IL-8 and iNos is also inhibited by Th-2 cytokines. Thus reduced expression of these innate immune factors may contribute to the increased susceptibility of AD skin to infection.

8.3.2 TLR and CARD/Nod proteins

As described above (Section 8.2.1.3), TLR2 and TLR4 polymorphisms are present in increased frequency in two subgroups of AD patients. The subgroup of AD patients carrying the TLR2 polymorphism R753Q is characterised by markedly increased IgE antibody levels to *S. aureus* superantigens and HDM allergens, and shows increased disease severity, whilst two TLR4 polymorphisms (D299G and T399I) present in a further subset of AD patients are associated with

LPS hyporesponsiveness. In addition, polymorphisms of the intracellular bacterial peptidoglycan receptors CARD15/Nod2 and CARD4/Nod1 have also been reported to be associated with AD. These findings suggest that patients with AD have inherently defective mechanisms for clearing infections, resulting in chronic colonisation with bacteria such as *S. aureus*.

8.4 Immunological abnormalities

Patients with AD have a range of different immunological abnormalities (Table 8.5). Some of these are reversible and return to normal when the disease is treated, suggesting that they are secondary to the disease. One example of this is T cell anergy to microorganisms. However others, such as increased IgE production, may have a genetic basis.

8.4.1 T lymphocyte responses *in vitro* and *in vivo*

Patients with AD have reduced numbers of circulating T cells, particularly of CD8$^+$ T cells, and decreased suppressor cell activity, impaired antibody-dependent cytotoxicity and decreased number or activity of NK cells. These deficiencies contribute to the inability of the immune system of these patients to fight off bacterial and viral infections.

Furthermore, T lymphocyte proliferation responses to bacterial antigens, such as *S. aureus* and PPD (purified protein derivative of Mycobacteria), and to herpes simplex virus are decreased. However, this anergy to microorganisms is reversible, manifesting itself when the skin condition is severe, and returning to normal when the skin is less active or after treatment. The T cell response to mitogens, plant lectins such as concanavalin A or phytohaemagglutinin which stimulate all T cells in a non antigen-specific manner, may also be decreased in AD, but this observation is less consistent than that relating to bacterial or viral antigens.

In keeping with their increased susceptibility to severe skin infections and decreased circulating T cell responses to bacteria, viruses and fungi, AD patients show cutaneous anergy to intracutaneous skin tests

---

Table 8.5 Immunological abnormalities in AD

- Decreased numbers of circulating T cells, particularly CD8$^+$ T cells
- Decreased suppressor cell activity *in vitro*
- Decreased antibody-dependent cytotoxicity
- Decreased number or activity of NK cells
- Decreased T lymphocyte proliferative response to bacterial antigens, and to a lesser extent, mitogens
- Unresponsive to intradermal skin tests with bacterial, viral and fungal antigens
- Reduced response to contact allergens
- Decreased sensitisation rate to DNCB
- Marked increase in total IgE, and IgE specific for ingested and inhaled allergens
- Increased proportion of B cells expressing surface-bound IgE

with organisms such as *Candida*, *Streptococcus* and *Trichophyton*. In addition, they have reduced responses to contact allergens e.g. poison ivy, and have a decreased sensitisation rate to DNCB, a very potent contact allergen for normal individuals, which is related to severity of disease.

In contrast to these findings, peripheral blood CLA$^+$ memory T cells (both CD4$^+$ and CD8$^+$) in patients with AD are activated *in vivo* and spontaneously release an IL-5- and IL-13-dominated Th-2 cytokine pattern which enhances eosinophil survival and induces IgE production by B cells, respectively, *in vitro* [39]. However, the CLA$^-$ memory T cells from the same patients are in a resting state and secrete low levels of cytokines and induce IgG$_4$ production. These findings suggest that activated skin-homing T cells play an important role in the pathogenesis of AD.

8.4.2 Leukocyte function

In patients with severe AD, PMNs and monocytes may exhibit decreased chemotaxis *in vitro*, which returns to normal when the skin lesions improve. This appears to be due to factors present in plasma as the patient's plasma inhibits the chemotactic function of cells from normal individuals. Histamine released by activated basophils, which has been shown to inhibit chemotaxis by PMNs from both normal and atopic individuals, is probably at least partly responsible. Basophils of AD patients with severe disease show increased spontaneous release of histamine; stimulation by anti-IgE, C5a or an ionophore results in a bigger and faster release of histamine, LTB$_4$, LTC$_4$ and possibly also PGE$_2$ [40].

Monocytes show other functional abnormalities in AD, such as a reduction in antibody-mediated cytotoxicity after stimulation by histamine or isoproterenol, which may be due to decreased cAMP levels [41]. This reduced cAMP response results from increased levels of phosphodiesterase 4 enzymes that degrade cAMP. Decreased intracellular cAMP levels leads to decreased activation of protein kinase C, resulting in reduced protein phosphorylation and associated cell activities such as proliferation, secretion etc. The increased phosphodiesterase activity, which may be secondary to skin inflammation or represent an intrinsic defect such as a heightened susceptibility to the effects of inflammatory mediators, correlates with increased PGE$_2$ production in AD monocytes. PGE$_2$, in turn, inhibits Th-1 responses and enhances IL-4 secretion by Th-2 cells.

Monocytes in atopic patients express higher levels of both low (FcεRII) and high affinity (FcεRI) receptors for IgE, and this expression is significantly higher in patients with allergic AD than in those with non-allergic AD [42]. Furthermore, activation-induced secretion of IL-15 and membrane bound IL-15 expression is decreased in monocytes of AD patients compared to that of normal individuals and psoriasis patients [43]. IL-15 stimulates T cell proliferation and the production of IgM, IgG$_1$ and IgA by B cells; in contrast, it suppresses IgE synthesis by PBMC from AD patients. Furthermore it is considered to be a Th-1-like cytokine since it induces IFN-γ expression. Thus the decrease in monocyte-derived IL-15 in AD may contribute to the elevated IgE levels (see below), and, in addition, may account for the decreased NK activity associated with this disease as IL-15 plays an important role in the development, survival and function of NK cells.

8.4.3 Dysregulation of IgE synthesis

8.4.3.1 Increased total and allergen-specific IgE

As mentioned above (Section 8.2.2), in many AD patients there is an excessive formation of total serum IgE antibodies, and of specific IgE to ingested or inhaled allergens. Furthermore, a proportion of circulating B cells express surface-bound IgE in AD.

The increased levels of IgE correlate with the decreased delayed hypersensitivity responses *in vitro* (T cell proliferation assays) and *in vivo* (skin tests). Furthermore, there is an inverse correlation between the total amount of serum IgE and the decreased numbers of CD8$^+$ T suppressor cells. Up to one-third of the serum IgE may be complexed with IgG and C3, but the levels of these immune complexes are not related to the concentrations of serum IgE or to disease severity. Furthermore, despite the marked increase in serum IgE levels, there does not appear to be selective diffusion of IgE into the skin from the blood in AD as shown by suction blister fluid analysis.

There is also a relationship between serum concentrations of IgE, and receptors for IgE on T cells. Lymphocytes expressing FcεRII, which is associated with isotype-specific IgE synthesis, are increased in atopic allergic patients. Most of these are B cells, but a small proportion of CD8$^+$ T and NK cells expressing FcεRII are present.

In contrast, the amounts of total IgG, IgA and IgM in AD are usually normal, although they may be increased in severe disease. Increased IgG may arise from increases in antibodies to bacteria as a result of secondary skin infections, or to antibodies to food antigens. Furthermore, normal total IgG may be accompanied by increases in the subclass IgG$_4$, which, because it makes the smallest contribution of the four subclasses, does not induce an increase in total IgG levels. Increased IgG$_4$ has been observed in children with AD accompanied by asthma, and who also have increased total IgE levels. IgG$_4$ does not, however, appear to induce mast cell degranulation, and may perhaps be protective as it prevents sensitisation of basophils by IgE *in vitro*.

8.4.3.2 Impaired regulation of IgE production by cytokines

The commitment of a B cell to switch isotype to an IgE-producing cell is a tightly regulated process. The classical pathway of IgE switching requires T cells, which express CD40L and secrete Th-2 type cytokines, IL-4 and/or IL-13, in response to antigen. Both CD40 ligation (which activates NF-κB), together with the activation of STAT6 (activation of signal transducer and activator of transcription 6) by IL-4/IL-13 are required to switch the B cells to IgE production. In addition, IgG$_4$ production by B cells is similarly induced by a T cell-dependent mechanism involving IL-4, which also up-regulates expression of the low affinity IgE receptor FcεRII on lymphocytes and LCs.

Negative regulators of IgE transcription include the cytokines IFN-γ, TGF-β and IL-21 and the B-cell receptors CD45 and CD23. However, IFN-γ stimulates rather than inhibits FcεRII expression by LCs.

In atopic patients, cytokine production by CD4$^+$ T cells in response to allergens such as HDM is skewed towards a Th-2 type response (IL-4, IL-5 and IL-13) with no IFN-γ. This is specific for allergens as atopic CD4$^+$ T cells can produce IFN-γ in response to microbial antigens such as tetanus toxoid and *C. albicans* [44]. Furthermore, B cells from these patients are stimulated to produce IgE

Figure 8.5   Dysregulated allergen-specific IgE production in atopics driven by Th-2 cytokines.

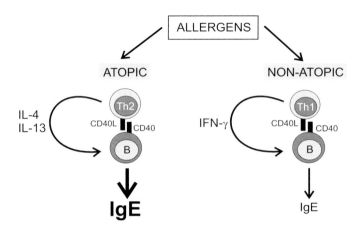

in response to supernatants from HDM–activated atopic T cell clones. Circulating $CD4^+$ T cells that recognise HDM allergens are also present in non-atopics. However, they respond to stimulation by allergens by producing Th-1 type cytokines including IFN-γ, which negatively regulates IgE production, and do not produce IL-4 [44].

Thus a preferential expansion of allergen-specific T cells producing Th-2 cytokines is probably responsible for the dysregulated production of IgE in atopic individuals (Fig. 8.5).

8.5 Defects of the epidermis

Defects of the epidermis, which may or may not be intrinsic, contribute to the pathogenesis of AD and include impairment of the skin barrier and alterations in cytokine/chemokine production by KCs (Table 8.6).

8.5.1 Impairment of the skin barrier

A basic defect in AD is the altered lipid composition of the stratum corneum, which results in increased permeability to allergens and irritants. The barrier function of the cornified envelope is provided by a matrix of structural proteins to which ceramides, the major water retaining molecules, are bound. In AD, ceramides are reduced in both uninvolved and lesional skin leading to increased transepidermal water loss and marked dryness. In addition, bacteria that colonise the lesional and uninvolved skin of AD patients release ceramidase, which breaks down ceramide into sphingosine and fatty acids.

Table 8.6 Epidermal defects in AD skin

Factor	Increase/ Decrease	Location	Functional consequences
Ceramides	Decrease	Stratum corneum	Transepidermal water loss Marked dryness
GM-CSF	Increase	KCs	Increased numbers of activated dendritic cells with enhanced antigen-presenting function

TSLP	Increase	KCs	Effects on dendritic cells:
			    Activation and migration
			    Prod. of Th-2 chemokines, TARC and MDC
			    Priming of Th-2 cells

RANTES	Increase	Basal KCs	Recruitment of monocytes, dendritic cells, Th-1 and Th-2 cells
MCP-1	Increase	Basal KCs	Recruitment of monocytes, dendritic cells, Th-1 and Th-2 cells

8.5.2 Keratinocyte defects

KCs in patients with AD have an intrinsically abnormal cytokine and chemokine production profile that contributes to the recruitment of specific leukocyte subsets to the skin. Firstly, spontaneous and induced production of GM-CSF is markedly increased in KCs isolated from AD patients compared to nonatopic controls [45]. This is reflected *in vivo* by heavy immunostaining for the cytokine in both epidermal and dermal compartments of AD lesional skin. GM-CSF is known to play a crucial role in the recruitment and survival, as well as maturation of dendritic cells/LCs into efficient antigen-presenting cells. The high levels of this cytokine could, therefore, explain the increased numbers of activated dendritic cells with enhanced antigen-presenting capacity present in AD skin lesions. The mechanism behind the overproduction of GM-CSF by KCs from AD patients may involve the accompanying higher (constitutive or induced) levels of members of the activator protein 1 (AP-1) family of transcription factors, including c-Jun, JunB and c-Fos, induced by functional abnormalities in protein kinase C translocation. AP-1 is activated by various cytokines including IL-4, IFN-γ and TNF-α, and AP-1 binding sites are located in the promoters of a vast array of cytokines and chemokines, including RANTES.

Thymic stromal lymphopoetin (TSLP), an IL-7-like cytokine, is also produced in high amounts by KCs in AD, and its expression is associated with LC migration to the lymph nodes [46]. TSLP has been shown to activate CD11c[+] dendritic cells and induce their production of two Th-2-attracting chemokines, TARC (CCL17) and MDC (CCL22). Furthermore dendritic cells activated by TSLP prime naïve CD4[+] T cells to produce Th-2 type cytokines.

In skin lesions of chronic AD, basal KCs strongly express the CCL chemokines, RANTES (CCL5) and MCP-1 (CCL2), which are chemoattractants for monocytes, dendritic cells, Th-1 and Th-2 cells [47]. This is compatible with the mixed Th-1/Th-2 inflammatory infiltrate found in the chronic phase (see below). However, in contrast to skin lesions from patients with psoriasis, CXCL chemokines such as IP-10 and IL-8, which primarily attract Th-1 cells and PMNs, are not consistently up-regulated in chronic AD skin lesions.

8.6 Immunopathology of AD

8.6.1 Immunohistology of skin lesions

The immunopathology of AD skin lesions is that of a non-specific dermatitis and, in common with allergic contact dermatitis (see Fig 7.2, colour plate), is characterised by spongiosis in the epidermis and a perivascular infiltrate of predominately T cells and dendritic cells in the papillary dermis. The ratio of CD4$^+$ to CD8$^+$ T cells in the dermal infiltrates tends to be higher than in other inflammatory dermatoses and can be as high 7:1, compared to 2:1 in peripheral blood. However, overall, the absolute numbers of T cells infiltrating AD skin lesions is less than that found in those of allergic contact dermatitis.

8.6.2 Epidermal dendritic cells

Increased numbers of dendritic cells are present both in the dermal infiltrates in close apposition to T cells, and in the epidermis. The epidermal dendritic cells can be divided into two populations, LCs and inflammatory dendritic epidermal cells (IDEC) based upon different immunophenotypic and ultrastructural characteristics [48]. IDEC differ from LCs in that they do not contain Birbeck granules, but both cell types express costimulatory molecules B7-1 (CD80) and B7-2 (CD86), MHC Class I and II antigens and markedly increased levels of the high affinity IgE receptor, FcεRI. Furthermore, FcεRI expression in lesional skin from allergic AD patients correlates significantly with serum IgE levels in these patients, and IgE can be detected bound to epidermal dendritic cells. In contrast, in non-allergic AD, the expression of FcεRI on LCs is significantly reduced with respect to allergic AD (Table 8.4).

Epidermal dendritic cells in AD are also characterised by their enhanced stimulatory capacity to autologous peripheral blood T cells in the absence of exogenous antigen. In addition, there is evidence that signal transduction events triggered in LCs from AD patients differ from those of normal individuals [49]. Cross-linking of FcεRI on LCs results in rapid tyrosine phosphorylation of several proteins and additionally, in the case of LCs from the lesional skin of AD patients, calcium mobilisation. Calcium mobilisation is dependent upon tyrosine phosphorylation and the activation of phospholipase C-γ, which is absent in LCs from normal skin.

8.6.3 Model for pathogenesis of AD

8.6.3.1 Antigen presentation

Allergens, which successfully penetrate the epidermis as a result of its reduced skin barrier

Figure 8.6   IgE-mediated allergen uptake by LCs.

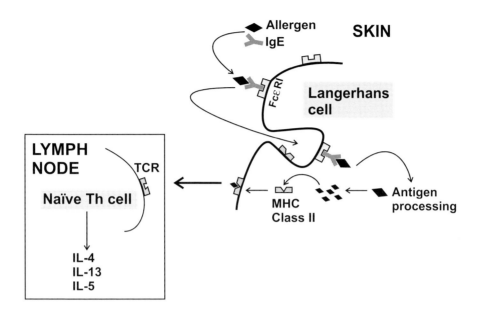

function, will be immediately taken up by LCs via FcεRI-bound antigen-specific IgE molecules on their surface (Fig. 8.6). (Allergens may also be ingested or inhaled and are taken to the skin by an unknown mechanism). These complexes will be internalised, processed and the resulting peptides expressed on the surface bound to MHC Class II molecules. The resulting activation of the LCs facilitates their migration to the lymph nodes where they present antigen to naïve T cells. In keeping with the known role of dendritic cells in inducing the polarisation of naïve T cells, it has been recently shown that LCs activated by FcεRI drive naïve T cells to become IL-4-producing Th-2 cells. In addition, FcεRI activation of LCs leads to the release of chemokines such as MCP-1, IL-16, TARC and MDC, which recruit various leukocyte populations into the skin.

It is likely that IDEC are attracted into the epidermis during the acute phase of AD in response to signals from LCs, and amplify the inflammatory skin response. The number of monocyte precursors of IDEC (which express FcεRI) correspondingly decreases in the peripheral blood during this active stage, and increase again when the skin lesions improve. In common with dendritic cells, FcεRI-activated IDEC prime naïve T cells to become IFN-γ-producing Th-1 cells, via production of IL-12 and IL-18. This may explain the switch from a Th-2 to Th-1 type cytokine profile in chronic AD skin lesions (see below).

8.6.3.2 Biphasic Th-2/Th-1 cytokine pattern

Studies of lesions induced by aeroallergen patch test reactions, and acute versus chronic AD skin lesions have established that the cytokine profile of the allergic inflammatory immune response is biphasic (Fig. 8.7). In the acute phase of AD, T cells expressing the Th-2 cytokines, IL-4, IL-13 and IL-5, predominate whilst IFN-γ-producing cells are low. In contrast, during the chronic

Figure 8.7 Biphasic cytokine pattern in acute/chronic AD. A predominantly Th-2 cytokine response in the acute stage of AD is replaced (with the exception of IL-5) by Th-1 cytokines in the chronic form of the disease due to the effects of IL-12 produced by dendritic cells (DC), macrophages (Macr) and eosinophils (Eos).

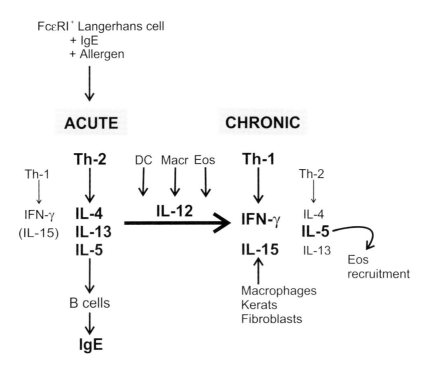

stage IL-4- and IL-13- expressing T cells are decreased, and IFN-γ- and IL-12-producing cells are increased, with respect to acute lesions. Furthermore, IL-5 increases during the chronic stage of AD, together with a significant increase in the number of activated eosinophils. This is more marked in the lesional skin of allergic compared to non-allergic AD patients.

Thus the expression of Th-2 and Th-1 type cytokines in AD is not mutually exclusive, but their expression varies at different stages of the development of skin lesions. IL-4 is associated with initiation, whilst IFN-γ appears to be responsible for the chronicity of skin lesions. In addition, the *in situ* expression of IFN-γ, but not of IL-4, corresponds to the clinical severity of AD, and decreases to levels observed in uninvolved skin following successful treatment of AD patients.

In keeping with the fact that most AD patients are hyper-responsive to HDM, CD4+ (and, to a lesser extent, CD8+) T cells with specificity for HDM allergens have consistently been isolated from chronic AD skin lesions. HDM-specific CD4+ T cells that produce predominately IL-4 and/or IL-13 have been shown to induce normal peripheral blood B cells to produce high levels of IgE, and to enhance the expression of FcεRII on APC [50]. In contrast, T cells isolated from skin lesions of patients with non-allergic AD, who are not sensitised to aeroallergens or food allergens, produce IL-5 and IL-13 at lower levels than those with allergic AD, and are only able to induce marginal IgE production by normal B cells.

In addition, the expression of the Th-1-like cytokine IL-15 is significantly increased in chronic versus acute AD skin lesions, although in both cases the levels are significantly less than in skin lesions of psoriasis [43]. This is consistent with the increased production of IFN-γ in chronic skin lesions as IL-15 can induce its production. In AD skin, IL-15 is produced by macrophages, basal KCs, T cells and dermal fibroblasts, in contrast to peripheral blood where it is exclusively expressed by monocytes/macrophages,

8.6.3.3 Chemokines

In addition to KC-derived chemokines, immune cells such as T cells, macrophages and dendritic cells in AD skin lesions also produce chemoattractants that contribute to the recruitment of leukocytes to the site of inflammation.

Dendritic cells and macrophages constitutively produce MDC (CCL22), which is a potent chemoattractant for chronically activated Th-2 cells. Activated T cells also produce MDC, in association with the synthesis of Th-2 cytokines, and inversely correlated with the production of Th-1 cytokines. In AD, MDC is produced by both dendritic cells and T cells in skin lesions, and is also present at high levels in serum [51].

Eotaxin, a CC chemokine, is a potent chemoattractant and activator of eosinophils, basophils and Th-2 cells which acts via the chemokine receptor CCR3. It is constitutively expressed at low levels in normal skin, but the number of eotaxin-expressing cells, including macrophages, eosinophils and T cells, in the papillary dermis of AD skin lesions is significantly increased [52]. Furthermore, eotaxin, which is also expressed in the epidermis of AD skin lesions, is more highly expressed in chronic than acute lesions correlating with the increased numbers of eosinophils. CCR3 expression on eosinophils and T cells is also increased in both lesional and uninvolved AD skin samples.

Another chemokine, MCP-4 (CCL13), which attracts macrophages as well as eosinophils and activated T cells, is also up-regulated in the lesional skin of AD patients with the same distribution as eotaxin [52]. It is also present at higher levels in chronic versus acute AD skin lesions, and its expression correlates with the numbers of macrophages.

8.6.4 *S.aureus* and AD

The inflammatory environment of lesional AD skin facilitates the colonisation of the Gram-positive bacteria, *S. aureus*. This organism exacerbates the skin immune response via the production of superantigenic toxins, which activate T cells and other cell types, and induce the production of specific IgE antibodies.

8.6.4.1 Colonisation of AD skin

As mentioned earlier, more than 90% of AD patients have *S. aureus* colonising their skin compared to only 5% of normal subjects. Furthermore, the density of the bacteria on lesional skin is greatly increased compared to uninvolved skin. *S. aureus* are tightly attached to the uppermost corneocytes, and can penetrate the epidermis via the intercellular spaces probably as a result of lipid deficiencies in AD skin. The antibacterial activities of skin surface lipids such as fatty acids, polar lipids and glycosphingolipids are well recognised. Furthermore, the dryness and cracking of AD skin, as a result of transepidermal water loss caused by altered lipid content, may facilitate bacterial colonisation.

Other factors contributing to the increased *S. aureus* colonisation of AD skin include disruption of the skin barrier by scratching which allows exudation of plasma proteins such as fibrinogen and fibronectin to which the bacteria can bind, defective innate and acquired immune responses to bacteria, and increased skin alkalinity. Furthermore, binding of *S. aureus* to KCs from inflamed atopic skin is increased, probably due to the enhancement of staphylococcal-binding protein levels and the down-regulation, by Th-2 type cytokines, of anti-microbial peptides required for control of bacterial proliferation. A role for Th-2–mediated inflammation in *S. aureus* colonisation is further supported by the observation that *S. aureus* numbers are reduced in AD skin after treatment with effective anti-inflammatory agents.

8.6.4.2 Staphylococcal superantigens

One mechanism used by *S. aureus* to exacerbate the allergic inflammatory response in AD skin is the production of enterotoxins, such as SEA, SEB and TSST-1, which can act as superantigens. Superantigens bind, without prior processing, to regions outside of the peptide-binding groove of MHC Class II molecules expressed by APC. They then cross-link the APC with T cells by binding to specific TCR Vβ chains (each superantigen recognises particular Vβ families) leading to polyclonal stimulation of a large number of T cells, of both CD4+ and CD8+ T cell subsets. The role for staphylococcal superantigens in AD is supported by the following observations (Table 8.7).

Superantigen-specific IgE

Superantigen-secreting *S. aureus* have been isolated from over 50% of AD patients, and many of these patients produce IgE antibodies specific for the toxins found on their skin [53]. In contrast, although *S. aureus* secreting SEA, SEB or TSST have also been isolated from the lesional skin of psoriasis patients, their sera did not contain IgE antibodies to the toxins. Basophils and mast cells from AD patients with anti-toxin IgE antibodies release histamine on exposure to toxins, but only those toxins against which they have raised specific IgE antibody. Furthermore, there is a correlation between the presence of IgE antibodies specific for staphylococcal superantigens and the severity of AD. Thus superantigen-specific IgE antibodies can bind to mast cells or basophils and induce histamine release, thereby inducing inflammation, but they may also bind to LCs via FcεRI and facilitate the presentation of superantigens, as shown for aeroallergens.

Superantigen-mediated T cell activation

It has been demonstrated that SEB applied to intact normal skin or uninvolved skin of patients with AD can induce erythema and dermatitis [54]. In addition, half of the AD patients tested experienced a flare of their disease in the elbow flexure of the same arm to which the superantigen was applied. These findings suggest that superantigens can initiate, exacerbate and maintain inflammation associated with AD. With relevance in this respect is the observation that 14 of 68 patients recovering from toxic shock syndrome caused by TSST-1, but no patients recovering from Gram-negative sepsis, developed chronic eczematous dermatitis [55].

The major effects of superantigens in AD are likely to be mediated via the activation of T cells. Superantigens can be presented to T cells by LCs, macrophages or even by MHC Class II-expressing

Table 8.7 Role of staphylococcal superantigens in AD

Superantigen-induced effects	Functional consequences
Application of SEB to uninvolved skin	Induces local erythema and dermatitis Sometimes causes disease flare
Superantigen-specific IgE production	Release of histamine by mast cells and basophils Facilitates toxin presentation by LCs to T cells Correlates with disease activity
Selective Vβ family expansion in lesional skin and blood	Activation of Th-2 cells in a Vβ-specific manner
CLA expression on activated Th-2 cells, circulating and in lesional skin	Induces homing of T cells to skin
Apoptosis of superantigen-reactive T cells	SEB-reactive Th-2 cells in AD are apoptosis-resistant, thus helping to maintain inflammation
Inhibition of CLA$^+$CD4$^+$CD25$^+$ regulatory T cell activity	Increases inflammation
Dermal eosinophils	Inhibits apoptosis, increases expression of surface activation antigens and enhances oxidative burst.
LCs and macrophages	Stimulates production of IL-1,TNF-α and IL-12
HLA-DR$^+$ KCs	TNF-α production Presentation of superantigen to Th-2 cells

KCs, which have been shown to preferentially activate Th-2 type cells in the presence of superantigens. T cells expressing Vβ chains specific for the superantigen accumulate selectively in superantigen-treated skin, but not in skin treated with sodium lauryl sulphate, supporting this hypothesis [56]. In addition, in the peripheral blood of AD patients whose skin was colonised by superantigen-secreting *S. aureus*, a relevant skewing of superantigen-reactive Vβ families was observed in CD4$^+$ and CD8$^+$ T cells coexpressing CLA [57]. Bacterial superantigens up-regulate CLA expression by T cells via stimulation of IL-12 production, facilitating their homing to the skin [58].

T cell activation by superantigens may be further augmented by an inhibitory effect (at least by SEB) on the immunosuppressive activity of circulating CLA$^+$CD4$^+$CD25$^+$ regulatory T cells which, surprisingly, are increased in patients with AD [59]. Furthermore, SEB-reactive CD4$^+$ T cells producing Th-2 cytokines in AD patients are more resistant to SEB-induced apoptosis than corresponding SEB-reactive Th-1 cells from healthy individuals [60].

Superantigen-mediated activation of other cell types

In addition to T cells, superantigens can also mediate effects on other cell types such as eosinophils, LCs, macrophages and KCs.

Increased levels of circulating eosinophils and eosinophil granule proteins in the sera and urine are characteristic of AD and correlate with disease activity. During flares of AD, eosinophils are recruited to the skin by chemoattractants such as RANTES and eotaxin, where they are activated and undergo degranulation and cytolytic degeneration. This leads to the deposition of various factors such as eosinophil cationic and major basic proteins, eosinophil-derived neurotoxin and reactive oxygen species which promote inflammation and tissue damage. Furthermore it has been demonstrated that SEB in AD skin lesions is localised predominately to eosinophils in the dermis, as well as to a lesser extent on LCs and IgE-bearing cells [61]. Superantigens modulate the effector function of eosinophils and, probably the course of AD, by inhibiting eosinophil apoptosis, increasing expression of activation antigens on the eosinophil surface, and enhancing oxidative burst of eosinophils in vitro.

Superantigens also bind to HLA-DR on LCs and macrophages and stimulate them to produce IL-1, TNF-α and/or IL-12. These cytokines either up-regulate the expression of adhesion molecules on endothelial cells, or increase CLA expression on T cells, respectively, thus facilitating the recruitment of CLA$^+$ memory T cells to the skin.

As mentioned above, KCs that have been induced to express MHC Class II molecules by stimulation with IFN-γ can present superantigens to T cells. However, because KCs do not synthesise IL-12, this results in the activation of Th-2 type cells that do not produce IFN-γ. Furthermore, KCs are induced to produce TNF-α by interaction with superantigenic toxins, and also by two other products of *S.aureus*, alpha toxin and staphylococcal protein A. Alpha toxin, which is produced by superantigenic toxin-negative strains of *S. aureus* isolated from AD skin, induces profound cytotoxicity of KCs with morphological and functional characteristics of necrosis. This effect contrasts with the superantigenic toxins (SEA, SEB, ST-1, exfoliative toxin), and staphylococcal protein A, which do not have significant cytotoxic effects on KCs.

8.6.5 *Malassezia* **and AD**

Malassezia (formerly known as *Pityrosporum orbiculare/ovale*) is part of the normal human skin flora. It is most abundant at sites of high sebum production such as the scalp, chest and back where it colonises the stratum corneum. Most healthy individuals have developed IgG antibodies to *Malassezia*, but in 30-80% of AD patients, IgE and/or T cell reactivity to the organism is present [62]. The defective skin barrier in AD may allow the whole *Malassezia* yeast cells and their allergens, nine of which have been isolated and cloned so far, to enter the skin and be taken up by LCs. *In vitro* studies show that the process of internalisation of *Malassezia* causes maturation of dendritic cells and the production of proinflammatory and immunoregulatory cytokines, but not IL-12, thereby favouring the induction of a Th-2 type response [63]. Furthermore, it has been demonstrated that a positive atopy patch test to *Malassezia* in AD patients correlates with a Th-2-like peripheral blood mononuclear cell response [64].

8.6.6 Auto-allergens

The frequent presence of IgE antibodies recognizing both exogenous allergens and structurally related human proteins in the sera of AD patients has led to the hypothesis that IgE autoreactivity may be a pathogenic factor in atopic diseases. Serum IgE from AD patients has been used to screen human epithelial copy DNA (cDNA) expression libraries and have identified intracellular proteins including Hom s 1, DSF70 (dense fine speckles 70 kDa) and alpha-nascent polypeptide-associated complex as IgE-reactive autoantigens [65-67].

Purified recombinant Hom s 1, which exhibited an almost complete sequence identity with an antigen recognized by cytotoxic T cells of a squamous cell carcinoma patient, specifically bound IgE from patients with severe atopy. IgE antibodies to DSF70, so called because of the characteristic nuclear immunostaining pattern by AD sera on tissue culture substrates directed against a 70 kDa protein, were found in approximately one-third of AD patients. The cDNA encoding DFS70 was identical to a transcription coactivator called p75, which had been shown to be required for RNA polymerase II-dependent transcription. The alpha-nascent polypeptide-associated complex, which represented a novel isoform, not only specifically bound IgE antibodies, but also induced specific peripheral blood lymphocyte proliferative responses in a sensitized AD patient.

These findings suggest that immune responses in AD patients are initiated by environmental antigens but may be maintained by cross-reactive endogenous intracellular proteins, which are released from tissue damaged by inflammation and scratching. This is supported by the observation that autoallergen IgE levels decrease when skin lesions are resolved by treatment.

8.7 Treatment

Successful treatment of AD requires a combination of topical and systemic measures to control the various aspects of the disease such as skin dryness and itching, exposure to allergens, inflammation and bacterial infection (Table 8.8).

8.7.1 Prevention

Preventative measures in AD include the use of emollients and the avoidance of exacerbating factors such as certain foods, aeroallergens, animals and irritants.

Patients with AD have a dry skin with a defective skin barrier, which facilitates the entry of irritants and microorganisms into the epidermis. Emollients, which contain fatty substances, can be used to prevent these inflammation-inducing factors gaining access and, in addition, prevent water loss allowing rehydration of the skin. However, emollients have no anti-inflammatory effects and will not, therefore, have any beneficial effects on eczematous skin.

Avoidance of aggravating factors can also prevent exacerbations of the disease. Food allergens have been implicated as a cause of AD in a subset of patients. However, elimination diets have not proved helpful in the majority of patients, partly perhaps because there is not a reliable test to determine which foods are responsible. Encouragement of breast-feeding, delayed introduction of solid foods until the child is one year old, and avoidance of food antigens in pregnancy have all been advocated with varying benefit.

Significant improvement in AD has been shown when various measures to decrease HDM antigens are employed. It is not possible to eradicate HDM totally, but a significant decrease in HDM exposure may benefit those patients with severe disease. Avoidance of animals may also be helpful, but whether cat, dog and horse dander directly cause AD or exacerbate existing lesions through their induction of type I responses is not clear. Contact irritants such as detergents and oils may also exacerbate AD, and, in these cases, should be avoided.

Table 8.8 Current treatments for AD

Topical treatments	Systemic treatments	New approaches to treatment
Corticosteroids ± antibiotics	UVA light	Subcutaneous IgE mAb injection
Tacrolimus	Corticosteroids	Subcutaneous rIFN-γ injection
Pimecrolimus	Cyclosporin	Subcutaneous TGF-β_1 injection
	Azathioprine	Intradermal killed *M. vaccae* immunisation
	Mycophenolate mofetil	Cysteinyl leukocyte antagonists

8.7.2 Topical corticosteroids ± antibiotics

The potent anti-inflammatory effect of topical glucocorticosteroids makes these drugs the mainstay for the treatment of AD. However, in addition to their well known side-effects, such as that on fibroblast collagen synthesis that results in thinner skin, the response by AD patients to low or moderate doses of these drugs can be variable. The observation that combined topical treatment with antibiotics and glucocorticosteroids is more effective in the treatment of AD than glucocorticosteroids alone may indicate that *S. aureus* on the skin secrete products that affect the efficacy of the latter. Indeed, it has been shown that T cells stimulated with staphylococcal superantigens *in vitro* become insensitive to the immunosuppressive effects of glucocorticosteroids [68](Fig. 8.8).

The anti-inflammatory effects of glucocorticosteroids are mediated by the α-isoform of a specific intracellular glucocorticosteroid receptor (GR-α) that, in its steroid-bound state, relocates to the nucleus where it binds to glucocorticosteroid-responsive elements in genes coding for cytokines. In contrast the β-isoform of GR (GR-β), which differs from GR-α only in its COOH terminus, is unable to bind glucocorticosteroids and antagonises the activity of GR-α. Interestingly, superantigens induce a marked increase in GR-β expression in T cells providing a possible mechanism for their ability to induce glucocorticosteroid insensitivity.

Both topical and systemic antibiotics induce clinical improvement in AD skin lesions by reducing or eliminating *S. aureus*, which produce superantigens and other toxins that trigger skin inflammation. In addition, antibiotics may also have anti-inflammatory effects, which reduce the attachment sites for *S. aureus* that are up-regulated in inflamed skin. Furthermore, the elimination of superantigens by antibiotics would increase glucocorticosteroid sensitivity and allow the use of lower doses of glucocorticosteroid than would be required if the drug was used alone. However, the routine use of topical antibiotics brings with it the risk of inducing resistant strains of *S. aureus*. It may therefore be more appropriate to use antiseptics such as chlorhexidine hydrochloride and benzalkonium chloride to reduce bacterial colonisation.

Figure 8.8 Superantigen-induced glucocorticosteroid insensitivity in T cells. Interaction of superantigens (superAg) with T cells induces a marked increase in the β-isoform of the intracellular glucocorticosteroid receptor (GR-β). GR-β antagonises the activity of the α isoform of the receptor (GR-α), preventing both binding of glucocorticosteroids in the cytoplasm, and repression of cytokine-specific genes in the nucleus.

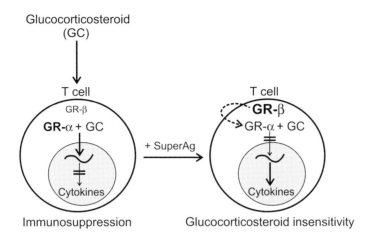

8.7.3 Topical tacrolimus and pimecrolimus

Tacrolimus (FK506) and pimecrolimus are calcineurin inhibitors with potent immunosuppressive properties (see Chapter 7). Both drugs applied topically are effective in the treatment of AD and provide alternatives to glucocorticosteroids with their attendant side effects. Tacrolimus has recently been given a licence for use in AD in adults, and children over two years of age for short-term use and intermittent long-term use. Both agents are as effective as a moderate-strength topical steroid and can be used on sites such as the face where the use of potent steroids are inappropriate.

8.7.4 UV light

It is well known that natural sunlight is beneficial for AD and other inflammatory diseases, and consequently artificial sources of ultraviolet (UV) light have been developed for therapeutic use. There are three types of UV light treatment, high intensity UVB (narrowband), high intensity UVA-1, and PUVA (psoralens plus UVA). (Psoralens are photosensitisers, which increase the effects of the UV light). UV light treatments are both immunosuppressive, affecting both lymphocytes and LCs, and antibacterial resulting in decreased numbers of *S. aureus* on the skin.

Narrowband UVB and PUVA are not suitable for treating infants and young children and would normally be used in cases of chronic and persistent AD which are resistant to topical treatments.

8.7.5 Systemic treatments

For the small number of AD patients who do not respond to topical treatments or UV light, systemic therapies may be used. These include systemic glucocorticosteroids and immunosuppressive drugs such as cyclosporin, azathioprine and mycophenolate mofetil. If systemic glucocorticosteroids are used in short courses to treat a flare of the disease, they are relatively safe and very effective. However, long-term use is usually avoided because of the side effects. Cyclosporin, an immunosuppressant that inhibits cytokine production by T cells, is effective in AD at relatively low doses. Its side effects include nephrotoxicity, hypertension and increased risk of malignancy. Both azathioprine, whose mode of action is the inhibition of DNA synthesis in T and B cell cells, and mycophenolate mofetil, which acts by inhibiting purine biosynthesis, have also been shown to be beneficial in AD. The main side effect of both these drugs is bone marrow suppression.

8.7.6 Biological response modifiers

To avoid the potentially serious side effects of the immunosuppressants currently in use, biological response modifiers such as monoclonal antibody to IgE, recombinant cytokines, anti-leukotrienes and *M. vaccae* vaccination are being investigated for treatment of AD.

A humanized monoclonal antibody (mAb) to IgE that blocks the binding of IgE to FcεRI on mast cells and basophils has been developed and given subcutaneously to individuals with a history of immediate hypersensitivity to peanuts [69]. On subsequent challenge with increasing amounts of peanut antigen, the threshold of sensitivity for initiation of a type I hypersensitivity response was increased in these individuals. The success of this approach raises the possibility that an IgE mAb could be used to suppress AD by blocking binding of IgE to LCs, and preventing allergen presentation.

When recombinant IFN-γ (rIFN-γ), which inhibits Th-2 responses, was given subcutaneously to AD patients, disease severity was significantly reduced as compared to a placebo [70]. The therapy, which appeared to be both safe and effective, did not decrease IgE levels but did partially correct the reduced circulating CD4/CD8 ratio of activated T cells, and reduced numbers of circulating total white blood cells, eosinophils, PMNs and lymphocytes. However, IFN-γ plays a role in the chronic phase of AD, raising the possibility that administration of the cytokine could exacerbate the disease in some patients.

Subcutaneous administration of a suppressive cytokine, TGF-β_1, has been shown to decrease serum IgE levels and the numbers of mast cells and eosinophils in AD-like skin lesions in the NC/Nga mouse model of AD [71] These effects, which appear to be partly mediated via down-regulation of IFN-γ, suggest that TGF-β_1 may be a useful tool for treatment of human AD.

Cysteinyl leukotriene antagonists have been used successfully in the treatment of asthma, both in the acute phase and in controlling the chronic development of bronchial asthma. Preliminary studies suggest that they may also be beneficial in suppressing the inflammation induced by leukotrienes released by mast cells in the skin.

A single intradermal injection of killed *M. vaccae* given to patients with moderate to severe AD resulted, 3 months later, in a significant reduction in the surface area and in the dermatitis severity score compared to those patients receiving an injection of buffer solution [72]. These findings suggest that immunisation with *M. vaccae* may induce immunomodulatory effects in AD which result in reduction of disease activity.

Summary

- AD is a common, chronic fluctuating disease that is increasing in prevalence in Westernised countries.
- 80% of patients have associated IgE-mediated allergies.
- Skin lesions are characterised by a type IV hypersensitivity response to environmental antigens, a biphasic Th-2/Th-1 cytokine profile and chemokines that attract Th-2 cells, eosinophils, basophils and macrophages to the skin.
- AD has a strong genetic component:
    - Linkage to loci on 4 chromosomes identified in genome scans of children with AD. These differ from atopy-associated loci.
    - Candidate genes include FcεRI-β, SPINK5, Th-1/Th-2 cytokines, IL-4R, RANTES, IRF2, CARD4/Nod1, CARD15/Nod2, TLR2/TLR4, Tim-1 and HSCCE.
- AD is precipitated and exacerbated by various environmental factors including allergens, secondary microbial infections, stress and contact with skin irritants.
- The innate immune system in AD patients is impaired due to Th-2 cytokine-mediated inhibition of antimicrobial peptide, IL-8 and iNOS production by KCs. In addition, TLR and CARD/Nod polymorphisms, which result in impaired recognition of microbial components, are expressed in subgroups of AD patients.
- Various functional defects of T cells and monocytes in AD decrease the response to infection and increase the Th-2 response to allergens.
- Antigen-specific IgE synthesis is dysregulated in AD due to a selectively skewed Th-2 cytokine response to allergens. AD patients also produce IgE to superantigens released by skin-colonising *S. aureus*, *Malassezia* (part of normal skin flora) and allergen cross-reactive endogenous intracellular proteins.
- The epidermis and its component cells have distinctive characteristics that contribute to the disease process:
    - Altered lipid composition of the stratum corneum, which increases permeability to allergens and irritants.
    - KCs have an abnormal cytokine/chemokine profile; LCs have increased FcεRI expression and altered signal transduction.
    - Allergens are taken up via FcεRI-bound antigen-specific IgE on LCs and processed for presentation to naïve T cells in the lymph node. This favours the induction of allergen-specific Th-2 cells.
- Conventional topical and systemic treatments include corticosteroids, antibiotics, calcineurin inhibitors, UV light and immunosuppressive drugs. Novel biological response modifiers being tested in AD include monoclonal antibodies to IgE, recombinant cytokines, anti-leukotrienes and *M. vaccae* vaccination.

References

1. Lee Y.A., Wahn U., Kehrt R. *et al*. A major susceptibility locus for atopic dermatitis maps to chromosome 3q21. Nat.Genet. 2000; **26:** 470-3.

2. Cookson W.O., Ubhi B., Lawrence R. *et al*. Genetic linkage of childhood atopic dermatitis to psoriasis susceptibility loci. Nat.Genet. 2001; **27:** 372-3.

3. Bradley M., Soderhall C., Luthman H., Wahlgren C.F., Kockum I., Nordenskjold M. Susceptibility loci for atopic dermatitis on chromosomes 3, 13, 15, 17 and 18 in a Swedish population. Hum.Mol.Genet. 2002; **11:**1539-48.

4. Cox H.E., Moffatt M.F., Faux J.A. *et al*. Association of atopic dermatitis to the beta subunit of the high affinity immunoglobulin E receptor. Br.J.Dermatol. 1998; **138:** 182-7.

5. Walley A.J., Chavanas S., Moffatt M.F. *et al*. Gene polymorphism in Netherton and common atopic disease. Nat.Genet. 2001; **29:** 175-8.

6. Kawashima T., Noguchi E., Arinami T. *et al*. Linkage and association of an interleukin 4 gene polymorphism with atopic dermatitis in Japanese families. J.Med.Genet. 1998; **35:** 502-4.

7. He J.Q., Chan-Yeung M., Becker A.B. *et al*. Genetic variants of the IL13 and IL4 genes and atopic diseases in at-risk children. Genes Immun. 2003; **4:** 385-9.

8. Liu X., Nickel R., Beyer K. *et al*. An IL13 coding region variant is associated with a high total serum IgE level and atopic dermatitis in the German multicenter atopy study (MAS-90). J.Allergy Clin.Immunol. 2000; **106:** 167-70.

9. Oiso N., Fukai K., Ishii M. Interleukin 4 receptor alpha chain polymorphism Gln551Arg is associated with adult atopic dermatitis in Japan. Brit.J.Dermatol. 2000; **142:**1003-6.

10. Callard R.E., Hamvas R., Chatterton C. *et al*; The ALSPAC Study team. Avon Longitudinal Study of Parents and Children. An interaction between the IL-4Ralpha gene and infection is associated with atopic eczema in young children. Clin.Exp.Allergy 2002; **32:** 990-3.

11. Tsunemi Y., Saeki H., Nakamura K. *et al*. Interleukin-12 p40 (IL12B) 3'-untranslated region polymorphism is associated with susceptibility to atopic dermatitis and psoriasis vulgaris. J.Dermatol. Sci. 2002; **30:** 161-166.

12. Takahashi N., Akahoshi M., Matsuda A. *et al*. Association of the IL12RB1 promotor polymorphisms with increased risk of atopic dermatitis and other allergic phenotypes. Hum. Mol.Genet. 2005; **14:** 3149-59.

13. Novak N., Kruse S., Potreck J. *et al*. Single nucleotide polymorphisms of the IL18 gene are associated with atopic eczema. J.Allergy Clin.Immunol. 2005; **115:** 828-33.

14. Rafatpanah H., Bennett E., Pravica V. *et al*. Association between novel GM-CSF gene polymorphisms and the frequency and severity of atopic dermatitis. J.Allergy Clin.Immunol. 2003; **112:** 593-8.

15. Nickel R.G., Casolaro V., Wahn U. *et al*. Atopic dermatitis is associated with a functional mutation in the promoter of the C-C chemokine RANTES. J.Immunol. 2000; **164:** 1612-6.

16. McElligott D.L., Phillips J.A., Stillman C.A., Koch R.J., Mosier D.E., Hobbs M.V. CD4[+] T cells from IRF-1 deficient mice exhibit altered patterns of cytokine expression and cell subset homeostasis. J.Immunol. 1997; **159:** 4180-6.

17. Hida S., Ogasawara K., Sato K. *et al*. CD8(+) T cell-mediated skin disease in mice lacking IRF-2, the transcriptional attenuator of interferon-alpha/beta signalling. Immunity 2000; **13:** 643-55.

18. Nishio Y., Noguchi E., Ito S. *et al*. Mutation and association analysis of the interferon regulatory factor 2 gene (IRF2) with atopic dermatitis. J.Hum.Genet. 2001; **46:** 664-7.

19. Girardin S.E., Hugot J.-P., Sansonetti P.J. Lessons from Nod2 studies: towards a link between Crohn's disease and bacterial sensing. Trends Immunol. 2003; **24:** 652-8.

20. Kabesch M., Peters W., Carr D., Leupold W., Weiland S.K., von Mutius E. Association between polymorphisms in caspase recruitment domain containing protein 15 and allergy in two German populations. J.Allergy Clin.Immunol. 2003; **111:** 813-7.

21. Weidinger S., Klopp N., Rummler L. *et al*. Association of NOD1 polymorphisms with atopic eczema and related phenotypes. J.Allergy Clin.Immunol. 2005; **116:** 177-84.

22. Ahmad–Nejad P., Mrabet-Dahbi S., Breuer K. *et al*. The Toll-like receptor 2 R753Q polymorphism defines a subgroup of patients with atopic dermatitis having severe phenotype. J.Allergy Clin.Immunol. 2004; **113:** 565-7.

23. Chae S.C., Song J.H., Lee Y.C., Kim J.W., Chung H.T. The association of the exon 4 variations of Tim-1 gene with allergic diseases in a Korean population. Biochem.Biophys. Res.Commun. 2003; **312:** 346-50.

24. Vasilopoulos Y., Cork M.J., Murphy R. *et al*. Genetic association between an AACC insertion in the 3'UTR of the stratum corneum chymotryptic enzyme gene and atopic dermatitis. J.Invest.Dermatol. 2004; **123:** 62-6.

25. Cookson W.O.C.M. & Moffatt M.F. The genetics of atopic dermatitis. Curr.Opin.Allergy Clin.Immunol. 2002; **2:** 383-7.

26. Wuthrich B. & Schmid-Grendelmeier P. The atopic eczema/dermatitis syndrome. Epidemiology, natural course, and immunology of the IgE-associated ("extrinsic") and the nonallergic ("intrinsic") AEDS. J.Invest.Allergol.Clin.Immunol. 2003; **13:** 1-5.

27. Ring J., Kramer U., Schafer T., Behrendt H. Why are allergies increasing? Curr.Opin. Immunol. 2001; **13:** 701-8.

28. Strachan D.P. Hay fever, hygiene and household size. Br.Med.J. 1989; **299:** 1259-60.

29. Kalliomaki M., Salminen S., Arvilommi H., Kero P., Koskinen P., Isolauri E. Probiotics in primary prevention of atopic disease: a randomized placebo-controlled trial. Lancet 2001; **357:** 1076-9.

30. Romagnani S. The increased prevalence of allergy and the hygiene hypothesis: missing immune deviation, reduced immune suppression, or both? Immunol. 2004; **112:** 352-63.

31. Redecke V., Hacker H., Datta S.K. *et al*. Cutting edge: activation of Toll-like receptor 2 induces a Th2 immune response and promotes experimental asthma. J.Immunol. 2004; **172:** 2739-43.

32. Gambineri E., Torgerson T.R., Ochs H.D. Immune dysregulation, poliendocrinopathy, enteropathy and X-linked inheritance (IPEX) a syndrome of systemic autoimmunity caused by mutations of Foxp3, a critical regulator of T-cell homeostasis. Curr.Opin.Rheumatol. 2003; **15:** 430-8.

33. Smits H.H., Engering A., van der Kleij D. *et al*. Selective probiotic bacteria induce IL-

10-producing regulatory T cells in vitro by modulating dendritic cell function through dendritic cell-specific intercellular adhesion molecule 3-grabbing nonintegrin. J.Allergy Clin.Immunol. 2005; **115:** 1260-7.

34. Ong P.Y., Ohtake T., Brandt C. *et al.* Endogenous antimicrobial peptides and skin infections in atopic dermatitis. N.Engl.J.Med. 2002; **347:** 1151-60.

35. Nomura I., Goleva E., Howell M.D. *et al.* Cytokine milieu of atopic dermatitis, as compared to psoriasis, skin prevents induction of innate immune response genes. J.Immunol. 2003; **171:** 3262-9.

36. Rieg S., Steffen H., Seeber S. *et al.* Deficiency of dermcidin-derived antimicrobial peptides in sweat of patients with atopic dermatitis correlates with an impaired innate defense of human skin in vivo. J.Immunol. 2005; **174:** 8003-10.

37. Stern U.M., Hornstein O.P., Salzer B. Do training-dependent differences in perspiration exist between healthy and atopic subjects? J.Dermatol. 2000; **27:** 491-9.

38. Imayama S., Shimozono Y., Hoashi M. *et al.* Reduced secretion of IgA to skin surface of patients with atopic dermatitis. J.Allergy Clin.Immunol. 1994; **94:** 195-200.

39. Akdis M., Simon H.U., Weigl L., Kreyden O., Blaser K., Akdis C.A. Skin-homing (cutaneous lymphocyte-associated antigen-positive) CD8[+] T cells respond to superantigen and contribute to eosinophilia and IgE production in atopic dermatitis. J.Immunol. 1999; **163:** 466-75.

40. James J.M., Kagey-Sobotka A., Sampson H.A. Patients with severe atopic dermatitis have activated circulating basophils. J.Allergy Clin.Immunol. 1993; **91:** 1155-62.

41. Herlin T. & Kragballe K. Impaired monocyte cyclic AMP responses and monocyte cytotoxicity in atopic dermatitis. Allergy 1980; **35:** 647-55.

42. Novak N., Kruse S., Kraft S. *et al.* Dichotomic nature of atopic dermatitis reflected by combined analysis of monocyte immunophenotyping and single nucleotide polymorphisms of the interleukin-4/interleukin-13 receptor gene: the dichotomy of extrinsic and intrinsic atopic dermatitis. J.Invest.Dermatol. 2002; **119:** 870-5.

43. Ong P.Y., Hamid Q.A., Travers J.B. *et al.* Decreased IL-15 may contribute to elevated IgE and acute inflammation in atopic dermatitis. J.Immunol. 2002; **168:** 505-10.

44. Wierenga E.A., Snoek M., de Groot C. *et al.* Evidence for compartmentalization of functional subsets of CD2[+] T lymphocytes in atopic patients. J.Immunol. 1990; **144:** 4651-6.

45. Pastore S., Fanales-Belasio E., Albanesi C., Chinni L.M., Giannetti A., Girolomoni G. Granulocyte macrophage colony-stimulating factor is overproduced by keratinocytes in atopic dermatitis. Implications for sustained dendritic cell activation in the skin. J.Clin. Invest. 1997; **99:** 3009-17.

46. Soumelis V. & Liu Y.J. Human thymic stromal lymphopoietin: a novel epithelial cell-derived cytokine and a potential key player in the induction of allergic inflammation. Springer Semin. Immunopathol. 2004; **25:** 325-33.

47. Giustizieri M.L., Mascia F., Frezzolini A. *et al.* Keratinocytes from patients with atopic dermatitis and psoriasis show a distinct chemokine production profile in response to T cell-derived cytokines. J.Allergy Clin.Immunol. 2001; **107:** 871-7.

48. Wollenberg A., Kraft S., Hanau D., Bieber T. Immunomorphological and ultrastructural characterization of Langerhans cells and a novel, inflammatory dendritic epidermal cell

(IDEC) population in lesional skin of atopic eczema. J.Invest.Dermatol. 1996; **106:** 446-53.

49. Kraft S., Wessendorf J.H., Haberstok J., Novak N., Wollenberg A., Bieber T. Enhanced expression and activity of protein-tyrosine kinases establishes a functional signaling pathway only in FcepsilonRIhigh Langerhans cells from atopic individuals. J.Invest. Dermatol. 2002; **119:** 804-11.

50. van der Heijden F.L., Wierenga E.A., Bos J.D., Kapsenberg M.L. High frequency of IL-4-producing CD4$^+$ allergen-specific T lymphocytes in atopic dermatitis lesional skin. J.Invest. Dermatol. 1991; **97:** 389-94.

51. Galli G., Chantry D., Annunziato F. *et al.* Macrophage-derived chemokine production by activated human T cells *in vitro* and *in vivo*: preferential association with the production of type 2 cytokines. Eur.J.Immunol. 2000; **30:** 204-10.

52. Taha R.A., Minshall E.M., Leung D.Y. *et al.* Evidence for increased expression of eotaxin and monocyte chemotactic protein-4 in atopic dermatitis. J.Allergy Clin.Immunol. 2000; **105:** 1002-7.

53. Leung D.Y.M., Harbeck R., Bina P. *et al.* Presence of IgE antibodies to staphylococcal exotoxins on the skin of patients with atopic dermatitis. J.Clin.Invest. 1993; **92:** 1374-80.

54. Strange P., Skov L., Lisby S., Nielsen P.L., Baadsgaard O. Staphylococcal enterotoxin B applied on intact normal and intact atopic skin induces dermatitis. Arch. Dermatol. 1996; **132:** 27-33.

55. Michie C.A. & Davie T. Atopic dermatitis and staphylococcal superantigens. Lancet 1996; **347:** 324.

56. Skov L., Olsen J.V., Giorno R., Schlievert P.M., Baadsgaard O., Leung D.Y. Application of staphylococcal enterotoxin B on normal and atopic skin induces up-regulation of T cells by a superantigen-mediated mechanism. J.Allergy Clin.Immunol. 2000; **105:** 820-6.

57. Davison S., Allen M., Vaughan R., Barker J. Staphylococcal toxin-induced T cell proliferation in atopic eczema correlates with increased use of superantigen-reactive Vbeta-chains in cutaneous lymphocyte-associated antigen (CLA)-positive lymphocytes. Clin.Exp.Immunol. 2000; **121:** 181-6.

58. Leung D.Y., Gately M., Trumble A., Ferguson-Darnell B., Schlievert P.M., Picker L.J. Bacterial superantigens induce T cell expression of the skin-selective homing receptor, the cutaneous lymphocyte-associated antigen, via stimulation of interleukin 12 production. J.Exp.Med. 1995; **181:** 747-53.

59. Ou L.S., Goleva E., Hall C., Leung D.Y. T regulatory cells in atopic dermatitis and subversion of their activity by superantigens. J.Allergy Clin.Immunol. 2004; **113:** 756-63.

60. Lin Y.T., Wang C.T., Hsu C.T. *et al.* Differential susceptibility to staphylococcal superantigen (SsAg)-induced apoptosis of CD4$^+$ T cells from atopic dermatitis patients and healthy subjects: the inhibitory effect of IL-4 on SsAg-induced apoptosis. J.Immunol. 2003; **171:** 1102-8.

61. Morishita Y., Tada J., Sato A. *et al.* Possible influences of *Staphylococcus aureus* on atopic dermatitis - the colonizing features and the effects of staphylococcal enterotoxins. Clin.Exp. Allergy. 1999; **29:** 1110-7.

62. Scheynius A., Johansson C., Buentke E., Zargari A., Linder M.T. Atopic eczema/dermatitis syndrome and *Malassezia*. Int.Arch.Allergy Immunol. 2002; **127:** 161-9.

63. Buentke E. & Scheynius A. Dendritic cells and fungi. A.P.M.I.S. 2003; **111:** 789-96.

64. Johansson C., Eshagi H., Linder M.T., Jakobson E., Scheynius A. Positive atopy patch test reaction to *Malassezia furfur* in atopic dermatitis correlates with a T helper 2-like peripheral blood mononuclear cell response. J.Invest.Dermatol. 2002; **118:** 1044-51.

65. Valenta R., Natter S., Seiberler S. *et al.* Molecular characterisation of an autoallergen, hom s 1, identified by serum IgE from atopic dermatitis patients. J.Invest.Dermatol. 1998; **111:**1178 –83.

66. Ochs R.L., Muro Y., Si Y., Ge H., Chan E.K., Tan E.M. Autoantibodies to DFS 70 kd/ transcription coactivator p75 in atopic dermatitis and other conditions. J.Allergy Clin. Immunol. 2000; **105:** 1211-20.

67. Mossabeb R., Seiberler S., Mittermann I. *et al.* Characterisation of a novel isoform of alpha-nascent polypeptide-associated complex as IgE-defined autoantigen. J.Invest.Dermatol. 2002; **119:** 820-9.

68. Hauk P.J., Hamid Q.A., Chrousos G.P., Leung D.Y.M. Induction of corticosteroid insensitivity in human peripheral blood mononuclear cells by microbial superantigens. J.Allergy Clin. Immunol. 2000; **105:** 782-7.

69. Leung D.Y., Sampson H.A., Yunginger J.W. *et al.* Effect of anti-IgE therapy in patients with peanut allergy. N.Engl.J.Med. 2003; **348:** 986-93.

70. Ellis C.N., Stevens S.R., Blok B.K., Taylor R.S., Cooper K.D. Interferon-gamma therapy reduces blood leukocyte levels in patients with atopic dermatitis: correlation with clinical improvement. Clin.Immunol. 1999; **92:** 49-55.

71. Sumiyoshi K., Nakao A., Ushio H. *et al.* Transforming growth factor-beta1 suppresses atopic dermatitis-like skin lesions in NC/Nga mice. Clin.Exp.Allergy 2002; **32:** 309-14.

72. Arkwright P.D. & David T.J. Intradermal administration of a killed *Mycobacterium vaccae* suspension (SRL 172) is associated with improvement in atopic dermatitis in children with moderate-to-severe disease. J.Allergy Clin.Immunol. 2001; **107:** 531-4.

Further Reading

1. Cookson W. Genetics and genomics of asthma and allergic diseases. Immunol.Rev. 2002; **190:** 195-206.

2. Novak N., Bieber T., Leung D.Y.M. Immune mechanisms leading to atopic dermatitis. J.Allergy Clin.Immunol. 2003; **112:** S128-39

PART III: Immunological Mechanisms of Skin Disease

9

Psoriasis

Psoriasis is a common, chronic skin disease characterised by epidermal hyperproliferation and an infiltrate of activated T lymphocytes and dendritic cells. It is a T cell-mediated disease (type IV hypersensitivity response), which may be autoimmune and/or the result of a chronic infection.

9.1 Clinical Features

Psoriasis is a chronic, inflammatory skin disease affecting approximately 2-3% of Caucasians. A seronegative arthopathy is present in 6-30% of patients, and both Crohn's disease and ulcerative colitis show a positive association. The onset of the disease is more frequent around puberty, and two further peaks of increased frequency occur at about 30 and 50 years of age. However, there is considerable overlap between the three groups, and the disease can potentially start at any age.

The commonest form of the disease is chronic plaque (CP) psoriasis in which skin lesions characteristically occur on the extensor surfaces of the knees and elbows, scalp and sacral region (Fig. 9.1, colour plate). The lesion is typically a raised red scaly patch with a sharply demarcated edge. In the less frequent guttate form of psoriasis, the lesions are smaller and have a different distribution, occurring over the upper trunk, and sometimes on the limbs, face and scalp (Fig. 9.2, colour plate). Guttate psoriasis typically appears 1-2 weeks after a streptococcal upper respiratory tract infection in children and young adults and, unlike CP psoriasis, often spontaneously resolves after 8-12 weeks. As 60-70% of patients with guttate psoriasis go on to develop the chronic form of the disease at a later date, it is likely that the two clinical types are linked by common factors. Other less frequently observed forms of psoriasis include erythroderma, in which the whole body surface area is involved, and pustular psoriasis, whose pathogenesis has not been widely studied and therefore will not be discussed here.

9.2 Histology of skin lesions

The major histological features of a psoriatic plaque are a hyperproliferative epidermal layer, and a mononuclear cellular infiltrate surrounding dilated and tortuous capillaries in the papillary dermis (Fig. 9.3, colour plate).

The epidermis is characterised by a parakeratotic stratum corneum containing aggregates of PMNs (Munro abscesses), absence of a granular layer, thinning of the suprapapillary plate, and regular elongation of the rete ridges with clubbing. These features result from a 4-fold increase in the numbers of epidermal cells, as compared to normal skin, accompanied by an abnormal differentiation pathway. The increase in the rate of production of epidermal cells within psoriatic lesions is probably not, however, the result of an altered cell cycle time as previously thought. Instead, there is evidence that suggests hyperproliferation is due to the activation of, but not increase in, the normally quiescent basal KC population, which includes the stem cells. This is accompanied by accelerated maturation and differentiation [1].

These epidermal changes are secondary to the appearance of a perivascular mononuclear cell infiltrate, together with dilation and tortuosity of the blood vessels in the dermal papillae, which are the earliest histological changes in the formation of a psoriatic lesion. The majority of mononuclear cells in the infiltrate of both early and fully developed psoriatic lesions are T lymphocytes, macrophages and dendritic cells, with rare B lymphocytes and few PMNs.

9.3 Aetiology

9.3.1 Genetics

9.3.1.1 Evidence for a genetic basis

Two large-scale epidemiology studies in the Faroe Islands and Sweden [2,3] revealed a significantly higher incidence of psoriasis in relatives compared to the general population, or to matched controls, and provided the first strong evidence for a genetic basis for psoriasis. The risk to first-degree relatives was estimated to be 8-23%, and the prevalence of psoriasis 2.0-2.8% in the study populations as a whole. Re-analysis of the data from these two studies approximately 30 years later showed that it was consistent with a multilocus model of inheritance.

The involvement of genetic factors in psoriasis was further suggested by twin studies, which showed that the concordance in monozygotic twins was 63-70% compared to 23% in dizygotic twins. Furthermore, the age of onset of the disease and its manifestations were very similar in the concordant monozygotic twins. Environmental factors are also implicated in the triggering of the disease as indicated by concordance rates of less than 100%.

The mode of inheritance in psoriasis remains unclear with reports of both autosomal dominant and recessive patterns of inheritance in families. However, much of the available data concerning the frequency of psoriasis in siblings with neither, one or both parents affected with the disease do not appear to fit either model, even after taking into account age-dependent penetrance.

9.3.1.2 Genomic imprinting

Genomic imprinting refers to the differential expression or activity of a gene depending upon whether it has been inherited from the mother or the father. It is a form of epigenetic modification in which changes occur in the transcriptional control of genes.

Two pieces of evidence have been presented that support the genomic imprinting of a major gene in psoriasis [4]. Firstly, the birth weight of children from psoriatics is influenced by the sex of the psoriatic parent; thus babies whose fathers have psoriasis are significantly heavier than those with psoriatic mothers. Secondly, the disease manifestation or penetrance depends in part upon the sex of the psoriatic parent, so that fathers with psoriasis have affected children more often than psoriatic mothers. This was also true in the case of offspring of male "gene carriers" i.e. clinically healthy individuals who had a first or second degree relative with psoriasis and therefore presumably carry a major gene for the disease in their family. Furthermore, recent evidence suggests that an increase in disease severity or decrease in age at onset in successive generations, known as genetic anticipation, is most marked if the disease is inherited from the father.

9.3.1.3 HLA Associations

Early genetic studies focused on the association of HLA alleles with psoriasis. The HLA genes, which are located within the MHC region on chromosome 6p, express a high degree of polymorphism and association with several Class I and II antigens have been reported. These include the Class I antigens, HLA-B13, -B17, -B37, -B57, -Cw6 and –Cw7, and the Class II antigens HLA-DR7 and HLA-DR4. The Cw6 allele (HLA-Cw*0602) shows the strongest and most consistent association in psoriasis in various ethnic groups, and has been proposed to correlate with early onset (up to 40 years of age) and positive family history, so called type I psoriasis [5]. Approximately 40-80% of affected individuals express HLA-Cw*0602, compared to approximately 20% of the normal population, although it has been reported to be as high as 100% in patients with guttate psoriasis. Heterozygosity for HLA-Cw*0602 is associated with a relative risk of developing psoriasis of 8.9 which increases to 23.1 for HLA-Cw*0602 homozygous patients. Furthermore, HLA-Cw*0602-positive psoriatic individuals have different clinical features to those who do not express the HLA-Cw*0602 allele, such as more extensive skin lesions and severe disease, a higher incidence of the Koebner phenomenon (trauma-induced skin lesions in patients with pre-existing skin disease), more frequently reported that their skin got worse during or after throat infections and generally had a better response to sunlight [6].

A strong association between psoriasis and the replacement of threonine by alanine at position 73 on HLA-C molecules has been reported in Japanese patients [7]. This amino acid is situated on the α1 domain helix that forms one side of the putative antigen-binding cleft of the HLA-C molecules and could therefore affect antigen presentation. The substitution at codon 73 is an important component of HLA-C genes and is present in Cw*04, Cw*0602, Cw*07, Cw*12, Cw*1503 and Cw*17 alleles. However, such an association has not been confirmed in Caucasian psoriatic patients.

The MHC genes characteristically show strong linkage disequilibrium because of low recombination frequencies between them. This results in the formation of conserved or ancestral haplotypes, groups of genes that are inherited in a block. A strong association between psoriasis and a number of extended haplotypes, which encompass alleles at HLA-C, -B, -DRB1 and -DQB1, has been demonstrated. In most cases the haplotypes contain HLA-Cw*0602, further implicating the Class I gene in disease susceptibility, but there is some controversy over whether it is the HLA-Cw*0602 gene itself or another gene in strong linkage disequilibrium that is responsible (see below).

The fact that only a small proportion (approximately 10%) of HLA-predisposed individuals go on to develop psoriasis implies that inheritance of a particular HLA allele is not sufficient by itself for initiation of the disease. Indeed it is now widely accepted that psoriasis is a complex multifactorial disease involving several genes that interact with both each other and with a variety of environmental factors.

9.3.1.4 Genetic linkage/Positional candidate genes

Since the mid 1990s, 10 genome-wide linkage scans of multiplex families with psoriasis have been performed in order to detect linkage with susceptibility loci for the disease (reviewed in [8]). The results of these studies are measured as a lod (logarithm of odds ratio) score, a score of ≥ 3.0 being taken as indicative of linkage. This is a statistical estimate that a DNA marker is segregating with psoriasis in families more often than expected by chance. As the mode of inheritance is unknown, non-parametric methods of data analysis, which identify regions of excess allele sharing, have also been used.

Nineteen potentially susceptible loci on 15 different chromosomes have been identified (Table 9.1). Nine of the candidate loci with evidence of linkage have been designated as PSORS1-9 (Psoriasis susceptibility 1-9), but a lod score of 3.0 was not reached for PSORS5-9 and non-parametric analysis giving suggestive evidence of linkage was reported. Only one locus, PSORS1 containing the associated HLA Class I region, has been consistently identified by several independent research groups. Evidence for linkage to PSORS1 is stronger than for the rest, presumably because its effects are greater than for the other regions identified. The weak effects of the non-HLA regions may indicate false positives, or, conversely that the linkage is true but that these susceptibility loci are found only in particular psoriasis phenotypes.

The candidate genes implicated by these genome-wide linkage scans code for proteins involved in epidermal differentiation, immune and inflammatory responses and response to pathogens. Some of these candidate loci are shared with other inflammatory diseases (Table 9.1) suggesting common genetic defects in the skin immune system (see Chapter 8).

PSORS 1

The PSORS1 locus containing HLA-Cw6 on chromosome 6p21.3 confers significant risk for disease and is estimated to account for between 35-50% of familial clustering in psoriasis. However three linkage disequilibrium studies of the PSORS1 region, using different statistical approaches, differed in the extent and location of the minimal PSORS1 region reported (Fig. 9.4). There was no overlap between these published minimal intervals; however, more conservative interpretations of the data suggest that these regions may extend further than presented [9]. A distance of approximately 160 kb encompassing HLA-C, and the genes OTF3, TCF19, HCR (α-helix coiled-coil rod homologue) and CDSN (corneodesmosin) telomeric to HLA-C, appears to be the critical site in which the susceptibility gene is located. Furthermore, patients with psoriatic arthritis also share a 100 kb susceptibility region telomeric to HLA-C.

The findings of most studies have excluded **HLA-C** as the susceptibility gene is this region. Candidate gene analysis using both robust family-based association studies, such as the transmission disequilibrium test (TDT), and case-control studies has, however, shown disease association for the genes coding for OTF3, HCR and CDSN.

A single **OTF3** allele (β allele) has been reported to show disease association, independently of the association of HLA Cw*0602, in a single study of Spanish psoriasis patients. This gene codes for a transcriptional factor involved in embryonic stem cell lineage commitment, and is not, therefore, an obvious candidate for psoriasis susceptibility. Furthermore, SNPs of a cell growth regulated gene, TCF19 (SC1), were not found to be associated with psoriasis.

Table 9.1 Susceptibility loci for psoriasis identified by genetic linkage

Locus name	Chromosome location	Proposed Candidate gene(s)	Linkage to other diseases
PSORS1*	6p21.3	CDSN, HCR	
PSORS2	17q24-25	SLC9A3R, NAT9, RAPTOR	Atopic dermatitis, multiple sclerosis, diabetes mellitis, inflammatory arthritis
PSORS3	4q34	IRF2	Asthma, multiple sclerosis
PSORS4	1q21	S100A8/S100A9	Atopic dermatitis
PSORS5	3q21	SLC12A8	Atopic dermatitis
PSORS6	19p13	JunB	Crohn's disease, ulcerative colitis
PSORS7	1p35-p34		
PSORS8	16q12-13	CARD15/Nod2	Crohn's disease, diabetes mellitis, psoriatic arthritis
PSORS9	4q31		
	2p14		
	2q		
	4q13		
	7p15		Asthma, multiple sclerosis, Crohn's disease, ulcerative colitis, diabetes mellitis, inflammatory arthritis
	8q		
	10q22		
	14q		
	15		Psoriatic arthritis
	18p		
	20p		Atopic dermatitis

* Locus names in bold show lod score ≥ 3.0

The genetic evidence for the involvement of CDSN and HCR is, in contrast, much stronger and is supported by functional studies. The **CDSN** gene (formerly known as the S gene) is located about 160 kb telomeric to HLA-C in the class I region (Fig. 9.4). CDSN encodes for an epidermal desmosomal glycoprotein (corneodesmosin), which is expressed exclusively in differentiating KCs and shares structural homology to granular cell layer components such as loricrin, keratin 1 and keratin 10. CDSN is important in corneocyte cohesion and its proteolysis may be involved in the process of desquamation. It is abnormally highly expressed in psoriasis (and other hyperproliferative skin disorders) and its synthesis is dysregulated. In common with other genes in the MHC region,

Figure 9.4   Proposed location of the minimal region containing the PSORS1 gene on chromosome 6p21. The approximate positions of the known genes are given at the top of the figure. Underneath, the regions shown in black are the minimal susceptibility regions reported in three different studies; the dotted lines indicate the extended regions suggested by refinement of this data by Capon et al, 2002 [9].

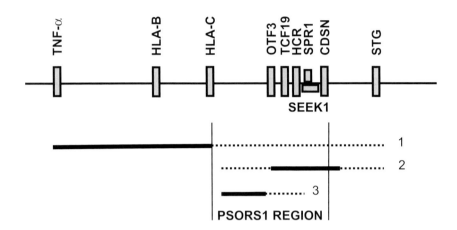

the CDSN gene is highly polymorphic, and the association between CDSN SNPs and psoriasis susceptibility has been extensively investigated [9]. Two SNPs that induce amino acid changes (+619, Ser → Phe; +1243, Ser → Leu) define an allele of the CDSN gene that shows linkage and association with psoriasis. Furthermore a high-risk haplotype of CDSN, which includes the high-risk allele, has been shown to be more closely associated with psoriasis than HLA-Cw*0602-B*5701 in German families. Thus CDSN is an attractive candidate gene for psoriasis because of its function and skin-specific expression; amino acid changes in the protein could lead to altered function.

The **HCR** gene is located only 110 kb telomeric of HLA-C and codes for a tricohyalin homologue with a-helical coiled-coil rod domains. The HCR protein, which is ubiquitously expressed throughout the body, is present in basal KCs in healthy skin but shows a different pattern in psoriatic skin. This altered pattern, in which HCR expression is increased in basal KCs at the tips of dermal papillae but is absent from the tips of rete ridges, is inversely related to the expression of Ki-67 (a cell proliferation marker) suggesting a role for HCR in regulation of keratinocyte differentiation or proliferation. In common with CDSN, the HCR gene is highly polymorphic and genotyping of 419 families from six populations showed that coding SNPs of HCR formed a conserved allele HCR*WWCC that associated highly significantly with psoriasis and with the HLA-Cw6 allele in all populations [10]. Three of the amino acid substitutions that constitute this high-risk haplotype are predicted to induce secondary structural alterations of the HCR protein. Thus altered HCR function could play a role in the altered proliferation and differentiation of KCs in psoriasis.

PSORS2

Linkage of psoriasis susceptibility was first reported to a locus on chromosome 17q25 (PSORS2) in a genome-wide scan of eight multiply affected US families. Four of the eight families showed linkage, and in the family where evidence for linkage was strongest, psoriasis susceptibility segregated as an autosomal dominant trait with high penetrance. In addition, in the 17q-linked families, no association with HLA-Cw6 was observed. Further independent studies of groups of psoriasis patients belonging to different Caucasian populations confirmed the linkage of psoriasis to 17q24-q25. However, there have also been studies that have failed to find a linkage to this region. Thus genetic heterogeneity appears to be a characteristic of psoriasis families suggesting that different combinations of genes may be responsible for disease susceptibility in individual families.

Family-based association tests have revealed two peaks of strong association with psoriasis on chromosome 17q25, separated by 6 Mb [11]. One peak contains SLC9A3R1 and NAT9, and the other RAPTOR (p150 target of rapamycin (TOR)-scaffold protein containing WD-repeats). SLC9A3R1 (solute carrier family 9, isoform A3, regulatory factor 1) is a PDZ domain-containing phosphoprotein that associates with the ezrin-radixin-moesin family, and is implicated in epithelial membrane function and immune synapse formation in T cells. It is predominantly expressed in the stratum corneum of normal and psoriatic skin and in inactive rather than active T cells. NAT9 is a new member of the N-acetyltransferase family. Five psoriasis-associated variants in the SLC9A3R1-NAT9 region have been identified, one of which lies between the two genes and leads to loss of a putative binding site for the transcription factor, RUNX1. RUNX1 is essential for haematopoietic cell development and can harbour mutations causing sporadic and familial myeloid leukaemias. Loss of a RUNX1 binding site has also been reported in SLE (see Chapter 6) and rheumatoid arthritis in relation to different genes. In psoriasis, the loss of a RUNX1 binding site may cause dysregulation of SLC9A3R1 or NAT9 in cells of haematopoietic origin. However, SLC9A3R1 is also expressed in polarised epithelial cells including KCs, and its dysregulation may affect KC response to immune signals.

PSORS3

In 1996, a scan of five Irish and one English family with psoriasis revealed evidence for linkage to a locus on chromosome 4q35 (PSORS3). Although some studies have failed to confirm this linkage, other linkage scans have identified a slightly more proximal region of chromosome 4q (4q32) to contain a psoriasis susceptibility gene. A recent meta-analysis of six previous linkage scans for psoriasis susceptibility loci has revealed that the second strongest peak of linkage (after the MHC region) was obtained with markers from a region on chromosome 4q28-q31 [12]. This region was detected previously only in families from the Chinese Han population. This raises the possibility that a number of psoriasis susceptibility loci may be present in the region 4q28-q35; such clusters of genes are not uncommon in complex traits.

Possible candidate genes within this region include IL-15, TLR2 and TLR3, vascular endothelial growth factor C (VEGFC) and IRF2. IRF2, which is involved in negative regulation of IFN-γ signalling, has been investigated in two studies as a possible candidate gene for psoriasis with conflicting results.

PSORS4

In 1999, linkage between psoriasis and a region on chromosome 1q21 (PSORS4) was reported in Italian families in which none of the previously described susceptibility loci had generated significant lod scores. Subsequent analysis, however, revealed evidence supporting an interaction between the 1q21 susceptibility locus and that on chromosome 6p21 (PSORS1). Some linkage to the 1q21 region, which contains the Epidermal Differentiation Cluster (EDC), was subsequently also found in a set of families from the USA. In each case, psoriasis was inherited as an autosomal dominant trait with reduced penetrance. The EDC, which spans approximately 2 Mb, contains gene families coding for small proline-rich proteins (SPRRs) and late envelope proteins (LEPs), which code for precursor proteins of the cornified cell envelope. Genes coding for the S100A calcium-binding protein family are also present, many members of which are over-expressed in psoriatic skin. S100 calcium-binding proteins, which are often secreted, have a wide range of immunological functions.

Fine mapping of the 1.6 Mb 1q21 region in Italian families, using linkage disequilibrium analysis, showed that PSORS4 lies within a 50 kb region on the distal portion of the EDC complex [13]. This region contains several genes including loricrin, a KC structural protein, with the genes coding for inflammatory proteins S100A7, S100A8 and S100A9 close by. S100A7 (also called psoriasin because it was first identified in psoriatic skin) has been further analysed for disease-associated nucleotide variants. S100A7 is a potent and selective chemotactic inflammatory protein for CD4[+] T cells and PMNs, and is highly up-regulated in psoriatic KCs. Although two polymorphisms were detected within the promotor for the gene, neither showed preferential association with psoriasis, excluding S100A7 as a candidate gene for disease susceptibility. However, overexpression of S100A8/S100A9 expression has subsequently been shown to be specific for 1q-linked pedigrees suggesting that these members of the S100 family may be more suitable candidates for psoriasis susceptibility.

PSORS5

Suggestive evidence (NPL score of 2.77) for linkage to chromosome 3q21 (PSORS5) has been reported in psoriasis patients from southwest Sweden. Genome scans carried out in Scandinavian patients with AD (see Chapter 8) and asthma, have also detected linkage to the same region suggesting that a mutation or variant may be found at the 3q21 locus which is present at a higher frequency in Scandinavians. Linkage disequilibrium mapping, using a SNP map spanning an approximately 1 Mb region of chromosome 3q21 containing the PSORS5 locus, led to the identification of a psoriasis susceptibility candidate gene SLC12A8 (solute carrier family 12 protein, member 8) coding for a potassium/chloride transporter [14]. A five SNP-marker haplotype spanning half of this gene is significantly associated with psoriasis, although a causative DNA variation has yet to be identified. Interestingly, a second solute carrier at chromosome 5q31, SLC22A4 (solute carrier family 22, member 4) is associated with rheumatoid arthritis suggesting that alterations in cation transport may be relevant to other inflammatory diseases.

Recent investigation of two further genes in the 3q21 region, coding for a cysteine protease inhibitor cystatin A which is up-regulated in psoriatic skin lesions, and zinc finger protein 148 which is involved in the regulation of T cell receptors, failed to find any association with psoriasis.

PSORS6

Suggestive evidence for linkage to chromosome 19p13 (PSORS6) has been obtained in a genome-wide scan of German families, and subsequently was one of three regions showing weak linkage in a study of British families. The candidate interval on 19p is ≥ 15 cM and contains numerous genes and expressed sequence tags. A recently proposed candidate gene for PSORS6 is JunB, a component of the AP-1 transcription factor, which regulates cell proliferation, differentiation and cytokine expression. JunB expression is downregulated in KCs in psoriatic lesions; furthermore, inducible epidermal deletion of JunB and its proposed antagonist, c-Jun in mice led to the development of psoriasis-like skin disease and arthritis [15].

PSORS6 coincides with a susceptibility locus for inflammatory bowel disease suggesting that common genetic factors may be involved in the susceptibility to both inflammatory conditions.

PSORS7

A possible psoriasis susceptibility locus has been identified on chromosome 1p35-p34 (PSORS7) in British families, but has yet to be replicated in independent studies. A number of immune-related genes have been mapped to this region including the gene coding for EPS15, a highly specific intracellular substrate for the EGF receptor, which is over-expressed in psoriatic skin lesions.

PSORS8

Suggestive linkage for a locus on chromosome 16q12-13 (PSORS8), which overlaps with a locus conferring susceptibility to Crohn's disease, has been reported in a study of US and German psoriasis pedigrees. In addition, linkage analysis conditioned on paternal transmission to affected individuals gave a significant lod score of 4.19 for Icelandic patients with psoriatic arthritis for this region.

Crohn's disease susceptibility has recently been localised to mutations in the CARD15/ Nod2 gene, which codes for an intracellular receptor for bacterial peptidoglycan fragments [16]. The prevalence of psoriasis is significantly increased in patients with Crohn's disease suggesting that the two diseases may share genetic susceptibility at this, and possibly other, chromosomal sites (Table 9.1). However three studies that have investigated Crohn's-associated mutations in psoriasis patients have failed to find any association. Furthermore, whilst an association was found between the Nod2 gene and psoriatic arthritis in a study of Canadian patients, this was not confirmed in a cohort of Italian psoriatic arthritis patients.

PSORS9

The locus at chromosome 4q31 (PSORS9) was detected in a linkage scan for psoriasis susceptibility loci using families from the Chinese Han population, but had not been a likely candidate for linkage in other studies of families of Northern European origin. However, as mentioned above, a meta-analysis of six linkage scans for psoriasis susceptibility loci has revealed that the second strongest peak of linkage (after the MHC region) was obtained with markers from a region on chromosome 4q28-q31 [12].

Several other weak linkages to loci on various chromosomes have been detected (Table 9.1) and various approaches are currently being used to determine their validity. A consortium of international psoriasis genetics investigators was recently established to investigate 14 previously reported potential psoriasis-susceptibility loci in a cohort of 710 families with psoriasis [17]. Analysis of allele sharing at chromosome 6p21 confirmed the presence of a major susceptibility locus within the MHC region. Apart from 6p21, it was demonstrated that the strongest evidence of allele sharing in affected sibling pairs was found on chromosomes 16q and 10q22-q23. Furthermore, an association between the expression of a MHC risk haplotype for psoriasis and linkage to 16q was shown.

9.3.1.5 Other candidate genes

Investigation of the frequencies of polymorphisms in candidate genes may reveal association to disease where genetic linkage studies have failed. Various cytokines, killer cell immunoglobulin-like receptors and MHC Class I chain-related-A antigen have been proposed as candidate susceptibility genes for psoriasis (Table 9.2). However, some of the polymorphisms reported are not consistently found in different patient populations or do not appear to be related to functional effects, which makes their significance questionable.

<u>**Cytokines**</u>

Polymorphisms of the **IL-1** gene family have been implicated in various chronic inflammatory and autoimmune diseases, including inflammatory bowel disease. In psoriasis, association between an allele (A2) at the locus for IL-1ra, a specific inhibitor of IL-1 activity, and early onset psoriasis has been reported. However, linkage to IL-1ra in psoriasis has been excluded using family linkage analysis. In contrast, a more recent study showed that carriage of the IL-1β -511*C homozygous genotype was associated with late onset psoriasis and with increased production of IL-1ra in response to LPS and IL-10 [18].

A strong association has been consistently reported in Caucasians between early onset psoriasis, especially in males, and a polymorphism at position –238 (allele 2; G to A transition) in the **TNF-α** promotor [18]. The TNF-α gene is located on chromosome 6p21.3 within the Class III region of the MHC, centromeric to HLA-B, and forms part of the ancestral haplotype 57.1, which is strongly associated with psoriasis. However, the functional consequences of this variant is not clear as both decreased secretion of TNF-α in response to mitogens and streptococcal antigens, and increased production in response to LPS have been shown to correlate with carriage of the TNF-238*2 allele in psoriatics and/or normal individuals.

In addition, the B1 allele of the NcoI polymorphism of the **TNF-β** gene is increased in psoriasis and associated with positive family history.

MIF, a macrophage-derived cytokine that induces TNF-α production and promotion of T cell activation, is also over-expressed in psoriatic skin lesions. Carriage of either the MIF –173*C or MIF CATT$_7$ promotor polymorphism, which are associated with increased production of MIF, has recently been reported to be positively correlated with CP psoriasis [19]. Furthermore, a haplotype containing both polymorphisms conferred an odds ratio of 1.7 for increased risk of susceptibility to psoriasis. This haplotype has also been associated with juvenile idiopathic arthritis and adult inflammatory polyarthritis.

Polymorphisms of the **IFN-γ** and **IL-10** genes associated with different levels of cytokine production have been investigated in patients with psoriasis. No difference in the genotypes

Table 9.2 Candidate gene polymorphisms

Candidate gene	Polymorphisms	Psoriasis subtypes	Functional outcome
IL-1β	-511*C	Late onset	Increased IL-1ra
TNF-α	Promotor -238, allele 2	Early onset, especially males	Increased/decreased
TNF-β	Ncol-B1 allele	Positive family history	Not known
MIF	-173*C CATT$_7$ -173*C/CATT$_7$ haplotype	CP psoriasis	Increased
IL-12p40	-1188, A allele	Japanese patients	Increased
IL-20	-1053, G allele HT3 GAA haplotype	Early or late onset, familial or sporadic disease	Not known
VEGF	+405CC, C allele	Type I psoriasis, severe disease	Increased
KIR	KIR2DS1 KIR2DL5	Psoriatic arthritis and/or psoriasis	Not known
MICA	MICA A5.1 allele	Positive family history, early onset	Secretion of molecule
	MICA*06 allele	Type I psoriasis	Not known

expressed by the patients compared to controls, or between early and late onset psoriasis were detected. However, an association between psoriasis and single nucleotide polymorphisms of the Th-1-inducing cytokine **IL-12** may explain the predominance of Th-1 cytokines in psoriatic skin lesions. The A allele of the SNP at position −1188 in the 3' untranslated region of the IL-12p40 gene present on chromosome 5q31-33 is increased in Japanese patients with psoriasis (and conversely decreased in AD) resulting in increased levels of IL-12p40 protein [20]. However, in another study of psoriasis patients carried out in the Netherlands, the frequencies of various genotypes for the promoter region of the IL-12p40 gene did not differ between psoriasis patients and controls. Furthermore, there was no association between these promoter genotypes and increased production of IL-12p40 and IL-12p70 in response to LPS demonstrated by psoriatic blood cells.

KCs in psoriasis synthesise **IL-20**, a cytokine that has autocrine effects on epidermal function (see below). Significant association between patients with psoriasis and the G allele at position −1053 of the IL-20 gene has been detected [21]. Polymorphisms at positions −1053, 1380 and 1462 are in linkage disequilibrium; patients with plaque psoriasis had a higher frequency of the HT3 GAA haplotype, which was associated with an increased risk of early or late onset, and of familial or sporadic disease [21]. The functional implications of these polymorphisms in the regulation of IL-20 expression are presently unknown.

VEGF is a stimulator of angiogenesis produced by KCs and up-regulated in psoriatic lesions. In both type I psoriasis and in severe disease, there is an increased frequency of the +405CC genotype and of the C allele of VEGF compared to controls [22]. This is accompanied by increased plasma levels of VEGF and of one of its receptors, flt-1. Increased VEGF production regulated by polymorphisms in the VEGF gene may explain the increased proliferation of blood vessels, which is a characteristic of psoriatic skin lesions.

Since many of the cytokine gene polymorphisms reported to be associated with susceptibility to psoriasis are not specific for the disease, it is likely that their expression is indicative of a susceptibility to inflammation in general.

KIR

Killer cell immunoglobulin-like receptors (KIRs) are members of the NK receptor family expressed on NK and NK-T cells, and are encoded by approximately 14 genes in the human leukocyte receptor cluster on chromosome 19q13.4. Structurally they can be divided into activating or inhibiting types. Typing of the KIR genes in psoriatic patients revealed a significantly increased frequency of KIR2DS1 (activating) and KIR2DL5 (inhibitory), and haplotypes containing these genotypes, compared with controls [23]. KIR2DS1 recognises group 2 HLA-C molecules, including HLA-Cw6, and has previously been reported to be correlated with psoriatic arthritis. Since T cells bearing NK receptors are present in psoriatic skin lesions, dysregulation of KIR function could contribute to the psoriatic process.

MICA

The MHC class I chain-related (MIC) gene family consists of five members, only two of which (MICA and MICB) are not pseudogenes. The MICA gene is located centromeric to HLA-B on chromosome 6p21.3 and codes for a MHC-like molecule which is transcribed selectively in epithelial cells and fibroblasts, is stress-inducible and recognised by $\gamma\delta$ T and NK cells. MICA molecules are polymorphic with 16 alleles in the extracellular domains, and 5 alleles in the transmembrane region which differ in the number of copies of a GCT triplet; A4, A5, A6, A9 and A5.1. An association between polymorphic triplet repeat alleles in the transmembrane region and various autoimmune diseases including psoriatic arthritis have been previously demonstrated. In patients with a positive family history and early onset, a significantly higher carrier frequency of the MICA A5.1 allele was found in Chinese patients with psoriasis [24]. This polymorphism causes premature termination of the molecule, which may result in its secretion. Furthermore, the MICA*06 allele, which includes polymorphisms of the transmembrane region containing 9 GCT monomers and the preceding intron 4, has also been shown to have increased frequency in type I psoriasis in a separate study [25]. In this case, the major determinant of the association is a SNP within intron 4. MICA is expressed in the basal KCs of skin including ducts and follicles suggesting that alterations in its expression and/ or function may be relevant to psoriatic pathogenesis.

9.3.1.6 Global gene expression in psoriatic skin

An alternative approach to the identification of psoriasis-specific genes is the investigation of the global expression of genes within lesional skin compared to uninvolved and normal skin. This has involved techniques such as cDNA differential display, and the subsequent cloning of differentially expressed cDNAs, or DNA microarray studies which employed oligonucleotide arrays specific for 7,000 to 63,000 known genes.

The cDNA differential display technique has revealed the presence of 4 genes not previously described in psoriasis: connexin 26, a gap junction protein; squamous cell carcinoma antigen-1 (SCCA1), a serine protease inhibitor; mitochondrial nicotine adenine dehydrogenase subunits 5 and 6 [26]. The expression of mRNA specific for each of these proteins was significantly up-regulated in psoriatic skin compared to normal tape-stripped (wounded) skin as shown by *in situ* hybridisation. Furthermore, cloning of cDNAs differentially expressed in psoriatic and normal skin has recently revealed a gene that codes for a new member of the type IV cytosolic phospholipase A (cPLA) (2) family, designated as cPLA(2)delta [27]. *In situ* hybridization and immunohistochemistry has demonstrated strong expression of cPLA(2) delta in the upper epidermal layers of psoriatic skin, but only weak or no expression in AD or normal skin, respectively.

DNA microarray studies allow the simultaneous comparison of thousands of messenger RNAs. Two groups using this technique to compare global mRNA expression in lesional, uninvolved and normal skin have shown 159/177 genes distinct for psoriasis, approximately 30 of which mapped to psoriasis susceptibility loci and/or had been described previously in psoriasis [28, 29]. A comparison of psoriasis and AD using this approach has revealed 62 genes, including several coding for chemokines, with more than a 2-fold increase in expression in psoriatic versus AD skin [8]. A further study, which profiled psoriasis on a 63,100-element oligonucleotide array, revealed 1338 genes with potential roles in psoriasis pathogenesis/maintenance. This included genes coding for proteins involved in immune and inflammatory responses, responses to wounding and to pathogens, cell proliferation and cytokine signalling cascades [30].

9.3.2 Environmental factors

Various environmental factors can initiate and/or exacerbate psoriasis (Table 9.3). However, their effects may vary between individuals presumably due to genetically determined modifying factors.

9.3.2.1 Infections

It was reported some 50 years ago that, in two-thirds of patients with guttate psoriasis, there is a history of an acute sore throat 1-2 weeks before the eruption, and serological evidence of a recent streptococcal infection. These observations have now been substantiated in several studies both by isolating streptococcal organisms from the tonsils and by serology. The triggering of guttate psoriasis was initially associated with Lancefield group A of β- haemolytic streptococci (*S. pyogenes*), although apparently with no particular streptococcal M serotype, but streptococci of groups C and G have also been isolated from the tonsils or skin of guttate patients. Similarly, good evidence exists that guttate flares in patients with CP psoriasis are also triggered by streptococcal throat infections. Furthermore, a higher incidence of recurrent sore throats and of positive throat swabs in CP psoriasis compared

Table 9.3 Environmental factors that provoke or exacerbate psoriasis

Type of Factor	Reported associations
Infections	
Bacteria	*Streptococcus pyogenes* *Staphylococcus aureus*
Fungi	*Candida albicans* *Malassezia (Pityrosporum)*
Viruses	HIV Retroviruses Papillomaviruses
Trauma	Physical, chemical, surgical (Koebner reaction)
Endocrine factors	Pregnancy Oestrogen therapy Stress
Drugs	Lithium Anti-malarials β-blockers Withdrawal of systemic corticosteroids
Metabolic factors	Hypocalcaemia
Alcohol	Heavy consumption

to controls implicates streptococci in the pathogenesis of the chronic form of the disease.

In patients infected with the HIV virus, the appearance and/or worsening of psoriasis have been reported. However, whether this is induced by the HIV virus itself, or by one or more of the accompanying opportunistic infections is not clear. Colonization of lesional psoriatic skin by *S. aureus* has been demonstrated in 20-50% of patients with psoriasis and is associated with exacerbation of the disease. *C. albicans* on the skin surface has also been implicated in the worsening of skin lesions. Furthermore, retroviruses, papillomaviruses and *Malassezia* yeasts have been proposed as possible triggers.

9.3.2.2. Koebner reaction (trauma)

The development of lesions at the site of injury of uninvolved skin (the Koebner phenomenon) is a characteristic feature of psoriasis, although it has been observed in other conditions. Positive Koebner responses by patients with psoriasis to a variety of different types of trauma including scratches, bites and tattoos have been documented, with damage to the epidermis being the necessary inducing factor. In a given patient, if a positive response is induced at one site, then positive responses will also be induced at any other site at the same point in time. However, a positive response will only be observed in a proportion (approximately 25%) of a randomly selected group of patients at any given time. Conversely, the clearing of existing psoriasis following an injury has also been reported and called the "reverse Koebner". This is also an all-or-none phenomenon, and the Koebner and reverse Koebner are mutually exclusive. These observations suggest that systemic factors that modulate disease expression are involved in the pathogenesis of psoriasis. The (unconfirmed) finding that serum from patients recovering from active psoriasis inhibits the Koebner reaction lends support to this hypothesis. However, these putative systemic factors have yet to be identified.

9.3.2.3 Hormones/drugs

Although psoriasis may worsen during pregnancy, it is more likely to improve or remain unchanged. In addition, stress is commonly associated with the exacerbation of psoriasis. In both cases, these effects could be explained by modulation of the immune system via alterations in hormone levels. Various drugs can also induce psoriasis especially the administration of lithium, β-blockers such as practolol, and anti-malarials, and the withdrawal of systemically administered corticosteroids.

Other factors that may affect disease activity include hypocalcaemia and heavy consumption of alcohol.

9.4 Innate immunity response

The recent progress made in elucidating the mechanisms involved in the innate immune response to microorganisms (see Chapter 3) has stimulated the investigation of innate immune-mediated reactions in psoriasis. Preliminary studies have revealed an altered pattern of TLR2 and TLR5 expression in psoriatic epidermis, the up-regulation of anti-microbial peptides/proteins, the presence of NK-T cells with KCs expressing CD1d, and expression of the heat shock protein (Hsp) receptor CD91 by dendritic cells.

9.4.1 Altered TLR expression

TLR2, the pattern recognition receptor for yeasts and Gram-positive bacterial components, is expressed by KCs throughout the epidermis of normal skin, but is highest in the cytoplasm of proliferating basal KCs (see Chapter 3). In contrast, in psoriatic epidermis TLR2 is more highly expressed in the non-proliferating keratinocytes close to the keratin layer, which is colonised by microorganisms such as *S. aureus* and *Malassezia* (Fig. 9.5, colour plate) [31]. Furthermore KCs have been shown to functionally respond, via TLR2, to peptidoglycan and lipoteichoic acid from *S. aureus* by NF-κB translocation and increased transcription of the NF-κB controlled genes, iNOS and IL-8, innate immune factors which are up-regulated in psoriatic lesions [32].

TLR5, which is a specific receptor for flagellin (a principle component of bacterial flagella), is highly expressed by basal KCs in normal skin, but is down-regulated in psoriatic compared with uninvolved epidermis suggesting ligand-induced activation (Fig. 9.6, colour plate) [31]. However, in addition to interaction with microorganisms, these changes in TLR expression in psoriatic epidermis could also be explained by other factors such as altered KC differentiation or the effects of proinflammatory cytokines such as IFN-γ and TNF-α present in the psoriatic lesion.

9.4.2 Anti-microbial peptides/proteins

Increased levels of anti-microbial β-defensin peptides, HBD-2 and HBD-3, and cathelicidin hCAP/LL-37 are present in the epidermis of psoriatic skin lesions as compared to normal epidermis [33,34]. Microorganisms, proinflammatory cytokines and/or injury to the skin can induce KC production of these innate immune factors. In addition, it has been shown that HBD-2 is synthesized in the cytoplasm of the upper KC layers, and is secreted into the intercellular space between corneocytes in the stratum corneum of psoriatic skin, thus facilitating interaction with invading microorganisms. Furthermore hCAP/LL-37 is stored in the granules of PMNs, which are characteristically found in clusters in the stratum corneum of psoriatic lesional skin. The up-regulated production of anti-microbial peptides probably accounts for the rarity of bacterial infection in psoriatic skin lesions, in contrast to those of AD in which HBD-2 and hCAP/LL-37 levels are low and *S. aureus* infection is common [33].

The S100A8 (myeloid-related protein (MRP)-8)/S100A9 (MRP-14) heterodimer is also found at high concentrations in the epidermis of psoriatic skin lesions and in PMNs, but is absent or expressed at minimal levels in normal epidermis. In addition to its various immunological functions, S100A8/S100A9 (also known as calprotectin) exerts anti-microbial effects and contributes to the killing of invading microorganisms in psoriatic skin. Furthermore, the overexpression of this S100 heterodimer has been shown to be specific for 1q (PSORS4)-linked pedigrees (see Section 9.3.1.4) suggesting that it may be a suitable candidate for psoriasis susceptibility.

9.4.3 NK-T cells/ keratinocyte CD1d expression

T cells coexpressing natural killer cell receptors (NK-T) are innate memory cells, which are activated by lipid antigens and play important roles in the initiation and regulation of the immune response. Presentation of glycolipid to NK-T cells by the non-polymorphic MHC Class I-like molecule, CD1d has been shown to activate NK-T cells to produce IFN-γ. Furthermore CD1d-restricted NK-T cells express a chemokine receptor profile that is similar to that of Th-1 inflammatory homing cells. NK-T cells expressing markers such as CD94, CD158 and CD161, and up-regulated CD1d expression by KCs have been detected by immunostaining in psoriatic skin lesions [35,36]. In addition, T cell lines expressing NK receptors have been shown to induce the phenotypic conversion of transplanted uninvolved to lesional psoriatic skin in a xenograft SCID (Severe Combined ImmunoDeficient) mouse model [37] (see Section 9.8.1). Thus activated NK-T cells producing IFN-γ may represent an important link between innate and acquired immune responses in psoriasis.

9.4.4 Dendritic cell CD91 expression

Recently it has been demonstrated that DDC and fibroblasts in psoriatic skin express CD91, an innate immune receptor for Hsps [38]. Hsps synthesized by KCs can induce NF-κB activation in fibroblasts, and activate dendritic cells leading to enhanced maturation, IL-12 production and antigen-presenting function. These observations suggest that Hsps may contribute to the Th-1 pathway in psoriasis via their effects on dendritic cells.

9.5 Peripheral blood T lymphocyte abnormalities

Various peripheral blood T lymphocyte functional abnormalities have been identified in psoriasis some of which may represent intrinsic immunological defects that contribute to the disease process (Table 9.4).

Table 9.4 Cellular defects in psoriasis: Intrinsic or secondary?

Peripheral blood T cells
T cell function
Decreased mitogen-induced proliferation *in vitro*   Decreased suppressor cell activity *in vitro*   Reduced intensity of DNCB and SKSD-induced DTH responses   Delayed resolution of PPD and (SKSD)-induced DTH responses   Th-1 cytokine bias
T cell homing
CLA induction: *S. pyogenes* > *C. albicans* antigens   Decreased L-selectin$^+$ T cells in response to streptococcal antigens   Increased binding to HUVEC   Endothelial cells resistant to inhibition of T cell binding by TGF-β_1
Keratinocytes
Response to cytokines
Resistance to inhibitory effects of IFN-γ Respond to IFN-γ or TNF-α with exaggerated expression of IL-8, MCP-1 and IP-10   Increased constitutive IL-8 production
Apoptosis
Resistance to apoptosis   Increased expression of molecules regulating apoptosis: Bcl-x$_L$, ICAD, Fas, Bax

9.5.1 T cell responses *in vitro* and *in vivo*

Numbers and ratios of CD4$^+$ and CD8$^+$ T cell subsets in the peripheral blood of patients with psoriasis are generally within normal limits, with the exception of patients with extensive skin lesions who have a significantly reduced systemic CD4$^+$ T cell subpopulation, probably as a result of marked infiltration of CD4$^+$ T cells into lesional skin.

Studies of mitogen-induced proliferation of peripheral blood lymphocytes (PBL) in psoriasis have produced conflicting results with both normal and decreased responses reported. Similarly, mixed findings have been reported in studies of polyclonal suppressor cell activity in psoriasis. These findings probably reflect the heterogeneity of the psoriasis populations studied.

In vivo, psoriasis patients exhibit decreased delayed hypersensitivity responses to certain antigens. For example, although the frequency of positive reactions to 2,4-dintrochlorobenzene (DNCB) is not altered, the intensity of the acquired DNCB sensitisation is significantly reduced in psoriatics compared to controls. This altered response appeared to be related to the activity rather than extent of the skin lesions. Furthermore, psoriatic individuals show a decrease in the amount, but not incidence, of both erythema and induration in response to streptokinase/streptodornase (SKSD), and a marked delay in resolution of the DTH reaction to purified protein derivative (PPD) and, to a lesser extent, SKSD.

These findings imply a subtle defect in T lymphocyte function in patients with psoriasis. However, it is unlikely that this represents a primary abnormality, and is probably secondary to the disease process.

9.5.2 T cell homing

Migration of T cells into the skin requires expression of skin homing receptors, the major receptor being CLA, which binds to E-selectin (CD62E) on endothelial cells (see Chapter 1). CLA is expressed on a minor subset of CD45RO$^+$ memory T cells in peripheral blood, but by the majority of such cells in cutaneous sites of chronic inflammation such as that of psoriasis in which E-selectin expression by endothelial cells is up-regulated.

CLA expression is selectively induced on T cells during virgin to memory transition in skin-draining peripheral lymph nodes, and is regulated by microenvironmental factors such as the cytokine TGF-β_1. In addition, bacterial superantigens (streptococcal and staphylococcal toxins) and group A streptococcal antigens can induce the expansion of skin-homing CLA$^+$ T cells via stimulation of IL-12 production [39, 40]. In psoriatic patients (but not in normal or disease controls), the streptococcal antigen-induced increase in mean percentage CLA$^+$ expression is significantly greater than that induced by *C. albicans* [40]. This increase is accompanied by a significant decrease in T cells positive for the peripheral lymph node homing receptor, L-selectin. These findings suggest that, in psoriatic patients, specific homing receptors on T cells are differentially modulated by antigens from group A streptococci, an organism associated with initiation and exacerbation of skin lesions (see Section 9.3.2.1).

In addition, the binding of PBL to cultured human umbilical vein endothelium *in vitro* has been shown to be increased in patients with psoriasis, in contrast to PBL from AD patients which show decreased binding compared to normal controls [41]. The mechanism for augmented PBL binding in psoriasis is not clear as increased LFA-1 expression by T cells or the presence of serum factors do not appear to be responsible. Moreover, dermal microvascular endothelial cells from psoriatic, but not normal, skin are resistant to the inhibitory effects by TGF-β_1 on the binding of PBL. These combined functional alterations may contribute to the targeting of T cells to the skin in psoriasis.

9.5.3 T cell cytokine profile

The cytokine profile of circulating T cells in psoriasis has been investigated using intracellular staining of PMBC stimulated non-specifically *in vitro* with a combination of ionomycin (a Ca^{2+} ionophore) and a phorbol ester, 12-O-tetradecanoyl-phorbol 13-acetate (PMA) [42]. The addition of Brefeldin A during activation prevents exocytosis of the induced cytokines from the cells and allows the frequency of cytokine-producing cells to be determined using cytokine-specific fluorescent-labelled monoclonal antibodies and flow cytometry. Although this method bypasses antigen-specific pathways, specificity for the cytokine profile is maintained allowing the cytokine-producing potential of the tested cells to be determined.

T cells producing IFN-γ or TNF-α were found in significantly higher frequency within psoriatic compared to control T cell populations, whilst numbers of IL-4-producing T cells were similar. More CD8$^+$ than CD4$^+$ psoriatic T cells were IFN-γ producers whereas equal numbers of both subpopulations produced TNF-α. Furthermore, the majority of IFN-γ^+ T cells co-expressed high levels of TNF-α, but IL-2$^+$ cells comprised a separate subpopulation. This shift towards a Th-1 cytokine profile was confirmed by a significantly decreased IL-4/IFN-γ ratio versus that of the controls. This contrasts with the findings of a similar study of peripheral blood T cells from AD patients, which showed a Th-2 cytokine bias (see Chapter 8).

9.6 Keratinocyte defects

KCs in psoriatic lesions display altered expression of a variety of different cytokines, chemokines and their receptors, the majority of which are probably changes secondary to the disease process (see below). However, altered production and/or responses by KCs from uninvolved skin of psoriatic patients may, in some cases, indicate intrinsic abnormalities in genetically predisposed individuals (Table 9.4).

9.6.1 Response to IFN-γ

IFN-γ interacts with specific receptors on KCs inducing surface expression of HLA-DR antigen and inhibition of cell growth. Two studies have demonstrated that the inhibitory growth effect of IFN-γ is reduced in psoriatic KCs (both uninvolved and lesional) whilst HLA-DR induction is unaffected in uninvolved, but decreased in lesional KCs [43,44]. The reduced inhibition of psoriatic KC growth by IFN-γ is in agreement with *in vivo* studies in which injection of IFN-γ into psoriatic plaques, or intraperitoneally into mice carrying psoriatic skin in diffusion chambers, failed to inhibit psoriatic epidermal DNA synthesis. This altered response to IFN-γ may reflect abnormal modulation of receptors and/or a defect in the signalling pathway, but the mechanism involved has yet to be elucidated. In contrast, psoriatic KCs do not differ from normal KCs in their response to other growth inhibitory cytokines such as TNF-α or TGF-β, or to stimulatory cytokines such as IL-8 or TGF-α [45,46] emphasising the significance of these findings.

9.6.2 Chemokine profile

KCs contribute to the inflammatory process by the regulated production of chemokines, which attract various leukocyte subpopulations such as monocytes, dendritic cells and T cells into the skin. A recent study has demonstrated distinct chemokine production profiles, in response to T cell-derived cytokines, by KCs from the uninvolved skin of patients with psoriasis and AD [47]. Thus psoriatic KCs responded to IFN-γ or TNF-α with an exaggerated expression of IL-8, MCP-1 and IP-10 compared to that of KCs from normal controls or patients with AD. In contrast, KCs from AD patients produced increased amounts of RANTES, but reduced levels of IP-10 in response to these cytokines. Furthermore, IL-8 was constitutively produced at much higher levels by unstimulated KCs from psoriasis than AD patients or controls, and IP-10 and IL-8 were consistently up-regulated in the epidermis of psoriatic, but not AD, skin lesions. IP-10 specifically attracts Th-1 cells expressing CXCR3, whilst IL-8 mainly functions as a PMN chemoattractant and activating factor, and, in addition, stimulates KC proliferation. Both RANTES and MCP-1 mRNA$^+$ KCs were detected in the basal epidermal layer of skin lesions from patients with AD and psoriasis; these chemokines are chemoattractants for both Th-1 and Th-2 cells, monocytes and dendritic cells.

Resistance to apoptosis

Apoptosis (or programmed cell death) is an active process of cell deletion, which can be differentiated from necrosis by characteristic features such as chromatin condensation, DNA fragmentation and blebbing of the plasma membrane. Apoptosis contributes to epidermal homeostasis in normal skin by removing excess cells and maintaining normal cell numbers. However, KCs from psoriatic skin do not have double-stranded DNA breaks and have a prolonged capacity to resist induction of apoptosis compared with normal skin-derived KCs [48]. Furthermore, psoriatic KCs resemble senescent (irreversibly growth arrested) KCs in that their resistance to UV-induced apoptosis is associated with a lack of p53 activation [49]. In addition, there is aberrant expression of molecules associated with regulating apoptosis in psoriasis. Thus both the anti-apoptotic molecules Bcl-x$_L$ (long form of Bcl-x) and ICAD (inhibitor of Caspase 3-related DNAse), and the pro-apoptotic Fas antigen and Bax are increased in psoriatic compared to uninvolved skin [50]. Furthermore the cytokine IL-15, a potent inhibitor of KC apoptosis, is up-regulated in psoriatic epidermis (see below). Whether this combination of molecules results in an inhibitory effect on apoptosis or whether there is an inherent defect of psoriatic KCs remains to be determined.

9.7 Immunohistology of skin lesions

9.7.1 T cell subpopulations

The transition from uninvolved to lesional skin in guttate psoriasis is associated with the influx and activation of CD4$^+$ T cells in the epidermis where they interact with epidermal dendritic cells in the basal layers [51]. In contrast, the appearance of a clinical lesion is not accompanied by detectable changes in the numbers of T cells in the dermis. As the lesions mature increased numbers of CD8$^+$ T cells are recruited into the epidermis and predominate over CD4$^+$ T cells, which gradually disappear. Both CD8$^+$ T cells, and to a lesser extent CD4$^+$ T cells, are seen in close proximity to dendritic cells. Finally a proportion of the CD8$^+$ T cells become activated, coinciding with spontaneous resolution of the lesion. These findings suggest a role for activated CD4$^+$ and CD8$^+$ T cells in initiation/ maintenance or resolution of the psoriatic process, respectively.

In common with resolving guttate lesions, CD8$^+$ T cells are present in a 2:1 ratio with CD4$^+$ T cells in the epidermis of stable CP lesions [52]. However in this case, equal numbers of epidermal CD4$^+$ and CD8$^+$ T cells are activated, whereas activated CD4$^+$ T cells are absent from mature guttate lesions. On the basis of increasing evidence, it seems likely that activated CD8$^+$ T cells act as effector cells which contribute to maintenance of the disease process in chronic lesions (see Section 9.10), in contrast to a possible suppressive role in resolving guttate lesions.

In the papillary dermis, CD4$^+$ T cell numbers exceed those of CD8$^+$ T cells by a factor of approximately 2.6, and the majority of activated T cells are CD4$^+$. As in the epidermis, the T cells are almost exclusively of the memory phenotype indicating that that they have already been primed to their specific antigenic determinant in the context of MHC Class I or Class II molecules. The total numbers and ratios of T cells in the dermis are similar in mature/resolving guttate and CP lesions. Thus the clinical activity of psoriasis appears to be associated with the interaction of CD4$^+$ and CD8$^+$

Table 9.5 Subsets of epidermal dendritic cells in lesional psoriatic skin

Epidermal dendritic cells	Comments
LC subsets (with Birbeck granules)	
DR⁺CD1a⁺	50% of cells in normal epidermis Increased in lesional psoriatic epidermis
DR⁻CD1a⁺	50% of cells in normal epidermis Decreased in lesional psoriatic epidermis
DR⁺CD1a⁻	18% of cells in lesional psoriatic epidermis Present in other inflammatory skin diseases Not present in normal or uninvolved psoriatic epidermis
Non-LC subsets (without Birbeck granules)	
DR⁺CD1a⁻	Express Hle1 antigen Includes monocytes and RFD1⁺ interdigitating cells
DR⁺CD1a^dim FcεRI⁺CD36⁺	Inflammatory dendritic epidermal cells 50% of epidermal CD1a⁺ population in lesional psoriatic skin Present in other inflammatory skin diseases, especially AD

T cells with APC in the epidermis.

9.7.2 Epidermal dendritic cells

There have been conflicting reports concerning the numbers of LCs in psoriatic epidermis from studies in which ATPase staining, or single staining with monoclonal anti-HLA-DR or anti-CD1a antibodies were used. In contrast, a marked increase in the total number of epidermal dendritic cells in CP lesions, compared to both uninvolved psoriatic and normal skin, was revealed by double-staining for HLA-DR and CD1a antigens [52]. (Total dendritic cell numbers were also increased in uninvolved compared to normal epidermis). Furthermore, 82% of LCs in lesional epidermis expressed HLA-DR, compared to only 50% in normal and uninvolved psoriatic epidermis, and included a subpopulation (18%) of cells on which CD1a antigen was not detected, but which contained Birbeck granules (Table 9.5). The latter feature suggests that these DR⁺CD1a⁻ cells can be characterised as a subpopulation of LCs. Although this minority LC subpopulation was rarely present in normal or uninvolved psoriatic epidermis, it is not unique to psoriasis but is found in other benign inflammatory skin diseases such as endogenous eczema, pityriasis rosea and lichen planus.

In addition, non-LC epidermal dendritic cell subpopulations have been reported in lesional psoriatic epidermis (Table 9.5). A DR⁺CD1a⁻ cell subpopulation expressing Hle1 antigen (found on all bone-marrow-derived leukocytes), which included monocytes and RFD1⁺ interdigitating cells, showed enhanced capacity to activate and induce proliferation of T cells. These cells differ from, but are analogous to, DR$^+$CD1a$^-$ epidermal cells that are present in skin following UV exposure. Furthermore, a variable sized subpopulation of epidermal dendritic cells with low CD1a expression, but high levels of HLA-DR, CD36 and FcεRI have also been described in lesional skin from patients with psoriasis and other inflammatory skin diseases. This subpopulation is referred to as "inflammatory dendritic epidermal cells".

In addition to increased numbers, the distribution of LCs in psoriatic epidermis is abnormal with marked clumping in the upper epidermal layers and scattered cells in the rete ridges [51]. This finding appears to be characteristic for psoriasis, as it has not been reported in other inflammatory skin conditions.

9.7.3 Dermal dendritic cells

DDC are markedly increased in psoriatic lesions and are observed in close conjunction with T cells in cellular infiltrates of the papillary dermis. The majority of these cells have high surface levels of HLA-DR, various adhesion molecules, costimulatory molecule B7 and CD1c, together with intracytoplasmic factor XIIIa [53]. In addition, DDC express the maturation markers CD83 and DC-lysosomal-associated membrane glycoprotein (DC-LAMP). Subpopulations of cells also express CD1a, RFD1 or CD14. Furthermore, DDC derived from lesional psoriatic skin are more potent stimulators of autologous T cell proliferation than DDC derived from normal skin, despite their indistinguishable immunophenotypic profiles. Psoriatic DDC induce a Th-1 cell response in autologous T cells in the absence of a stimulator, but the addition of PHA or a superantigen can additionally stimulate IL-4, but not IL-10 production [53].

Plasmacytoid dendritic cells (natural IFN-α-producing cells) are also present in psoriatic skin, but comprise a minority of the total dendritic cell population. These cells, which are absent from normal skin, express TLR9 that recognises bacterial unmethylated CpG DNA. Simultaneous ligation of surface CD40 and activation by CpG DNA results in the production of high levels of both IFN-α and IL-12.

9.7.4 Endothelial cells

Histological studies have shown that the earliest changes in psoriatic skin occur in the dermal microvasculature. Microvessels in the papillary dermis are elongated, dilated and hyperpermeable, and undergo angiogenesis (formation of new capillary blood vessels) and high endothelial venule (HEV) formation.

There is increased ^{3}H-thymidine labelling of dermal endothelial cells, and increased number and mass of capillary blood vessels. In addition, the enzyme capillary enzyme phosphatase, a marker of new dermal capillaries, is increased in developing psoriatic plaques. Sera from patients with active psoriasis can induce new blood vessel formation *in vitro*, probably as a result of the presence of increased levels of angiogenic cytokines such as IL-6, TGF-α and TNF-α. Furthermore TGF-α stimulates KCs to secrete VEGF, a selective endothelial cell mitogen that stimulates microvascular permeability. In psoriasis there is increased VEGF production, probably regulated by polymorphisms in the VEGF gene (see Section 9.3.1.5), and overexpression of VEGF receptors by dermal microvascular endothelial cells, which may account for the increase in blood vessel formation in skin lesions.

HEVs are specialised post-capillary venules in which the flat squame-like endothelial cell lining is replaced by that of tall columnar or cuboidal endothelial cells. HEVs, which are normally selectively present in lymphoid tissue, can also be found at sites of chronic inflammation such as the dermis in psoriasis and the synovium in RA and play an important role in lymphocyte recruitment to tissues. To gain entry into the dermis, T lymphocytes of the memory CD45RO$^+$ phenotype expressing LFA-1 and VLA-4 (CD49d) integrin receptors bind to the endothelial cells via the adhesion molecules ICAM-1 and VCAM-1, respectively (see Chapter 1). *In vitro*, normal or psoriatic PBL (preferentially CD4$^+$ T cells) bind selectively to dermal microvascular endothelial cells in frozen sections of biopsied psoriatic plaques, but not to those of uninvolved psoriatic or normal skin due to differences in adhesion molecule expression.

9.8 Role of T cells in psoriasis

9.8.1 Evidence that psoriasis is T cell-mediated

Various different observations have revealed the extent of involvement of T cells in the immunopathogenesis of psoriasis (reviewed in [54]) (Table 9.6).

9.8.1.1 Immunosuppressive treatments

Firstly, the resolution of psoriasis using immunosuppressive drugs, anti-CD4$^+$ monoclonal antibodies (mAbs) or lymphocyte-selective (DAB$_{389}$IL-2) toxin has provided compelling evidence for a pivotal role for T cells in psoriasis.

The immunosuppressive drug cyclosporin, whose primary action is the selective inhibition of cytokine production by CD4$^+$ T cells, has proved to be effective in clearing psoriasis. Furthermore, the macrolide antibiotic tacrolimus (FK-506), which shares a number of immunosuppressive properties with cyclosporin, is also a potent anti-psoriatic agent. Resolution of psoriasis by treatment with cyclosporin or tacrolimus, and also by other anti-psoriatic treatments such as topical steroids and psoralens plus UV light (PUVA), is accompanied by depletion of CD4$^+$ and CD8$^+$ T cells from the epidermis and dermis of skin lesions. In addition, the effects of some of these immunosuppressive treatments are not confined to T cells; modulation of APC cell numbers and/or function probably contributes to their efficacy. The evidence for a direct action by cyclosporin on KC proliferation is, however, unconvincing; furthermore, tacrolimus has been shown to have no direct effects on epidermal cells.

Rapid clinical improvement has also been observed in small groups of psoriasis patients after intravenous injection of anti-CD4 mAbs. This was accompanied by a decrease in circulating CD4$^+$ T cell numbers and loss of T cells from lesional skin.

To further address the role of T cells in psoriasis, patients were treated with a fusion protein (DAB$_{389}$IL-2) in which human IL-2 replaced the receptor-binding domain of diphtheria toxin, whilst its membrane-translocating and cytotoxic domains were retained [55]. Of 10 patients with extensive CP psoriasis that were administered the toxin, 4 showed striking improvement, 4 moderate

Table 9.6 Evidence in support of psoriasis as a T cell-mediated disease

Factors	Outcome
Cyclosporin Tacrolimus (FK-506)	Decrease in $CD4^+$ and $CD8^+$ T cells from epidermis and dermis of skin lesions Modulation of APC numbers/function
Anti-CD4 monoclonal antibodies	Decrease in circulating $CD4^+$ T cells Depletion of skin $CD4^+$ T cells
Lymphocyte-selective toxin ($DAB_{389}IL$-2)	Reduction in skin T cells correlating with clinical response Marked reduction in intraepidermal $CD3^+$ or $CD8^+$ T cells associated with reversal of disease-induced epidermal changes
SCID/human skin mouse model	Conversion of uninvolved to lesional psoriatic skin after injection of activated $CD4^+$ T cells into graft on SCID mouse
Bone-marrow transplantation	Transfer or clearance of severe psoriasis
Stimulatory T cell supernatants	Induction of KC proliferation and CDw60 expression by lesional skin T cell supernatants
Low $CD4^+$/HIV infection	Initiation and/or exacerbation of disease Small numbers of activated $CD4^+$ T cells in epidermis Increased numbers of $CD8^+$ T cells may contribute to disease activity and maintenance

and 2 minimal improvement after two cycles of treatment. $DAB_{389}IL$-2 selectively eliminated cells expressing IL-2 receptors (activated T cells) in skin lesions, the extent of which correlated with clinical response. Furthermore, a marked reduction in intraepidermal $CD3^+$ or $CD8^+$ T cells was associated with the reversal of several molecular markers of epidermal dysfunction.

9.8.1.2 Psoriasis xenograft model in SCID mice

Further evidence in support of a pathological role for T cells in psoriasis came from the development of a psoriasis xenograft model in Severe Combined Immunodeficient (SCID) mice [56]. SCID mice are genetically incapable of producing either T or B cells, resulting in an inability to reject human skin grafts, but retain their ability to produce PMNs and NK cells.

When transplanted uninvolved psoriatic skin was injected with autologous, blood-derived immunocytes (lymphocytes and monocytes) preactivated with IL-2 and superantigens, conversion into a fully-fledged psoriatic plaque was consistently observed [56]. In contrast, 4 transplanted normal skins injected with autologous immunocytes failed to convert to psoriatic plaques. Subsequently it was shown that $CD4^+$, but not $CD8^+$ T cells, were able to induce the transformation of pre-psoriatic skin into a psoriatic lesion [57]. The injection of $CD4^+$ T cells triggered a series of local immunologically mediated stimulatory events and the appearance of both $CD4^+$ and $CD8^+$ T cells expressing NK receptors (NKRs) [57]. Furthermore, T cell lines expressing NKRs were also shown to induce the phenotypic conversion of transplanted uninvolved to lesional psoriatic skin, but only if the NK-T cells and skin were taken from psoriasis patients [58]. In contrast, NKR-expressing cells from non-psoriatic controls induced psoriasiform dermatitis changes in transplanted normal or uninvolved psoriatic skin, rather than true psoriasis.

In a new animal model using AGR129 mice, which are deficient in type I and type II IFN receptors and have a deleted recombination-activating gene 2, spontaneous conversion of uninvolved to lesional psoriatic skin was recently demonstrated without injection of CD4$^+$ T cells [59]. Selective agents used to block T cell proliferation or TNF-α production prevented this conversion implicating resident human T cells in the development of a psoriatic phenotype.

9.8.1.3 Bone-marrow transplantation

Both the transfer of psoriasis and, conversely, the clearance of severe psoriasis following allogeneic or syngeneic bone-marrow transplantation have been reported. The remission induced by replacement of a psoriatic patient's bone-marrow-derived immune system by that of a genetically distinct non-psoriatic donor is long-standing, suggesting that marrow-derived lymphocytes are essential in the pathogenesis of psoriasis. However, it is not known to what extent the intensive immunosuppression necessary for successful transplantation contributes to the resolution of the psoriatic process.

9.8.1.4 Stimulatory T cell supernatants

Supernatants from T cell clones isolated from psoriatic skin lesions have been shown to stimulate normal KC proliferation *in vitro* [60]. Mitogenic activity was largely abolished by the addition of antiserum to IFN-γ, but as IFN-γ alone is a potent inhibitor of normal KC growth, the ultimate effect appears to be decided by the presence of additional cytokines. Furthermore, the decreased responsiveness of psoriatic KCs to inhibition by IFN-γ (see Section 9.6.1) may contribute to the overall stimulatory effects of these T cell-derived cytokines.

Soluble factors derived from lesional T cells also induce the expression of CDw60 on normal KCs. CDw60, which is expressed by basal and suprabasal KCs in lesional epidermis but is absent from normal skin, is thought to be a costimulatory molecule for T cell activation. Its KC-related function has yet to be determined, but the up-regulation of CDw60 on hyperproliferating cells in basal cell carcinoma suggests that it may play a role in proliferation.

9.8.1.5 Low CD4+ T cells/HIV infection

It has been argued that the appearance and exacerbation of psoriasis in patients with HIV infection is not consistent with the mediation of psoriasis by CD4$^+$ T cells. However, by analogy to a delayed-type hypersensitivity response to contact allergen in the skin, it is likely that only a very small number of antigen-specific CD4$^+$ T cells would be required to initiate the psoriatic process. Thus AIDS patients who still possess circulating CD4$^+$ T cells should potentially be able to develop psoriasis, but the skin lesions would be expected to clear (as has been observed in some patients) when peripheral CD4$^+$ T cells are depleted in the terminal stages of the disease.

Furthermore, a patient with widespread, recalcitrant psoriasis accompanied by a profound CD4$^+$

lymphocytopenia, but who was negative for the HIV virus, was shown to have similar numbers of activated epidermal CD4[+] T cells as a group of psoriasis patients with normal circulating CD4[+] T cell counts, although total numbers of epidermal CD4[+] T cells were decreased in the patient [61]. In AIDS patients, CD8[+] (rather than CD4[+]) T cells predominate in the dermis of psoriatic skin lesions. Furthermore, total and activated epidermal CD8[+] T cell numbers were greatly increased in the patient with CD4[+] lymphocytopenia [61]. Since CD8[+] T cells are now generally regarded as having an effector role in CP psoriasis, (see Section 9.10), it is possible that the increased activity of psoriasis observed in these lymphopenic patients may be explained by an increased contribution by activated CD8[+] T cells to the psoriatic process, presumably via the release of cytokines such as IFN-γ.

9.8.2 T cell antigen specificity

9.8.2.1 T cell clonality

Various studies have analysed the T cell repertoire within psoriatic skin lesions using PCR, CDR3 length spectratyping and/or CDR3 region sequencing analysis techniques. In most studies a preferential usage of certain TCR Vβ families by infiltrating T cells has been demonstrated implicating a role for antigens or microbial superantigens in T cell activation in psoriasis. However, there is a discrepancy between studies as to which Vβ families are preferentially expanded in lesional skin, which may result from differences in the PCR techniques and skin sample preparation used and/or the disease activity of the patients studied.

In guttate psoriasis patients infected by streptococci producing the toxin SPE-C, polyclonal activation of T cells expressing Vβ2 was demonstrated in very early skin lesions implicating superantigen-induced T cell activation [62]. In contrast, in CP psoriasis, oligoclonal expansions of T cells have been consistently reported in skin lesions suggesting that conventional antigens rather than superantigens are responsible for triggering the chronic form of the disease. Thus one study, which examined T cells in full thickness skin biopsies of lesional skin (containing predominately dermal CD4[+] T cells), reported clonal expansions of TCR Vβ2 and Vβ6 families [63]. In contrast, in another study when T cells were isolated from the epidermis of CP lesions and separated into CD4[+] and CD8[+] T cells, only the CD8[+] T cells expressing Vβ3 and Vβ13.1 showed clonal expansion [64]. A further study of total intraepidermal T cells in skin lesions from five patients with psoriasis showed abnormal CDR3 DNA length distribution, indicating the presence of monoclonal or oligoclonal T cell expansion, in approximately half of the TCR Vβ chain families in each patient's lesion [65]. Furthermore, sequence similarity between the CDR3 junctional sequences found in these patients and those reported in other studies [63, 64, 66] were identified. Thus it is possible that conserved CDR3 motifs, expressed by infiltrating T cells expressing one of several different TCR Vβ families in different patients, may be present in psoriatic lesions and recognise a common disease-associated antigen(s) [67]. The identity of this antigen(s) is currently unknown; both microbial antigens and autoantigens have been investigated as possible stimuli for pathogenic T cells in psoriasis (see below).

9.8.2.2 Microbial antigens

In skin lesions of psoriasis, a type 1 cytokine profile of IL-2, IFN-γ and TNF-α, but no IL-4 or IL-10 has been demonstrated using PCR and/or analysis of T cell clone supernatants [68,69]. This is consistent with the Th-1 cytokine bias reported in the peripheral blood of psoriasis patients (see Section 9.5.3). Since throat infections with group A streptococci are associated with the induction and exacerbation of psoriatic skin lesions, and bacterial antigens are known to induce a Th-1 type cytokine response, T cells from skin lesions have been investigated for response to streptococcal antigens.

A subset of Th-1 cells that recognises cell wall antigens isolated from group A streptococci, and is specific for psoriatic skin lesions, has been identified [70-72]. M protein, a major virulence factor and type-specific antigen of group A streptococci, has been excluded as the antigen responsible for activation of these T cells [71,72]. However, recently it has been shown that at least half of the streptococcal-specific Th-1 cells isolated from psoriatic lesions are specific for a major structural cell wall component of streptococci, peptidoglycan. Furthermore, macrophages carrying bacterial peptidoglycan have been demonstrated in dermal infiltrates in close association with T cells in psoriatic lesions [73]. Psoriatic T cell lines responded to streptococcal peptidoglycan only when presented by self HLA-DR alleles, suggesting that peptidoglycan induced T cell activation in a classical manner, rather than as a superantigen or mitogen. These findings are consistent with the TCR Vβ analysis studies of psoriatic skin, which implicated the involvement of a specific antigen(s) in T cell activation. However, it remains to be determined whether CD4+ T cells expressing specificities for streptococcal antigens are pathogenic in psoriasis.

T cells showing a differential reactivity to *Pityrosporum orbiculare* versus *Pityrosporum ovale* have been cultured from biopsies of skin lesions of CP psoriasis taken from the scalp, a region in which the fungi form part of the normal skin flora [74]. However, T cells with similar reactivity, but of lower frequency and degree of response, have also been isolated from scalp lesions of alopecia areata. This does not necessarily exclude *Pityrosporum*-reactive CD4+ T cells from being pathogenic in psoriasis since functional differences (e.g. cytokine profile) could exist between the antigen-specific CD4+ T cell subpopulations in the two groups of patients.

9.8.2.3 Autoantigens

Psoriasis is assumed to be a T cell-mediated autoimmune disease, but T cells specific for autoantigen(s) have yet to be isolated from skin lesions. However, there is some evidence for increased T cell reactivity to autoantigens in the peripheral blood of psoriatic patients. Thus an increased frequency of IFN-γ-producing T cells specific for keratin-derived peptides that share sequences with M proteins has been reported in the PBMC of psoriasis patients compared to healthy controls [75]. The most frequent and strongest responses were observed to a peptide from keratin 17 that shares the ALEEAN sequence with M-protein. Subsequently, when keratin and M protein peptides with sequence homology were additionally selected on the basis of predicted HLA-Cw*0602 binding, CLA+ CD8+ T cells were identified as the predominant responding cells to both sets of peptides in HLA-Cw*0602+ psoriatic patients [76]. In contrast, CLA+CD8+ T cells isolated from HLA-Cw*0602+ non-psoriatic individuals responded to some M peptides, but rarely to the keratin peptides.

Screening of cDNA libraries of lesional epidermis with patients' sera in a search for autoantigens in psoriasis identified three autoantigens with prominent reactivity: keratin 13, heterogenous nuclear ribonucleoprotein-A1 (RNP-A1) and a previously uncharacterised protein, FLJ00294 [77]. Keratin 13, which is not normally present in adult skin, is up-regulated in regenerating epidermis and has significant homology with keratin 17. RNP-A1 has a carboxy terminal domain that is homologous to basic keratins, and, furthermore, FLJ00294 also shows some sequence homology to keratins. Indeed, most positive serum samples (both psoriatic and control) reacted with all three autoantigens due to cross-reactivity between them. In addition, a peripheral blood T cell IFN-γ response to these proteins was also demonstrated in both patients and controls. Studies of autoreactive T cells in other autoimmune diseases have generally shown similar reactivity of peripheral blood T cells in patients and normal controls. This is taken as evidence that recognition of an autoantigen is insufficient alone to induce disease and that a dysregulated inflammatory response within the target organ is required for disease manifestation.

Thus the evidence suggests that keratin is a candidate autoantigen for psoriasis and could be a possible stimulus for antigen-specific CD8$^+$ T cells in the epidermis. Further studies are required to investigate this possibility.

9.8.3 Antigen presentation

Interaction between a T cell and an APC carrying antigen peptides bound to MHC molecules is mediated by a cluster of molecules termed the immune synapse [78]. This multimolecular complex consists of the TCR surrounded by a ring of adhesion molecules including LFA-1, which can bind to ICAM-1 expressed by the APC. Other adhesion and costimulatory cell surface molecules involved include CD2 and CD28 on T cells which interact with LFA-3 and CD80/CD86 (B7-1/B7-2), respectively on APC. T cell activation results in stimulation of the TCR signalling pathway linked to the immune synapse, activation of transcription factors and the triggering of target gene expression.

In addition to specialized APC such as macrophages or dendritic cells, KCs may also present antigens in psoriasis as they can be induced to express MHC Class II antigens and accessory proteins, such as CD40, in response to IFN-γ. However, recognition of antigen presented by KCs has generally been shown to lead to a state of specific non-responsiveness, characterized by a failure of T cells to produce IL-2. In contrast, IFN-γ-treated KCs have been shown to provide costimulation via ICAM-1 for superantigen-activated T cells, inducing their proliferation and the production of IL-2 and IL-4, but not IFN-γ. [79,80]. Of interest in this respect, a recent study has demonstrated the presence of human neutrophil peptides (HNP) 1 and 2, belonging to the alpha-subfamily of defensins, as dominant HLA class II bound self-peptides on KCs in psoriasis [81]. Both peptides inhibited superantigen-mediated T-cell activation *in vitro*, suggesting that they may be involved in the regulation of T cell responses within psoriatic skin lesions.

9.9 Cytokines/Chemokines in skin lesions

The activation of T cells by antigen-presenting dendritic cells in psoriatic skin lesions leads to the production of a vast array of cytokines, chemokines and growth factors produced both by immune

Table 9.7 Major cytokines produced by dendritic cells, T cells and KCs in skin lesions

Cell type	Cytokine	Functional effects
T cell	IFN-γ	Activation of >65 genes e.g. up-regulates adhesion molecule expression, chemokine and iNos production by KC
	TNF-α	Multifunctional e.g. inhibition of KC growth, induction of adhesion molecules on endothelial cells, cytotoxicity Synergistic with IFN-γ
	IL-17	Regulates adhesion molecule expression and production of GRO-α, GM-CSF and IL-6 by KC
Dendritic cell	IL-12	Induces T cell IFN-γ production Promotes expansion of Th-1 cells
	IL-23	Induces T cell IFN-γ production Promotes expansion of Th-1 cells
KC	IL-1β, IL-6, TNF-α	Pleiotropic effects on a variety of cell types
	IL-7	T cell growth factor Synergises with IL-2 and IL-12 to stimulate T cell IFN-γ production
	IL-15	Inhibits KC apoptosis Stimulates CD8⁺ T cell growth and IFN-γ, TNF-α and IL-17 production, induces angiogenesis and inflammatory cell recruitment
	IL-18	Growth and differentiation factor for Th-1 cells Induces IFN-γ production by T and NK cells Chemoattractant for dendritic cells Up-regulates dendritic cell adhesion and costimulation molecules
	IL-20	May regulate epidermal differentiation

cells and by skin cells, such as KCs and endothelial cells, in response to activation by immune cells. The major factors involved in the psoriatic process are shown in Tables 9.7 and 9.8.

9.9.1 Cytokines

9.9.1.1 T cell cytokines

As stated previously, activated T cells in psoriasis have a Th-1 cytokine profile producing predominately IL-2, IFN-γ and TNF-α. **IFN-γ** is a major cytokine in the immunopathogenesis of psoriasis being responsible for the activation of more than 65 genes, or approximately 5% of the psoriasis transcriptome (total expressed transcripts) as shown by genomic profiling [30]. Thus IFN-γ induces the up-regulation of KC production of chemokines Mig (CXCL9), IP-10 (CXCL10) and I-TAC (CXCL11), which attract T cells expressing CXCR3 receptor into the epidermis, and of IL-8 (CXCL8), a key chemokine for regulating PMN trafficking into the psoriatic stratum corneum. IFN-γ also up-regulates iNOS, which regulates vascular dilation via the production of nitric oxide. Increased nitric oxide levels are probably responsible for the dilated capillaries that characterise psoriatic skin lesions. Furthermore, in support of a pathogenic role for IFN-γ in psoriasis, subcutaneous injection of the cytokine induces the formation of psoriatic lesions at the site of administration.

TNF-α also appears to be a key cytokine in psoriasis as shown by the beneficial effects of anti-TNF-α therapies (see Section 9.11), and acts in synergy with IFN-γ to exert its effects. Both cytokines are inhibitory for normal KC growth, but psoriatic KCs are selectively resistant to the inhibitory effects of IFN-γ whilst responding normally to TNF-α (see Section 9.6).

In addition, activated T cells in psoriasis produce **IL-17**, a cytokine that regulates adhesion molecule expression and chemokine production by KCs. Thus IL-17 decreases the IL-1ra to IL-1α ratio, and stimulates the release of GRO-α (CXCL1), GM-CSF and IL-6 by KCs, with synergistic or additive effects by IFN-γ.

9.9.1.2 Dendritic cell cytokines

Activated dendritic cells produce two cytokines, IL-12 and IL-23, which are present at increased levels in psoriatic skin lesions. Both of these cytokines induce IFN-γ synthesis by T cells and probably also promote the expansion of Th-1 type cells.

IL-12 is a heterodimeric molecule composed of two covalently linked chains, p35 and p40, which have no biological activity alone. Specific mRNA for both chains have been detected in the epidermis of normal skin and psoriatic lesions, but the levels of p40 IL-12 mRNA were considerably higher in the latter [82]. Furthermore immunoreactivity for IL-12 p70 was markedly increased in psoriatic lesions, and predominately expressed on mononuclear cells in the dermis [82].

In addition, mRNAs coding for p19 and p40 subunits of **IL-23** are consistently, and markedly up-regulated in psoriatic skin lesions [83]. IL-23 shares its p40 subunit with IL-12 so that the increased levels of this subunit reported in psoriasis probably contributes to the formation of biological forms of both cytokines. Interestingly, overexpression of IL-23 in mice with endogenous p19 production who were transfected with the p40 subunit gene produced inflammatory skin lesions resembling psoriasis, with markedly increased activated dendritic cell infiltration and epidermal hyperproliferation [84].

9.9.1.3 Keratinocyte cytokines

Various KC-derived cytokines are up-regulated in psoriatic skin lesions, some of which are likely to play significant roles in the interplay between KCs and T cells.

In addition to the proinflammatory cytokines, IL-1β, IL-6 and TNF-α, psoriatic KCs produce significantly increased levels of **IL-7**, a T and B cell growth factor which, together with IL-2 and IL-12, has been shown to stimulate IFN-γ production by T cells. Furthermore, three further cytokines (IL-15, IL-18 and IL-20) have been shown to be up-regulated in lesional KCs, suggesting that they play a role in psoriasis [85-87]. **IL-15** triggers inflammatory cell recruitment, angiogenesis, T cell proliferation (particularly CD8[+] T cells) and the production of other inflammatory cytokines, including IFN-γ, TNF-α, and IL-17. In addition, IL-15 is a potent inhibitor of KC apoptosis. Since receptors for IL-15 are also up-regulated on lesional KCs, it has been suggested that IL-15 may be responsible for the abnormally low KC apoptosis in psoriasis. Blockade of IL-15 biological activity in a psoriasis xenograft mouse model, using a specific mAb that interferes with the assembly of the IL-15 receptor complex, resulted in a reduction in the severity of psoriasis supporting a role for IL-15 in the disease process [88].

IL-18 (IFN-γ-inducing factor), another growth and differentiation factor for Th-1 cells with similar functions to that of IL-12, is also over-expressed in the epidermis of psoriatic skin lesions. In addition to inducing IFN-γ production by T cells and NK cells, IL-18 also acts as a chemoattractant for dendritic cells and up-regulates their surface expression of adhesion and costimulatory molecules.

IL-20 is a functionally distinct member of the IL-10 gene family, the receptor subunits for which are expressed in skin. In psoriatic skin lesions, IL-20 is synthesized focally by basal and suprabasal KCs above the dermal papillae, whilst IL-20 receptor subunits are markedly up-regulated throughout the epidermis [87]. Overexpression of IL-20 in transgenic mice causes neonatal lethality with skin abnormalities including aberrant epidermal differentiation [89]. These findings suggest that IL-20 may play a role in the regulation of epidermal function in psoriasis.

9.9.2 Chemokines

Constitutive production and release of **CTACK** by epidermal KCs, with subsequent binding to endothelial cells, ensures that T cells expressing the CCR10 receptor can gain access to uninflamed skin for immune surveillance. Once activated in psoriatic skin, the T cells produce IFN-γ and TNF-α, which induce the production of chemokines by various skin cell types, particularly KCs. These chemokines not only attract Th-1 cells, dendritic cells and PMNs into the skin, but also activate the responding cells to produce cytokines and growth factors, which further perpetuates the disease process.

KCs in psoriatic lesions produce various chemokines that attract Th-1 and/or dendritic cells into the dermis. Thus Th-1 cells expressing the CXCR3 receptor can respond to **IP-10** (CXCL10), **Mig** (CXCL9) and **I-TAC** (CXCL11) which are all up-regulated in lesional epidermis, whilst **RANTES** (CCL5) and **MCP-1** (CCL2) expressed in the basal layer of the epidermis attract activated T cells and APC that express CCR5 or CCR2, respectively. In addition, CCR6 is selectively expressed on CLA$^+$ T cells and immature dendritic cells, which migrate into the skin in response to **MIP-3α** (CCL20), which is highly expressed in psoriatic epidermis.

In addition, endothelial cell-derived chemokines **MDC** (CCL22) and **TARC** (CCL17) activate T cells bearing the CCR4 receptor, which are also increased in the dermis of psoriatic lesions.

A proportion of CXCR3-positive CD8$^+$ (and CD4$^+$) T cells migrate from the dermis into the epidermis, along the IP-10, Mig and I-TAC chemokine gradients. **IL-8** also contributes to the selective movement of effector CD8$^+$ T cells expressing CXCR1 into the epidermis, and, together with **GRO-α** (CXCL1), induces the migration and activation of PMNs, which are characteristically found in clusters in the stratum corneum of psoriatic lesions.

Gene profiling using oligonucleotide micro-array analysis has revealed the presence of additional chemokines not previously reported in psoriatic skin lesions [30]. Surprisingly, these included **MIP-3β** (CCL19) and **SLC** (CCL21), ligands for the chemokine receptor CCR7, which was subsequently demonstrated on T cells and dendritic cells in lesional skin. CCR7 is normally expressed on T cells that migrate to lymph nodes or other lymphoid tissues and are not differentiated for skin homing.

9.8 Chemokines produced by keratinocytes in psoriatic skin lesions

hemokines	Chemokine receptor	Responding cell types
CXCL1 (GRO-α)	CXCR1/CXCR2	PMN
CXCL8 (IL-8)	CXCR1/CXCR2	PMN, CD8[+] T cells
CXCL9 (Mig)	CXCR3	Activated Th-1 cells, NK
CXCL10 (IP-10)	CXCR3	Activated Th-1 cells, NK
CXCL11 (I-TAC)	CXCR3	Activated Th-1 cells, NK
CCL2 (MCP-1)	CCR2	Monocytes, activated T cells, immature dendritic cells, NK
CCL5 (RANTES)	CCR5	Monocytes, activated T cells, immature dendritic cells, NK
CCL20 (MIP-3α)	CCR6	Memory T cells, immature dendritic cells
CCL22 (MDC)	CCR4	Activated T cells (Th-2), immature dendritic cells
CCL27 (CTACK)	CCR10	Activated T cells

MIP-3β (CCL19) and SLC (CCL21), together with **SDF-1**(CXCL12), whose gene expression was also identified as being up-regulated in skin lesions, are lymphoid tissue chemokines suggesting that psoriatic skin could function as a secondary lymphoid tissue.

9.10 Model for pathogenesis of psoriasis

The immunopathogenic pathway leading to the development of CP psoriasis remains to be fully elucidated. However, the evidence so far suggests that the interaction between both CD4[+] and CD8[+] T cells, and KCs is pivotal to the disease process. A model describing the possible mechanisms involved is discussed below, and presented in Fig. 9.7.

Activated CD4[+] and activated CD8[+] T cells coexist in equal numbers in the epidermis of CP lesions and both subsets appear to play vital roles. The disease is initiated and maintained by the presentation of antigen by MHC Class II-positive dendritic cells to CLA[+]CD4[+] T cells in the epidermis and/or dermis. Once it has been initiated, dominant epidermal CD8[+] T cell clones contribute to the persistence of the disease process. It is proposed that antigen (or superantigen) derived from streptococci or other microorganisms are responsible for CD4[+] T cell activation, whilst CD8[+] T cells are specific for a skin-derived antigen, such as keratin, up-regulated in KCs by cytokines produced by activated T cells.

Production of IL-12 and IL-23 by dendritic cells during antigen presentation induces (epi)dermal CD4[+] and epidermal CD8[+] T cells to produce type 1 cytokines including IFN-γ and TNF-α. These

Figure 9.7   Model of pathogenesis of psoriasis

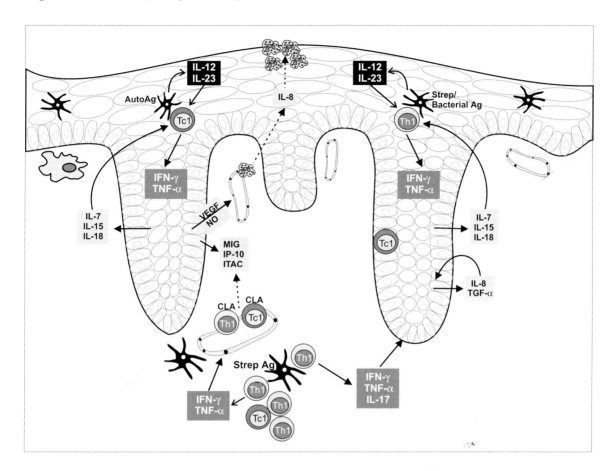

cytokines play a key role in the disease process via their effects on KCs. These include the up-regulation of adhesion and accessory molecule expression, promoting binding and interaction between the two cell types, and the enhanced production of Th-1 cell-attracting chemokines, various cytokines including the PMN chemoattractant IL-8, and iNos, which regulates vascular dilation via the production of nitric oxide. Adhesion molecules are also up-regulated on endothelial cells by IFN-γ and TNF-α thereby facilitating the further extravasation of leukocytes, including skin-homing CD4+ memory T cells expressing CLA, from the blood into the lesion. In turn, cytokines produced by activated KCs such as IL-8 and TGF-α have autocrine effects on KC proliferation, whilst other KC-derived cytokines such as IL-7, IL-15 and IL-18 stimulate T cell growth and IFN-γ production. This sets up a self-perpetuating cycle of events in which activated T cells and KCs interact via the production of a complex mixture of cytokines/chemokines, thus maintaining the pathology of the psoriatic skin lesion.

In contrast, in the acute guttate form of psoriasis, activated CD8+ T cells are associated with spontaneous resolution rather than persistence of skin lesions (Fig. 9.8). This suggests that they may have a suppressive role. Suppression of antigen-activated CD4+ T cells by CD8+ T cells stimulated

Figure 9.8   Resolution of guttate skin lesions

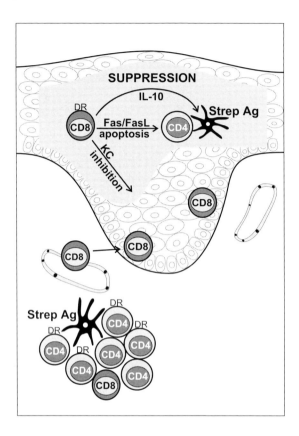

by superantigen has been shown to result from their ability to induce CD4[+] T cell apoptosis via ligation of Fas, whilst they are themselves resistant. Thus it is conceivable that activated CD8[+] T cells delete activated CD4[+] T cells associated with initiation/maintenance of guttate skin lesions, resulting in termination of the disease process. Other possible mechanisms include effects on LC function, inhibition of KC proliferation and/or Tc-2 cytokine production.

9.11 Treatment

Established treatments for psoriasis, such as corticosteroids, PUVA and cyclosporin, have various side effects including lack of consistent efficacy over time, and a risk of toxicity and/or carcinogenesis due to their broad mechanisms of action. Progress in the elucidation of the role of the immune system in the pathogenesis of psoriasis has led to the development of a new class of immuno-modulating biological agents for use in psoriasis, which specifically target specific steps involved in the disease process. In addition, novel systemic therapies (pimecrolimus, rosiglitazone maleate and tazarotene) are emerging as further options for the treatment of psoriasis.

Table 9.9 Established treatments for psoriasis

Treatment	Topical/ Systemic	Main cellular target	Mechanism of action
Steroid hormones			
Corticosteroids	Topical	T cells	Bind to nuclear receptors; resulting complex regulates gene transcription by binding to promotor region of target genes
Vitamin D analogues (eg. Dovonex)	Topical	T cells and KC	
Vitamin A analogues (eg. tazarotene, acitretin)	Topical/ systemic	T cells and KC	
Immunosuppressive drugs			
Cyclosporin Tacrolimus	Systemic	T cells	Bind to immunophilin; inhibit calcineurin, translocation of NF-AT and cytokine transcription
Methotrexate	Systemic	T cells and KC	Apoptosis via Fas-independent pathway
PUVA/UVB	Systemic	T cells	Apoptosis via Fas/FasL pathway
Dithranol	Topical	T cells and KC	DNA inhibition KC apoptosis via a mitochondrial pathway dependent upon oxidative respiration
Fumaric acid esters	Systemic	T cells and KC	Modulate dendritic cell polarisation leading to decreased T cell IFN-γ production Inhibit NF-κB activation

9.11.1 Established treatments for psoriasis

The established treatments for psoriasis that are currently in use are shown in Table 9.9.

9.11.1.1 Steroid hormones

Glucocorticosteroids, and the vitamin D and vitamin A analogues are steroid hormones which, when bound to specific nuclear receptors, regulate gene transcription by binding to a specific DNA sequence in the promotor region of target genes.

Glucocorticosteroids are potent immunosuppressive drugs that are commonly used topically to treat mild to moderate psoriasis. They induce resolution of skin lesions by inhibiting proliferation and cytokine production by T cells, and can also induce lymphocyte apoptosis.

Various vitamin D$_3$ analogues have been shown to be effective in psoriasis, and probably mediate their effects via modulation of epidermal growth, keratinisation and inflammation. A topical preparation of calcipotriol (Dovonex) is commonly used in combination with other therapies such as PUVA.

Vitamin A analogues (retinoids) have been used to treat psoriasis with variable success. Second generation retinoids, etrinate and its active metabolite acitretin, are only used in severe and recalcitrant forms of psoriasis due to their attendant side effects. Retinoids have potent effects on proliferation, keratinisation and differentiation of epidermal cells. Topical tazarotene has also been shown to decrease inflammation in psoriatic skin.

9.11.1.2 Immunosuppressive drugs

The effective clearing of psoriatic skin lesions can also be induced by systemic treatment with low doses of the immunosuppressant drugs, cyclosporin and tacrolimus (FK506). These drugs act primarily on activated T cells inhibiting their production of cytokines such as IL-2 and IFN-γ. Although cyclosporin and tacrolimus are structurally different (undecapeptide and macrolide, respectively), they have the same mode of action. Each binds to an intracellular receptor or immunophilin to form cyclosporin-cyclophilin and FK506-FK506-binding protein complexes, respectively. These complexes bind to and inhibit calcineurin, which prevents NF-AT translocation to the nucleus resulting in a failure to activate NF-AT regulated cytokine genes.

Methotrexate is a folate antagonist and potent antiproliferative agent that, after conversion to polyglutamate forms, blocks the synthesis of DNA by inhibiting thymidine monophosphate production. The drug also has a variety of anti-inflammatory properties, but unlike cyclosporin, tacrolimus and glucocorticosteroids, has no effect on cytokine release from T cells or monocytes. Furthermore, methotrexate has been shown to induce apoptosis of activated peripheral blood T cells via a Fas-independent pathway, and of KCs in an epidermal explant/dermal model *in vitro*.

9.11.1.3 PUVA, Dithranol and Fumaric acid esters

Treatment of psoriasis with PUVA or UVB results in clinical resolution preceded or accompanied by a reduction in CD4$^+$ and CD8$^+$ T cell numbers in the epidermis. Furthermore, repeated exposure of psoriatic skin lesions to PUVA, but not UVB, also results in a marked depletion of epidermal LC numbers. The mechanism of action of UVB/PUVA in clearing psoriasis is likely to be the induction of apoptosis in epidermal T cells via KC FasL-T cell Fas interactions. KCs, in contrast, are resistant to UVB-induced apoptosis.

Dithranol (anthralin) is a synthetic preparation of a natural product, chrysarobin, which has been used as an anti-psoriatic agent for more than 80 years. The drug appears to mediate its anti-psoriatic effects via inhibition of KC and lymphocyte proliferation, and by inducing KC apoptosis via a novel mitochondrial pathway dependent on oxidative respiration [90].

Fumaric acid esters (a mixture of dimethylfumarate, and ethylhydrogenfumarate salts) have proved to be both effective and safe in the treatment of severe psoriasis. However, compared to other systemic treatments for psoriasis, such as cyclosporin, relatively high doses are required to give a pharmacological effect. Although their exact mode of action in psoriasis is unknown, fumaric acid esters predominately target T cells and KCs, inducing Th-2 cytokine synthesis and inhibiting KC proliferation and chemokine production. In addition, the respiratory burst of PMNs and the TNF-α-induced up-regulation of adhesion molecules on endothelial cells are also inhibited.

9.11.2 Current and emerging biological therapies for psoriasis

Psoriasis is at the forefront in the development of novel treatments for skin disease. Currently there are three types of biological agents approved, or in development, for use in psoriasis; mAb, fusion proteins and recombinant human cytokines. These agents are targeted at specific points in the immune cell pathway leading to psoriasis: T cell activation/costimulation, T cell proliferation and cytokines (Table 9.10; reviewed in Refs 91-93).

9.11.2.1 Blocking T cell activation/costimulation

The interaction between T cells and APC has been the main target for the development of biological agents for psoriasis. These include efalizumab, alefacept and siplizumab, which bind to molecules on T cells, and CTLA4Ig and IDEC114 that are directed against costimulatory molecules on APC (Fig. 9.9).

Efalizumab (Raptiva) is a humanized IgG$_1$ mAb directed against the CD11a subunit in LFA-1. (In a humanized mAb, individual amino acids in a human backbone are replaced by specific murine binding sequences). Binding of efalizumab to LFA-1 on T cells blocks their interaction with APC

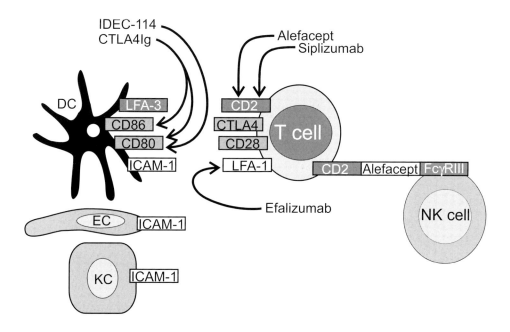

Figure 9.9 Sites of action of biological agents that block T cell-APC interaction.

Table 9.10   Current and emerging biological therapies for psoriasis

Target	Biological Agent (Brand name)	Trial phase	Mechanism of action
T cell activation/ costimulation	Efalizumab (Raptiva)	Approved by FDA* Submitted to EAEMP**	Humanized antibody to CD11a chain of LFA-1. Blocks binding of T cells to ICAMs on APC, endothelial cells and activated KCs
	Alefacept (Amevive)	Approved by FDA	LFA-3-IgG fusion protein. Binds to CD2 on T cells blocking costimulation and inducing T cell apoptosis
	Siplizumab (MEDI-507)	Phase II	Humanized antibody to CD2. Blocks CD2-LFA-3 costimulation and stimulates memory T cell lysis
	CTLA4Ig	Phase I	CTLA4-IgG fusion protein. Binds to B7 molecules on APC blocking B7-CD28 T cell costimulation
	IDEC-114	Phase II	Primatized antibody to B7-1. Binds to B7-1 blocking B7-1-CD28 interaction
T cell proliferation	Daclizumab (Zenapax)	Phase II	Humanized antibody to p55 (Tac) chain of high affinity IL-2 receptor. Inhibits IL-2 binding and T cell proliferation
	Basiliximab (Simulect)	Phase I	Chimeric antibody to p55 (Tac) chain of high affinity IL-2 receptor. Inhibits IL-2 binding and T cell proliferation
	Denileukin diftitox ($DAB_{389}IL-2$)	Phase II	Diphtheria toxin-IL-2 fusion protein. Binds to activated T cells and induces apoptosis

Target	Biological Agent (Brand name)	Trial phase	Mechanism of action
Cytokines	Etanercept (Enbrel)	Approved for psoriatic arthritis	TNF-receptor-IgG fusion protein. Binds to and inactivates soluble TNF-α and TNF-β
	Infliximab (Remicade)	Phase III	Chimeric antibody to TNF-α. Binds to and inhibits soluble and membrane-bound TNF-α
	Adalimumab (Humira)	Phase III	Human IgG_1 antibody to TNF-α. Binds to TNF-α and blocks its interaction with TNF receptors
	Onercept	Phase II	Recombinant human soluble p55 TNF-α binding protein
	HUZAF	Phase I	Humanized antibody to IFN-γ
Th-1 cytokines (immune deviation)	IL-4 (RhuIL-4)	Phase I	Recombinant Th-2 cytokines. Skew Th-1 cells to Th-2 phenotype
	IL-10 (Tenovil)	Phase II	
	IL-11 (Oprelvekin)	Phase I	

* FDA, US Food and Drug Administration; ** EAEMP, European Agency for the Evaulation of Medicinal Products

via ICAM-1, -2 and -3 preventing T cell activation, and also blocks T cell adhesion and migration into the skin via ICAMs expressed by endothelial cells and KCs. The administration of this mAb is associated with an early onset of action, which can be as early as 14 days, although extended treatment is more beneficial to maintain and improve responses.

Alefacept (Amevive) is a recombinant fusion protein composed of the terminal portion of LFA-3 and the Fc portion of human IgG_1. The LFA-3 domain on alefacept binds to CD2 on T cells and blocks its interaction with LFA-3 on APC through competitive inhibition. This prevents transduction of costimulatory signals between APCs and T cells. In addition, alefacept acts as a bridging molecule between up-regulated CD2 on memory T cells and the FcγRIII receptor (CD16) on NK cells. This interaction results in the release of granzyme by NK cells and induction of T cell apoptosis. The period of remission after cessation of successful treatment was found to be 4 times longer for alefacept than for efalizumab (7 or 8 months compared to 2). This may be related to the selective depletion of peripheral blood memory T cells, which correlated with the improvement in psoriasis induced by alefacept.

CD2 is also the target for the humanized mAb, siplizumab (Medi-507). Binding of siplizumab to CD2 on T cells also prevents costimulation by LFA-3 on APC and may induce prolonged clinical remissions.

Blockade of the interaction between CD28 on T cells and B7 on APC interferes with T cell activation, proliferation, cytokine production and overall survival. This can be achieved by the use of mAbs to B7-1 (CD80) and B7-2 (CD86), or the fusion protein CTLA4Ig. CTLA4Ig consists of the extracellular binding domain of CTLA-4 combined with IgG_1 to form a soluble, antibody-like protein that binds with high affinity to both CD80 and CD86. Preliminary studies suggested some beneficial effects of this fusion protein in psoriasis, accompanied by reductions in the expression of various costimulatory and accessory molecules on lesional dendritic cells and KCs. IDEC-114, a mAb directed against CD80 on APC, has also shown some evidence of clinical activity at higher doses. However, optimal blockade of CD28-B7 interactions may require the combined use of mAbs to both CD80 and CD86, as IDEC-114 was unable to affect interactions of APC with CTLA-4.

9.11.2.2 Inhibiting T cell proliferation

Activation of T cells results in up-regulation of the α subunit (CD25 or Tac) of the IL-2 receptor that confers high affinity binding, and increased synthesis of the T cell growth factor, IL-2. Two mAbs to CD25, which block binding of IL-2 to its receptor and inhibit T cell proliferation, have been tested out in a limited number of patients with psoriasis with some efficacy: Daclizumab (Zenapax), a humanised mAb which caused a reduction in disease that correlated with IL-2 receptor blockade, and Basiliximab (Simulect), a chimeric mAb (fused segments of mouse and human mAbs) which proved to be effective in the treatment of severe psoriasis.

Another biological agent that is specific for IL-2 receptor-positive T cells and has been used in psoriasis is $DAB_{389}IL-2$, a fusion protein in which the receptor-binding domain of diphtheria toxin is replaced by human IL-2 (see Section 9.8.1). The enzymatic fragment of the toxin, which inhibits protein synthesis, is released after receptor-mediated endocytosis of the bound protein, inducing the activated T cells to undergo apoptosis. The treatment induced a reduction in activated T cells together with resolution of skin lesions. However, in the multicentre phase II trial, one quarter of the patients discontinued treatment because of adverse symptoms suggesting that this agent may not be suitable for general use.

9.11.2.3 Cytokine blockade

Proinflammatory cytokines released as a result of T cell activation are responsible for inducing effector responses in various skin cell types in psoriasis. Blockade of cytokines using mAbs or fusion proteins is another approach that is being increasingly used to control disease with some success. TNF-α is currently the main focus for this strategy in psoriasis, both because of its increased levels in lesional skin and the demonstrated efficacy of anti-TNF-α agents such as etanercept and infliximab (also adalimumab and onercept) in rheumatoid arthritis.

Etanercept (Enbrel) is a fusion protein, comprising the human TNF-α p75 receptor fused to the Fc portion of IgG_1, whilst infliximab (Remicade) is a chimeric mAb; both bind to and inactivate

TNF-α, preventing interactions with its cell surface receptors. Both TNF-α inhibitors have proved to be beneficial in psoriasis and psoriatic arthritis. Etanercept can be used in conjunction with other systemic modalities such as methotrexate, acitretin, cyclosporin or PUVA without added toxicity, providing a further treatment option for patients with recalcitrant disease. Infliximab has also been used in combination with methotrexate in rheumatoid arthritis to prevent the loss of efficacy caused by the production of antibodies to the murine component of the chimera antibody. Furthermore infliximab, and also a human IgG_1 antibody to TNF-α called adalimumab (Humira) used in rheumatoid arthritis, induce complement-mediated lysis of cells resulting in a higher incidence of tuberculosis compared with the background population. For this reason, tuberculin skin testing is required on all patients undergoing therapy with these antibodies. In addition, a recombinant human soluble p55 tumour necrosis factor binding protein (onercept) is also under development for use in psoriasis and psoriatic arthritis, and other Th-1 type diseases.

Other proinflammatory cytokines important in psoriasis such as IL-8 and IFN-γ are also being explored as targets for humanized antibodies. An antibody to IL-8 (Abx-IL8) gave only modest improvement in preliminary trials and is no longer being developed for psoriasis. However, an antibody to IFN-γ (HUZAF) is currently undergoing phase I clinical trials.

9.11.2.4 Immune deviation

Th-1 cytokines such as IFN-γ and IL-12 can be inhibited and down-regulated by the exogenous administration of Th-2 cytokines such as IL-4, IL-10 and IL-11. As Th-2 cytokines influence endogenous differentiation of Th-2 cells, the differentiation of Th-1 cells can potentially be deviated to the production of Th-2 cytokines. This therapeutic manipulation of the Th-1/Th-2 (and Tc-1/Tc-2) balance is termed "immune deviation". As predicted, anti-psoriatic effects of recombinant IL-10 (Tenovil) were linked to reductions in Th-1 cytokines in phase II clinical trials; costimulatory molecules were also down-regulated on skin-derived dendritic cells affecting their T cell-stimulatory function. Psoriatic patients treated with recombinant IL-11 (oprelvekin) or IL-4 (RhuIL-4) have also shown decreases in Th-1 cytokines (and, in the case of IL-4, increased numbers of circulating Th-2 cells) associated with disease improvement. However, the therapeutic activity of these Th-2 cytokines is less than that of other immunosuppressive agents, and experimental evidence suggests that this may be improved by simultaneous neutralisation of IL-12.

9.11.3 New systemic therapies for psoriasis

Three new systemic therapies are currently being investigated for the treatment of psoriasis; pimecrolimus, rosiglitazone maleate and tazarotene.

Pimecrolimus (SDZ-ASM-981) is a macrolam ascomycin derivative, which, in its topical form (Elidel) is currently being investigated for treatment of inflammatory skin disorders such as AD and psoriasis. Pimecrolimus inhibits T cell activation by disrupting intracellular signalling following antigen stimulation, leading to down-regulation of IL-2 and IFN-γ production. In psoriasis, topical pimecrolimus was only slightly less effective than clobetasol ointment at a 1% concentration. Preliminary data from a study of psoriasis patients treated with an oral form of the drug looks promising and warrants further investigation.

Rosiglitazone maleate (Avandia) is an oral thiazolidinedione used in type II diabetes mellitis currently being studied as a possible treatment for psoriasis. It is a selective and potent agonist of the peroxisome proliferators-activated receptor-γ (PPAR-γ), which inhibits cytokine production and promotes cell differentiation, in addition to its insulin/glucose related functions. PPAR-γ is highly expressed in KCs, and rosiglitazone maleate and another PPAR-γ agonist, troglitazone, may improve psoriasis by reducing proliferation and normalising the differentiation of KCs in psoriatic skin lesions. Furthermore, low blood sugar is not a problem associated with the use of these agents, as rosiglitazone maleate is an insulin sensitiser rather than a hypoglycaemic agent.

Tazarotene (Tazaroc), a retinoid has been recently approved for use in psoriasis in its oral form. Since its active metabolite, tazarotenic acid, has a short half-life, oral tazarotene is probably a safer alternative than other retinoids such as acitretin.

Summary

- Psoriasis is a common, chronic inflammatory disease that presents with hyperproliferation of the epidermis and altered epidermal differentiation.
- Characteristic features of skin lesions include a type IV hypersensitivity response to microbial and/or auto- antigens, Th-1 cytokines and a chemokine profile that attracts Th-1 cells, dendritic cells, macrophages and PMNs.
- Psoriasis is associated with the Class I allele, HLA-Cw*0602, which correlates with early onset, positive family history, and more severe disease.
- Psoriasis has a strong genetic basis involving multiple genes:
  - 19 potential susceptibility loci on 15 different chromosomes; 9 are designated as PSORS1-PSORS9.
  - PSORS1, containing the HLA Class I region, accounts for between 35-50% of familial clustering.
  - Candidate genes code for proteins involved in epidermal differentiation, immune and inflammatory responses, and responses to pathogens.
- Psoriasis is triggered and/or exacerbated by various environmental factors including infections (particularly those caused by streptococci), stress, hormones and drugs.
- Innate immune responses appear activated in psoriatic skin lesions:
  - Modulation of KC expression of TLR2 and TLR5
  - Up-regulation of anti-microbial peptide production by KCs
  - NK-T cells present in skin lesions close to KCs expressing CD1d
  - DDCs and fibroblasts express the Hsp receptor CD91
- Peripheral blood T cells show altered functional responses *in vitro* and *in vivo*, and a shift towards Th-1 cytokine production.
- Dermal CD4$^+$ and epidermal CD8$^+$ T cells show oligoclonality and express conserved TCR CD3 motifs suggesting that they recognise a common disease-associated antigen(s). Possible candidates include microbial (bacterial peptidoglycan) and auto-antigens (keratin).
- KCs show insensitivity to growth inhibition by IFN-γ, a resistance to apoptosis and a distinct cytokine/chemokine pattern, which may represent inherent defects that confer susceptibility to disease.
- Conventional topical and systemic treatments include corticosteroids, calcineurin inhibitors, UV light, fumaric acid esters, Vitamin D and A analogues, and immunosuppressive drugs. Novel biological therapies currently being tested are targeted at specific points in the immune cell pathway; T cell activation/costimulation, T cell proliferation and cytokine production.

References

1. Bata-Csorgo Z., Hammerberg C., Voorhees J.J., Cooper K.D. Flow cytometric identification of proliferative subpopulations within normal human epidermis and the localization of the primary hyperproliferative population in psoriasis. J.Exp.Med. 1993; **178:** 1271-81.

2. Lomholt G. Psoriasis: Prevalence, Spontaneous Course and Genetics 1963; G.E.C. Gad, Copenhagen.

3. Hellgren I. Psoriasis: The prevalence in sex, age and occupational groups in total populations in Sweden. Morphology, inheritance and association with other skin and rheumatic diseases 1967; Almqvist & Wiksell, Stockholm.

4. Traupe H., van Gurp P.J., Happle R., Boezeman J., van de Kerkhof P.C. Psoriasis vulgaris, fetal growth, and genomic imprinting. Am.J.Med.Genet. 1992; **42:** 649-54.

5. Henseler T. & Christophers E. Psoriasis of early and late onset: characterization of two types of psoriasis vulgaris. J.Am.Acad.Dermatol. 1985; **13:** 450-6.

6. Gudjonsson J.E., Karason A., Antonsdottir A.A. *et al.* HLA-Cw6-positive and HLA-Cw6-negative patients with psoriasis vulgaris have distinct clinical features. J.Invest.Dermatol. 2002; **118:** 362-5.

7. Asahina A., Akazaki S., Nakagawa H. *et al.* Specific nucleotide sequence of HLA-C is strongly associated with psoriasis vulgaris. J.Invest.Dermatol. 1991; **97:** 254-8.

8. Bowcock A.M. & Cookson W.O.C.M. The genetics of psoriasis, psoriatic arthritis and atopic dermatitis. Hum.Mol.Genet. 2004; **13:** R43-R55.

9. Capon F., Munro M., Barker J., Trembath R. Searching for the major histocompatibility complex psoriasis susceptibility gene. J.Invest.Dermatol. 2002; **118:** 745-51.

10. Asumalahti K., Veal C., Laitinen T. *et al.* Coding haplotype analysis supports HCR as the putative susceptibility gene for psoriasis at the MHC PSORS1 locus. Hum.Mol.Genet. 2002; **11:** 589-97.

11. Helms C., Cao L., Krueger J.G. *et al.* A putative RUNX1 binding site variant between SLC9A3R1 and NAT9 is associated with susceptibility to psoriasis. Nat.Genet. 2003; **35:** 349-56.

12. Sagoo G.S., Tazi-Ahnini R., Barker J.W.N. *et al.* Meta-analysis of genome-wide studies of psoriasis susceptibility reveals linkage to chromosomes 6p21 and 4q28-q31 in Caucasian and Chinese Han population. J.Invest.Dermatol. 2004; **122:** 1401-5.

13. Capon F., Semprini S., Chimenti S. *et al.* Fine mapping of the PSORS4 susceptibility region on chromosome 1q21. J.Invest.Dermatol. 2001; **116:** 728-30.

14. Hewitt D., Samuelsson L., Polding J. *et al.* Identification of a psoriasis susceptibility candidate gene by linkage disequilibrium mapping with a localised single nucleotide polymorphism map. Genomics 2002; **79:** 305-14.

15. Zenz R., Eferl R., Kenner L. *et al.* Psoriasis-like skin disease and arthritis caused by inducible epidermal deletion of Jun proteins. Nature 2005; **437:** 369-75.

16. Girardin S.E., Hugot J.-P., Sansonetti P.J. Lessons from Nod2 studies; towards a link between

Crohn's disease and bacterial sensing. Trends Immunol. 2003; **24:** 652-8.

17. The International Psoriasis Genetics Consortium. The International Psoriasis Genetics Study: Assessing Linkage to 14 Candidate Susceptibility Loci in a Cohort of 942 Affected Sib Pairs. Am.J.Hum.Genet. 2003; **73:** 430–7.

18. Reich K., Mossner R., Konig I.R., Westphal G., Ziegler A., Neumann C. Promotor polymorphisms of the genes encoding tumor necrosis factor-α and Interleukin-1β are associated with different subtypes of psoriasis characterised by early and late disease onset. J.Invest.Dermatol. 2002; **118:** 155-63.

19. Donn R.P., Plant D., Jury F. *et al.* Macrophage migration inhibitory factor gene polymorphism is associated with psoriasis. J.Invest.Dermatol. 2004; **123:** 484-7.

20. Tsunemi Y., Saeki H., Nakamura K. *et al.* Interleukin-12 p40 gene (IL12B) 3'-untranslated region polymorphism is associated with susceptibility to atopic dermatitis and psoriasis vulgaris. J.Dermatol.Sci. 2002; **30:** 161-6.

21. Kingo K., Koks S., Nikopensius T., Silm H., Vasar E. Polymorphisms in the interleukin-20 gene: relationships to plaque-type psoriasis. Genes Immun. 2004; **5:** 117-21.

22. Young H.S., Summers A.M., Bhushan M., Brenchley P.E., Griffiths C.E. Single-nucleotide polymorphisms of vascular endothelial growth factor in psoriasis of early onset. J.Invest. Dermatol. 2004; **122:** 209-15.

23. Suzuki Y., Hamamoto Y., Ogasawara Y. *et al.* Genetic polymorphisms of killer cell immunoglobulin-like receptors are associated with susceptibility to psoriasis vulgaris. J.Invest.Dermatol. 2004; **122:** 1133-6.

24. Cheng L., Zhang S.Z., Xiao C.Y. *et al.* The A5.1 allele of the major histocompatibility complex class I chain-related gene A is associated with psoriasis vulgaris in Chinese. Br.J.Dermatol. 2000; **143:** 324-9.

25. Tay G.K., Hui J., Gaudieri S. *et al.* PERB11 (MIC): a polymorphic MHC gene is expressed in skin and single nucleotide polymorphisms are associated with psoriasis. Clin.Exp.Immunol. 2000; **119:** 553-8.

26. Rivas M.V., Jarvis E.D., Morisaki S., Carbonaro H., Gottlieb A.B., Krueger J.G. Identification of aberrantly regulated genes in diseased skin using the cDNA differential display technique. J.Invest.Dermatol. 1997; **108:** 188-94.

27. Chiba H. Michibata H., Wakimoto K. *et al.* Cloning of a gene for a novel epithelium-specific cytosolic phospholipase A2, cPLA2delta, induced in psoriatic skin. J.Biol.Chem. 2004; **279:** 12890-7.

28. Oestreicher J.L., Walters I.B., Kikuchi T. *et al.* Molecular classification of psoriasis disease-associated genes through pharmacogenomic expression profiling. Pharmacogenomics J. 2001; **1:** 272-87.

29. Bowcock A.M., Shannon W., Du F. *et al.* Insights into psoriasis and other inflammatory diseases from large-scale gene expression studies. Hum.Mol.Genet. 2001; **10:** 1793-1805.

30. Zhou X., Krueger J.G., Kao M.C. *et al.* Novel mechanisms of T-cell and dendritic cell activation required by profiling of psoriasis on the 63,100-element oligonucleotide array. Physiol.Genomics 2003; **13:** 69-78.

31. Baker B.S., Ovigne J.-M., Powles A.V., Corcoran S., Fry L. Normal keratinocytes express

Toll-like receptors (TLRs) 1, 2 and 5: modulation of TLR expression in chronic plaque psoriasis. Br.J.Dermatol. 2003; **148:** 670-9.

32. Mempel M., Voelcker V., Kollisch G. *et al.* Toll-like receptor expression in human keratinocytes: Nuclear factor κB controlled gene activation by *Staphylococcus aureus* is Toll-like receptor 2 but not Toll-like receptor 4 or platelet activating factor receptor dependent. J.Invest.Dermatol. 2003; **121:** 1389-96.

33. Ong P.Y., Ohtake T., Brandt C. *et al.* Endogenous antimicrobial peptides and skin infections in atopic dermatitis. New Engl.J.Med. 2002; **347:** 1151-60.

34. Harder J., Bartels J., Christophers E., Schroder J.-M. Isolation and characterization of human β-defensin-3, a novel human inducible peptide antibiotic. J.Biol.Chem. 2001; **276:** 5707-13.

35. Bonish B., Jullien D., Dutronc Y. *et al.* Overexpression of CD1d by keratinocytes in psoriasis and CD1d-dependent IFN-gamma production by NK-T cells. J.Immunol. 2000; **165:** 4076-85.

36. Cameron A.L., Kirby B., Fei W., Griffiths C.E. Natural killer and natural killer-T cells in psoriasis. Arch.Derm.Res. 2002; **294:** 363-9.

37. Nickoloff B.J., Bonish B., Huang B.B., Porcelli S.A. Characterization of a T cell line bearing natural killer receptors and capable of creating psoriasis in a SCID mouse model system. J.Dermatol.Sci. 2000; **24:** 212–25.

38. Curry J.L., Qin J.-Z., Bonish B. *et al.* Innate immune-related receptors in normal and psoriatic skin. Arch.Pathol.Lab.Med. 2003; **127:** 178-86.

39. Leung D.Y., Gately M., Trumble A., Ferguson-Darnell B., Schlievert P.M., Picker L.J. Bacterial superantigens induce T cell expression of the skin-selective homing receptor, the cutaneous lymphocyte-associated antigen, via stimulation of interleukin 12 production. J.Exp.Med. 1995; **181:** 747-53.

40. Baker B.S., Garioch J.J., Hardman C., Powles A., Fry L. Induction of cutaneous lymphocyte-associated antigen expression by group A streptococcal antigens in psoriasis. Arch.Dermatol. Res.1997; **289:** 671-6.

41. LeRoy F., Brown K.A., Greaves M.W. *et al.* Blood mononuclear cells from patients with psoriasis exhibit an enhanced adherence to cultured vascular endothelium. J.Invest.Dermatol. 1991; **97:** 511-6.

42. Austin L.M., Ozawa M., Kikuchi T., Walters I.B., Krueger J.G. The majority of epidermal T cells in psoriasis vulgaris lesions can produce type 1 cytokines, interferon γ, and tumor necrosis factor α defining TC1 (cytotoxic T lymphocytes) and TH1 effector populations: a type 1 differentiation bias is also measured in circulating blood T cells in psoriasis patients. J.Invest.Dermatol. 1999; **113:** 752-9.

43. Baker B.S., Powles A.V., Valdimarsson H., Fry L. An altered response by psoriatic keratinocytes to gamma interferon. Scand.J.Immunol. 1988; **28:** 735-40.

44. Nickoloff B.J., Mitra R.S., Elder J.T., Fisher G.J., Voorhees J.J. Decreased growth inhibition by recombinant gamma interferon is associated with increased transforming growth factor-α production in keratinocytes cultured from psoriatic lesions. Br.J.Dermatol. 1989; **121:** 161-74.

45. Malkani A., Baker B.S., Garioch J.J., *et al*. Normal response to tumor necrosis factor-alpha and transforming growth factor-beta by keratinocytes in psoriasis. Exp.Dermatol. 1993; **2:** 224-30.

46. Olaniran A.K., Baker B.S., Garioch J.J., Powles A.V., Fry L. A comparison of the stimulatory effects of cytokines on normal and psoriatic keratinocytes *in vitro*. Arch.Dermatol.Res. 1995; **287:** 231-6.

47. Giustizieri M.L., Mascia F., Frezzolini A. *et al*. Keratinocytes from patients with atopic dermatitis and psoriasis show a distinct chemokine production profile in response to T cell-derived cytokines. J.Allergy Clin.Immunol. 2001; **107:** 871-7.

48. Wrone-Smith T., Mitra R.S., Thompson C.B., Jasty R., Castle V.P., Nickoloff B.J. Keratinocytes derived from psoriatic plaques are resistant to apoptosis compared with normal skin. Am.J.Pathol. 1997; **151:** 1321-9.

49. Qin J.Z., Chaturvedi V., Denning M.F. *et al*. Regulation of apoptosis by p53 in UV-irradiated human epidermis, psoriatic plaques and senescent keratinocytes. Oncogene 2002; **21:** 2991-3002.

50. Takahashi H., Manabe A., Ishida-Yamamoto A., Hashimoto Y., Iizuka H. Aberrant expression of apoptosis-related molecules in psoriatic epidermis. J.Dermatol.Sci. 2002; **28:** 187-97.

51. Baker B.S., Swain A.F., Fry L. Valdimarsson H. Epidermal T lymphocytes and HLA-DR expression in psoriasis. Brit.J.Dermatol. 1984; **110:** 555-64.

52. Baker B.S., Swain A.F., Griffiths C.E.M., Leonard J.N., Fry L., Valdimarsson H. Epidermal T lymphocytes and dendritic cells in chronic plaque psoriasis: the effects of PUVA treatment. Clin.Exp.Immunol. 1985; **61:** 526-34.

53. Nestle F.O., Turka L.A., Nickoloff B.J. Characterisation of dermal dendritic cells in psoriasis. Autostimulation of T lymphocytes and induction of Th1 type cytokines. J.Clin.Invest. 1994; **94:** 202-9.

54. Baker B.S. Psoriasis is a T cell-mediated disease. *In* Recent Advances in Psoriasis: The Role of the Immune System 2000; Imperial College Press, London, p50-60.

55. Gottlieb S.L., Gilleaudeau P., Johnson R. *et al*. Response of psoriasis to a lymphocyte-selective toxin (DAB$_{389}$IL-2) suggests a primary immune, but not keratinocyte, pathogenic basis. Nat.Med. 1995; **1:** 442-7.

56. Wrone-Smith T. & Nickoloff B.J. Dermal injection of immunocytes induces psoriasis. J.Clin. Invest. 1996; **98:** 1878-87.

57. Nickoloff B.J. and Wrone-Smith T. Injection of pre-psoriatic skin with CD4[+] T cells induces psoriasis. Am.J.Pathol. 1999; **155:** 145–58.

58. Gilhar, A., Ullmann Y., Kerner H. *et al*. Psoriasis is mediated by a cutaneous defect triggered by activated immunocytes: induction of psoriasis by cells with natural killer receptors. J.Invest.Dermatol. 2002; **119:** 384–91.

59. Boyman O., Heftil H.P., Conrad C., Nickoloff B.J., Suter M., Nestle F.O. Spontaneous development of psoriasis in a new animal model: essential role for resident T cells and tumour necrosis factor alpha. J.Exp.Med. 2004; **199:** 731-6.

60. Prinz J.C., Gross B., Vollmer S. *et al*. T cell clones from psoriasis skin lesions can promote keratinocyte proliferation *in vitro* via secreted products. Eur.J.Immunol. 1994; **24:** 593-8.

61. Hardman C.M., Baker B.S., Lortan J., Surentheran S., Powles A., Fry L. Active psoriasis in a patient with a profound CD4+ lymphocytopenia. Br.J.Dermatol. 1997; **136**: 930-2.

62. Leung D.Y.M., Travers J.B., Giorno R. *et al*. Evidence for a streptococcal superantigen-driven process in acute guttate psoriasis. J.Clin.Invest. 1995; **96**: 2106-12.

63. Menssen A., Trommler P., Vollmer S. *et al*. Evidence for an antigen-specific cellular immune response in skin lesions of patients with psoriasis vulgaris. J.Immunol. 1995; **155**: 4078-83.

64. Chang J.C.C., Smith L.R., Froning K.J. *et al*. CD8+ T cells in psoriatic skin lesions preferentially use T-cell receptor Vβ3 and/or Vβ13.1 genes. Proc.Natl.Acad Sci. USA 1994; **91**: 9282-6.

65. Lin W.-J., Norris D.A., Achziger M., Kotzin B.L. Tomkinson B. Oligoclonal expansion of intraepidermal T cells in psoriasis skin lesions. J.Invest.Dermatol. 2001; **117**: 1546-53.

66. Prinz J.C., Vollmer S., Boehncke W.-H., Menssen A., Laisney I., Trommler P. Selection of conserved TCR VDJ rearrangements in chronic psoriatic plaques indicates a common antigen in psoriasis vulgaris. Eur.J.Immunol. 1999; **29**: 3360-8.

67. Hwang H.Y., Bahk Y.Y., Kim T.-G., Kim T.-Y. Identification of a commonly used CDR3 region of infiltrating T cells expressing Vβ13 and Vβ15 derived from psoriasis patients. J.Invest.Dermatol. 2003; **120**: 359-64.

68. Uyemura K., Yamamura M., Fivenson D.F., Modlin R.L., Nickoloff B.J. The cytokine network in lesional and lesion-free psoriatic skin is characterised by a T-helper type 1 cell-mediated response. J.Invest.Dermatol. 1993; **101**: 701-5.

69. Schlaak J.F., Buslau M., Jochum W. *et al*. T cells involved in psoriasis vulgaris belong to the Th1 subset. J.Invest.Dermatol. 1994; **102**: 145-9.

70. Brown D.W., Baker B.S., Ovigne J.-M., Hardman C., Powles A.V., Fry L. Skin CD4+ T cells produce interferon-gamma *in vitro* in response to streptococcal antigens in chronic plaque psoriasis. J.Invest.Dermatol. 2000; **114**: 576-580

71. Brown D.W., Baker B.S., Ovigne J.-M. *et al*. Non-M protein on the cell wall and membrane of group A streptococci induces IFN-γ production by dermal CD4+ T cells in psoriasis. Arch. Dermatol.Res. 2001; **293**: 165-70.

72. Baker B.S., Ovigne J.-M., Fischetti V.A., Powles A., Fry L. Selective response of dermal Th-1 cells to 20-50 kDa streptococcal cell wall proteins in chronic plaque psoriasis. Scand. J.Immunol. 2003; **58**: 335-41.

73. Baker B.S., Laman J.D., Powles A. *et al*. Peptidoglycan and peptidoglycan-specific Th1 cells in psoriasis lesions. J.Pathol. 2006; In Press.

74. Baker B.S., Powles A.V., Garioch J.J., Hardman C., Fry L. Differential T cell reactivity to the round and oval forms of *Pityrosporum* in the skin of patients with psoriasis. Brit. J.Dermatol.1997; **136**: 319-25.

75. Gudmundsdottir A.S., Sigmundsdottir H., Sigurgeirsson B., Good M.F., Valdimarsson H., Jonsdottir I. Is an epitope on keratin 17 a major target for autoreactive T lymphocytes in psoriasis? Clin.Exp. Immunol. 1999; **117**: 580–6.

76. Johnston A., Gudjonsson J.E., Sigmundsdottir H., Love T.J., Valdimarsson H. Peripheral blood T cell responses to keratin peptides that share sequences with streptococcal M proteins

are largely restricted to skin-homing CD8[+] T cells. Clin.Exp.Immunol. 2004; **138:** 83–93.

77. Jones D.A., Yawalkar N., Suh K.-Y., Sadat S., Rich B., Kupper T.S. Identification of autoantigens in psoriatic plaques using expression cloning. J.Invest.Dermatol. 2004; **123:** 93-100.

78. Bromley S.K., Burack W.R., Johnson K.G. *et al*. The immunological synapse. Ann.Rev. Immunol. 2001; **19:** 375-96.

79. Nickoloff B.J., Mitra R.S., Green J. *et al*. Accessory cell function of keratinocytes for superantigens. Dependence on lymphocyte function-associated antigen-1/intercellular adhesion molecule-1 interaction. J.Immunol. 1993; **150:** 2148-59.

80. Goodman R.E., Nestle F., Naidu Y.M. *et al*. Keratinocyte-derived T cell costimulation induces preferential production of IL-2 and IL-4 but not IFN-gamma. J.Immunol. 1994; **152:** 5189-98.

81. Boehncke W.H. The alpha-defensins HNP-1 and HNP-2 are dominant self-peptides presented by HLA class-II molecules in lesional psoriatic skin. Eur.J.Dermatol. 2004; **14:** 142-5.

82. Yawalkar N., Karlen S., Hunger R., Brand C.U., Braathen L.R. Expression of interleukin-12 is increased in psoriatic skin. J.Invest.Dermatol. 1998; **111:** 1053-7.

83. Lee E., Trepicchio W.L., Oestreicher J.L. *et al*. Increased expression of interleukin 23 p19 and p40 in lesional skin of patients with psoriasis vulgaris. J.Exp.Med. 2004; **199:** 125-30.

84. Kopp T., Lenz P., Bello-Fernandez C., Kastelein R.A., Kupper T.S., Stingl G. IL-23 production by cosecretion of endogenous p19 and transgenic p40 in keratin 14/p40 transgenic mice: evidence for enhanced cutaneous immunity. J.Immunol. 2003; **170:** 5438-44.

85. Ruckert R., Asadullah K., Seifert M. *et al*. Inhibition of keratinocyte apoptosis by IL-15: a new parameter in the pathogenesis of psoriasis? J.Immunol. 2000; **165:** 2240-50.

86. Ohta Y., Hamada Y., Katsuoka K. Expression of IL-18 in psoriasis. Arch.Derm.Res. 2001; **293:** 334-42.

87. Romer J., Hasselager E., Norby P.L., Steiniche T., Thorn Clausen J., Kragballe K. Epidermal overexpression of interleukin-19 and -20 mRNA in psoriatic skin disappears after short-term treatment with cyclosporine A or calcipotriol. J.Invest.Dermatol. 2003; **121:** 1306-11.

88. Villadsen L.S., Schuurman J., Beurskens F. *et al*. Resolution of psoriasis upon blockade of IL-15 biological activity in a xenograft mouse model. J.Clin.Invest. 2003; **112:** 1571-80.

89. Blumberg H., Conklin D., Xu W.F. *et al*. Interleukin 20: discovery, receptor identification, and role in epidermal function. Cell 2001; **104:** 9-19.

90. McGill A., Frank A., Emmett N., Turnbull D.M., Birch-Machin M.A., Reynolds N.J. The anti-psoriatic drug anthralin accumulates in keratinocyte mitochondria, dissipates mitichondrial membrane potential, and induces apoptosis through a pathway dependent on respiratory competent mitochondria. FASEB J. 2005; **19:** 1012-4.

91. Krueger J.G. The immunologic basis for the treatment of psoriasis with new biologic agents. J.Am.Acad.Dermatol. 2002; **46:** 1-23.

92. Kormeili T., Lowe N.J., Yamauchi P.S. Psoriasis: immunopathogenesis and evolving immunomodulators and systemic therapies; U.S. experiences. Br.J.Dermatol. 2004; **151:** 3-15.

93. Walsh S.R.A. & Shear N.H. Psoriasis and the new biologic agents: interrupting a T-AP

dance. Can.Med.Assoc.J. 2004; **170:** 1933-41.

Further Reading

1. Bowcock A.M. & Krueger J.G. Getting under the skin: the immunogenetics of psoriasis. Nat.Rev.Immunol. 2005; **5:** 699-711.

Glossary

ACD	Allergic contact dermatitis
ACE	Angiotensin converting enzyme
ACTH	Adrenocorticotropic hormone
AD	Atopic dermatitis
ADCC	Antibody-dependent cellular cytotoxicity
AEDS	Atopic eczema/dermatitis syndrome
AICD	Activation-induced cell death
ALP	Antileukoprotease
ANA	Anti-nuclear antibody
AP-1	Activator protein-1
APC	Antigen-presenting cells
AR	Amphiregulin
BCG	Bacille Calmette-Guérin
Bcl-xL	Long form of Bcl-x
BCR	B cell receptor
β-EP	β-endorphin
β-LPH	β-lipotropic hormone
BP	Bullous pemphigoid
BPAG1/2	Bullous pemphigoid antigen 1/2
CARD4/15	Caspase recruitment domain 4/15
CD40L	CD40 ligand
cDNA	Copy DNA
CDR	Complementarity determining region
CDSN	Corneodesmosin
c-FLIP	Cellular homologue of viral FLICE inhibitory protein
CGRP-α/β	Calcitonin gene-related peptide-α/β
CLA	Cutaneous lymphocyte-associated antigen
CLIP	Corticotropin-like intermediate lobe peptide
cM	CentiMorgans
COX-1/2	Cyclooxygenase-1/2
CP	Chronic plaque
cPLA(2)	Cytosolic phospholipase A (2) family
cpm	Counts per minute
CR	Complement receptor
CR3	Complement receptor type 3
CREB	cAMP response element binding protein

CREM	cAMP response element modulator
CRLR	Calcitonin-like receptor
CTACK	Cutaneous T cell-attracting chemokine
CTGF	Connective tissue growth factor
CTLA-4	Cytotoxic T lymphocyte-associated antigen-4
DAF	Decay accelerating factor
DC-LAMP	DC-lysosomal-associated membrane glycoprotein
DDC	Dermal dendritic cells
DNCB	Dinitrochlorobenzene
DNFB	Dinitrofluorobenzene
dsDNA	Double-stranded DNA
DSF70	Dense fine speckles 70 kDa
Dsg 1/3	Desmoglein 1/3
dsRNA	Double-stranded RNA
ECM	Extracellular matrix proteins
EDC	Epidermal differentiation complex
EGF	Epidermal growth factor
ELISA	Enzyme-linked immunosorbent assay
ENA78	Epithelial-neutrophil activating peptide 78
ESR	Erythrocyte sedimentation rate
ET-1	Endothelin-1
F	Phenylalanine
FasL	Fas ligand
FcϵR	Fc receptor for IgE
FcγR	Fc receptor for IgG
FCGR	Gene for IgG Fc receptor
FGF	Fibroblast growth factor
GC	Glucocorticosteroid
G-CSF	Granulocyte-colony stimulating factor
GITR	Glucocorticoid-induced TNF receptor
GM-CSF	Granulocyte/macrophage-colony stimulating factor
GR-α/β	Glucocorticosteroid receptor-α/β
H	Histidine
H_2O_2	Hydrogen peroxide
HB-EGF	Heparin-binding EGF-like growth factor
HCR	α-helix coiled-coil rod homologue
HDM	House dust mite
15-HETE	15-hydroxyeicosatetraenoic acid

HEV	High endothelial venule
HGF/SF	Hepatocyte growth factor/scatter factor
HLA	Human leukocyte antigen
13-HODE	13-hydroxyoctadecadienoic acid
Hsp	Heat shock protein
I	Isoleucine
IκB	Inhibitor kappa B
iC3b	Inactivatable C3b fragments
ICAD	Inhibitor of Caspase 3-related DNAse
ICAM-1	Intercellular adhesion molecule-1
ICSBP	Interferon consensus sequence-binding protein
IDEC	Inflammatory dendritic epidermal cells
IFN	Interferon
IgE	Immunoglobulin E
IGF	Insulin growth factor
IGFBP	Insulin growth factor-binding proteins
IL	Interleukin
iNOS	Inducible nitric oxide synthase
InsP$_3$	1,4,5-inositol triphosphate
IP-10	IFN-γ-inducible protein-10
IRAK	IL-1R-associated kinase
IRF-1/3	Interferon response factor-1/3
ITAM	Immunoreceptor tyrosine-based activation motif
ITIM	Immunoreceptor tyrosine-based inhibitory motif
JNK	c-Jun NH$_2$-terminal kinase
KCs	Keratinocytes
KGF	Keratinocyte growth factor
KGFR	Keratinocyte growth factor receptor
KIR	Killer cell immunoglobulin-like receptor
LAT	Linker for activation of T cells
LCs	Langerhans cells
LEEP-CAM	Glycoprotein lymphocyte endothelial-epithelial cell adhesion molecule
LEKT1	Lympho-epithelial Kazal-type-related inhibitor
LEP	Late envelope protein
LFA-1	Lymphocyte function-associated antigen-1
lod	Logarithm of odds
LPS	Lipopolysaccharide
LTC$_4$	Leukotriene C$_4$

mAb	Monoclonal antibody
MC	Melanocortin
MCP	Membrane cofactor of proteolysis
MCP-1	Monocyte chemoattractant protein-1
MCP-3	Monocyte chemoattractant protein-3
M-CSF	Macrophage-colony stimulating factor
MDC	Macrophage-derived chemoattractant
MHC	Major Histocompatibility Complex
MICA/B	MHC class I chain-related A/B
MIF	Macrophage migration inhibition factor
Mig	Monokine induced by interferon-gamma
MIP-1α/3α	Macrophage inflammatory protein-1α/3α
MMP-1/3	Matrix metalloproteinase −1/3
MRP	Myeloid-related protein
MSH	Melanocyte-stimulating hormone
NAT1/2	N-acetyltransferases 1/2
NF-κB	Nuclear Factor kappa B
NF-AT	Nuclear Factor of Activated T cells
NGF	Nerve growth factor
NK	Natural killer
NKA	Neurokinin A
NKB	Neurokinin B
NKR	NK receptors
NK-T	T cells coexpressing natural killer cell receptors
NO	Nitric oxide
NSAIDs	Non-steroidal anti-inflammatory drugs
O^{2-}	Superoxide anions
O-GlcNAc	O-N-acetylglucosamine
PACAP	Pituitary adenylate cyclase-activating polypeptide
PAF	Platelet-activating factor
PAMPs	Pathogen-associated molecular patterns
PAR	Proteinase-activated receptor
PARC	Pulmonary and activation-regulated chemokine
PARP	Poly (ADP-ribose) polymerase
PBL	Peripheral blood lymphocytes
PBMC	Peripheral blood mononuclear cells
PC1	Prohormone convertase 1
PC2	Prohormone convertase 2
PDCD1	Programmed cell death 1
PDGF	Platelet-derived growth factor

PECAM-1	Platelet endothelial cell adhesion molecule-1
PF	Pemphigus foliaceous
PGD_2	Prostaglandin D_2
PGE_2	Prostaglandin E_2
$PGF_{2\alpha}$	Prostaglandin $F_{2\alpha}$
PGI_2	Prostaglandin I_2
PHM	Peptide histidine methionine
PKA-1	c-AMP-dependent protein kinase A type I
PMA	12-O-tetradecanoyl-phorbol 13-acetate
PMN	Polymorphonuclear neutrophil
PNP	Paraneoplastic pemphigus
POMC	Proopiomelanocortin
PPAR-γ	Peroxisome proliferator-activated receptor-gamma
PPD	Purified protein derivative of Mycobacteria
PRR	Pattern-recognition receptor
PSORS1-9	Psoriasis susceptibility 1-9
PUVA	Psoralens plus UV light
PV	Pemphigus vulgaris
R	Arginine
RAMP-1/2/3	Receptor-activity modifying protein –1/2/3
RANTES	Regulated on activation, normal T expressed and secreted
RAPTOR	p150 target of rapamycin (TOR)-scaffold protein
RAST	Radioallergosorbent test
RNP-A1	Nuclear ribonucleoprotein-A1
RSV	Respiratory syncytial virus
RT-PCR	Reverse-transcriptase polymerase chain reaction
SCCA1	Squamous cell carcinoma antigen-1
SCF	Stem cell factor
SCID	Severe combined immunodeficient
SDF-1α	Stromal cell-derived factor-1α
SE	Staphylococcal enterotoxins
SIS	Skin Immune System
SKSD	Streptokinase/streptodornase
SLC12A8	Solute carrier family 12 protein, member 8
SLC22A4	Solute carrier family 22, member 4
SLC9A3R1	Solute carrier family 9, isoform A3, regulatory factor 1
SLE	Systemic lupus erythematosus
SNP	Single nucleotide polymorphism
SOCS/CIS	Suppressors of cytokine signalling/ cytokine-inducible SH2 containing protein
SPE	Streptococcal pyrogenic exotoxins

SPRR	Small proline-rich protein
ssDNA	Single-stranded DNA
ssRNA	Single-stranded RNA
STAT	Signal transducer and activator of transcription
T	Threonine
TAP1/2	Transporter associated with antigen processing 1/2
TARC	Thymus- and activation-regulated chemokine
Tc	$CD8^+$ cytotoxic T cell
TCR	T cell receptor
TDT	Transmission disequilibrium test
TGF-α	Transforming growth factor-α
TGF-β_1	Transforming growth factor- β_1
Th	$CD4^+$ T helper cell
TIM-1	T-cell immunoglobulin domain and mucin domain protein-1
TIMP-1	Tissue inhibitor of metalloproteinase-1
TIR	Toll/IL-1 receptor
TLR	Toll-like receptor
TNF-β	Tumour necrosis factor-β
TPA	12-O-tetradecanoylphorbol-13-acetate
Tr	Regulatory T cells
TRAF6	TNF receptor-activated factor 6
TRIF	TIR-domain-containing adaptor inducing IFN-β
TSLP	Thymic stromal lymphopoetin
TSST-1	Toxic shock syndrome toxin-1
UV	Ultraviolet light
V	Valine
VCAM-1	Vascular cell adhesion molecule-1
VEGF(C)	Vascular endothelial growth factor (C)
VIP	Vasoactive intestinal peptide
VLA-4	Very late antigen-4
VR-1	Vanilloid receptor-1

Index

Symbols

A

B

Colour Plates

Chapter 1

Figure 1.4 Langerhans cells in normal epidermis stained for HLA-DR antigen. (Source: Baker B.S. *In* Recent Advances in Psoriasis: The Role of the Immune System, 2000, with permission from World Scientific Publishing Co. Pte. Ltd, Singapore.)

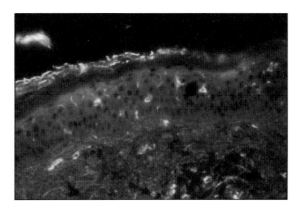

Chapter 3

Figure 3.4 TLR2 (A) and TLR5 (B) staining of normal epidermis. (Source: Baker B.S. *et al*. Brit.J.Dermatol. 2003; **148:** 670-9, with permission from Blackwell Publishing Ltd, Oxford, UK.)

A

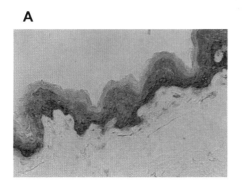

B

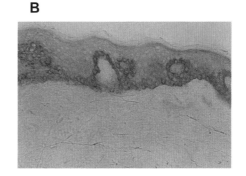

Chapter 4

Figure 4.7 Patch testing of a patient with allergic contact dermatitis. (Courtesy of Prof.Lionel Fry, Emeritus Professor of Dermatology, Imperial College, London.)

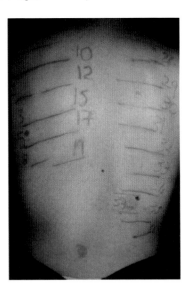

Chapter 5

Figure 5.1 Typical clinical appearance of urticarial skin lesions. (Courtesy of Prof.Lionel Fry, Emeritus Professor of Dermatology, Imperial College, London.)

Figure 5.2 Histology of urticaria. (Courtesy of Dr.Nick Francis, Charing Cross Hospital, London.)

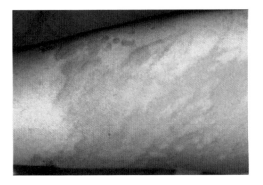

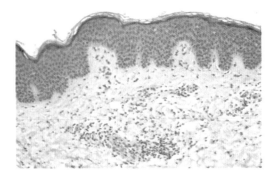

Chapter 5

Figure 5.6 Clinical presentation of skin lesions in A) Pemphigus vulgaris and B) Bullous pemphigoid. (Courtesy of Prof.Lionel Fry, Emeritus Professor of Dermatology, Imperial College, London.)

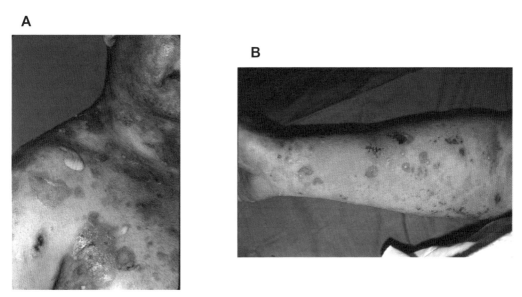

Figure 5.7 Immunofluorescence of skin lesions of A) Pemphigus vulgaris and B) Bullous pemphigoid. A) Linear IgG deposition on the surface of keratinocytes, excluding the basement membrane zone, present in PV skin lesions. B) Linear IgG deposition along the basement membrane zone, characteristic of BP skin lesions. (Courtesy of Prof.Lionel Fry, Emeritus Professor of Dermatology, Imperial College, London.)

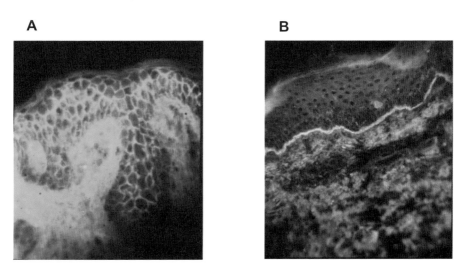

Chapter 6

Figure 6.1 Butterfly skin rash on the face of a SLE patient. (Courtesy of Prof.Lionel Fry, Emeritus Professor of Dermatology, Imperial College, London.)

Figure 6.2 Histology of SLE butterfly skin rash. (Courtesy of Dr Nick Francis, Charing Cross Hospital, London.)

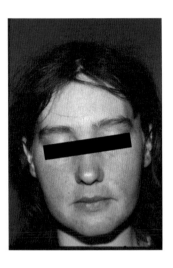

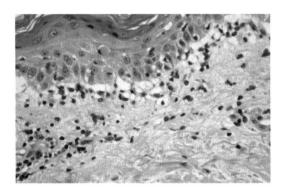

Chapter 7

Figure 7.1 Allergic contact dermatitis due to nickel in belt buckle. (Courtesy of Prof.Lionel Fry, Emeritus Professor of Dermatology, Imperial College, London.)

Figure 7.2 Histological appearance of allergic contact dermatitis. (Courtesy of Dr Nick Francis, Charing Cross Hospital, London.)

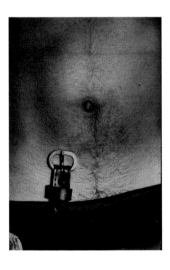

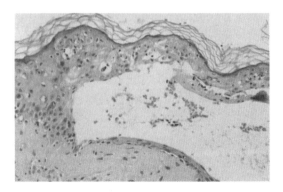

Chapter 7

Figure 7.6 Sequential production of chemokines by KCs in the elicitation of ACD, and their relationship to the formation of a mononuclear cell infiltrate. MCP-1 = monocyte chemoattractant protein-1; RANTES = regulated upon activation, normal T-cell expressed and secreted; Mig = monokine-induced by gamma interferon; IP-10 = interferon-inducible protein-10; MDC = macrophage-derived chemoattractant; TARC = thymus and activation-regulated chemokine; PARC = pulmonary and activation-regulated chemokine.

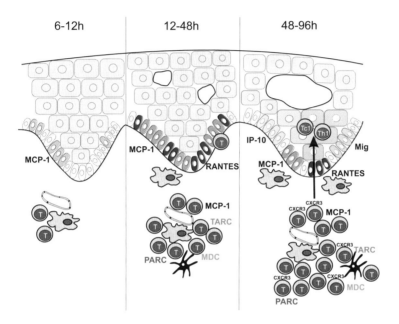

Chapter 8

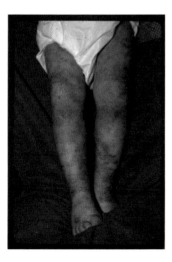

Figure 8.1 Clinical presentation of atopic dermatitis in an infant. (Courtesy of Prof. Lionel Fry, Emeritus Professor of Dermatology, Imperial College, London.)

Chapter 9

Figure 9.1 Clinical presentation of chronic plaque psoriasis.

Figure 9.2 Clinical presentation of guttate psoriasis.

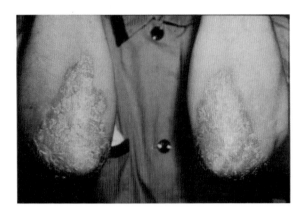

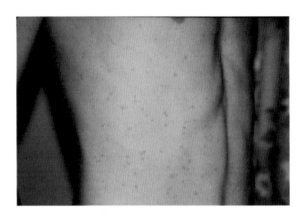

Figure 9.3 Histology of a psoriatic plaque. (Source: Baker B.S. *In* Recent Advances in Psoriasis: The Role of the Immune System, 2000, with permission from World Scientific Publishing Co. Pte. Ltd, Singapore.)